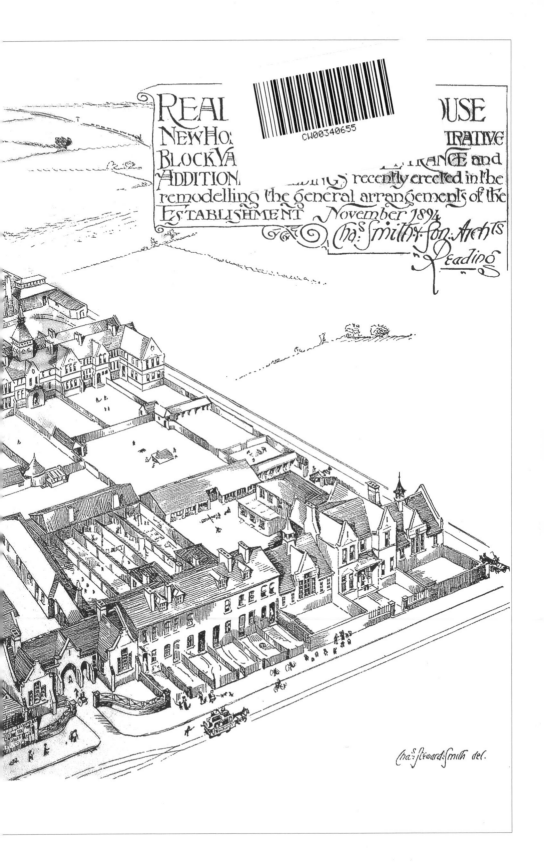

REAL ... USE
NEW HO... ...RATIVE
BLOCK YA... ...RANCE and
ADDITION... ...DINGS recently erected in the
remodelling the general arrangements of the
ESTABLISHMENT November 1894
Cha:s Smith & Son, Arch:ts Reading

Cha:s Steward-Smith del.

BATTLE WORKHOUSE
AND HOSPITAL
1867–2005

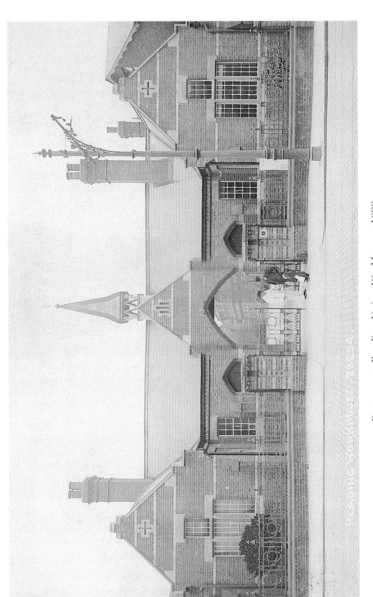

Entrance to Reading Union Workhouse *c*1890

——BATTLE—— WORKHOUSE AND HOSPITAL ——1867~2005——

MARGARET RAILTON

MARSHALL BARR

BERKSHIRE MEDICAL HERITAGE CENTRE

First published in 2005 by the Berkshire Medical Heritage Centre

Part I and Appendix © Copyright Margaret Railton 2005
Part II © Copyright Marshall Barr 2005

ISBN 0-9539417-1-X

Typeset in 11 on 12pt Baskerville by Columns of Reading
Printed by Cambridge University Press

CONTENTS

PART I
READING UNION WORKHOUSE

PART II
BATTLE HOSPITAL

LIST OF ILLUSTRATIONS

PART I

ACKNOWLEDGEMENTS

The material for Part 1 of this book has been obtained almost entirely from primary sources. I would particularly like to thank Dr Peter Durrant, County Archivist, Miss Sabina Sutherland, Senior Archivist, and the staff of the Berkshire Record Office for all their help, for giving me access to the relevant records and for allowing me to photograph some for inclusion in this book.

I would also like to thank Mr Gwylym Games, Local Studies Librarian, Mr David Cliffe, Mr Michael Hancock and the staff of the Local Studies section of Reading Central Library for their help with old newspaper files, various minute books and publications and for allowing many of the photographs in their collection to be copied and reproduced. The *Reading Evening Post*, who own the copyright of the former *Reading Standard*, have kindly allowed me to reproduce their photographs (listed below) now in Reading Central Library.

Mrs Helen Pugh, Archivist at the British Red Cross Museum and Archives, and Mrs Ann Yeater of the Wokingham Branch of the British Red Cross, are thanked for all their help with records of the Red Cross during the First World War and also Dr Catherine Crawford, who has given me information about Professor Juda Quastel.

I am most grateful to Sir William and Lady Benyon, Mrs Caroline Benson of the Museum of English Rural Life, Mrs Valerie Ayres, Mrs Joan Dunn, Mr Peter Delaney, Mr Brian Eighteen, Mrs M Franklin, Mr Ken Goatley, Mr Sidney Gold, Mr John Green, Mr Graham Parlour, Reading Pathological Society, Mr Ian Sainsbury of Reading University Library, Mr and Mrs Roy Sheppard, the Directors of Windsor Homes PLC and the staff of the Department of Medical Photography at the Royal Berkshire Hospital who have all helped me in various ways.

The help given by Mr Lionel Williams with photography and scanning has been invaluable and without him and the diligent work of our Editor, Miss Moyna Kitchin and our Graphic Designer, Mr Chris Harper, this book would have never been completed.

Margaret Railton

Dealing with the past 75 years has posed something of a difficulty: the presentation is necessarily skewed, depending at the start on written records alone, with oral history becoming more available and increasingly detailed as we approach the present day. From the 1950s onwards, the problem has been information overload. Since imbalance cannot be avoided, a judgement has been made to favour those specialities which started at Battle almost from scratch and went on to spectacular advancement. I particularly regret that the non-clinical departments could not be better served.

Scores of people, some sadly now deceased, have provided information. My thanks go to them all and apologies if any have been missed from the list of those whose stories and material have been used:

Mr Frank Cheadle, Mrs Betty Eggleton, Mr Robert Eggleton, Dr Walter Hausmann, Dr R A Ratcliff, Mr Gordon Bohn, Mrs Barbara Pires, Mr Ernest Ingarfill, Mrs Margaret Pilgrim, Mr Denis Petty, Miss Gladys Morgan, Dr G Shaw, Mr Peter Wheeler, Mrs Jean Ridout, Dr Moira Tarnoky, Mrs Doreen Thomas, Miss Evelyn Aust, Mrs Barbara White, Dr George Patey, Dr K Salzmann, Mr Frank Rackham, Dr Ian Meanock, Dr Sam Vine, Mr Stuart Robinson, Dr David Stone,

Mrs Ruth Clark, Dr Tom Boulton, Ms Joyce Benham, Ms May Cook, Mrs Pam Miller, Dr David Price, Dr Malcolm Evans, Mr Clem Grimshaw, Mrs Pat Saker, Mrs Sue Mears, Mr Richard Faber, Mr Andrew Pengelly, Mr Derek Fawcett, Dr Tony Mee, Dr John Bell, Dr Chris Newman, Dr Mike Pearson, Ms Kate Ignatowski, Mrs Miriam Palk, Dr Tony Bradlow, Dr Christine Collin, Mr Keith Westwood, Mr Peter Malone, Dr Andrew Boon, Miss Jennie Ingram, Mrs Margaret Jones, Mr Chris Bradby, Mrs Val Bradby, Ms Jacky Chandler, Mrs Sheila Dindar, Ms Barbara Gatward, Mr Mike Lacey, Dr Leo Horton, Mr Rob Marshall, Dr Clive Charlton, Ms Brenda Morton, Ms Maggie Netherwood, Ms Ros Crowder, Mr Bill O'Donnell, Dr Joan Thomas, Dr Tom Walker, Ms Neila Warner, Ms Mandy Odell, Ms Jane Williams, Mr Matthew Williams, Ms Jane Wooldridge, Mrs Evelyn Yardley, Ms Meta Muncaster, Mr Alan Hudson, Ms Samantha Byles, Mr Joe Devanny, Mr Rajinder Sohpal, Mrs Louise Griffiths.

I thank the Royal Berkshire and Battle Hospitals NHS Trust for permission to use information from the Archives and Annual Reports and for supplying statistical tables. My particular thanks to the staffs of the Local Studies section of Reading Central Library and of the Berkshire Record Office and to Lionel Williams for his encyclopaedic local hospital knowledge as well as his photographic skills.

Marshall Barr

The authors would like to thank the following people and organisations for their kind permission to reproduce the illustrations on the pages listed below:

Berkshire Record Office: First endpaper, 2, 6, 43, 47, 63, 64, 72, 74, 83, 91 (right), 100, 106, 111, 117, 118, 144, 223.
Mr and Mrs Roy Sheppard: ii, 174, 177 (top), 178, 186 (top), 195 (bottom), 198 (top).
Local Studies section, Reading Central Library: 26, 81, 177 (bottom), 189, 202, 238, 242.
Mr Brian Eighteen: 82
Mr Lionel Williams: 84
Museum of English Rural Life: 88, 154 (top), 158, 179, 188, 243.
Reading Pathological Society: 17, 91 (left), 201.
Mrs M Railton: 137, 156, 162, 163 (bottom), 164 (bottom), 171, 172, 173, 181, 182, 183 (top), 184 (bottom), 191 (top), 196, 198 (bottom), 199 (top).
Reading Evening Post/Local Studies section, Reading Central Library: 153, 159, 166, 169, 170, 176, 184 (top), 193, 203 (bottom), 204–205, 225 (top), 317, 345, 360 (bottom right).
Sir William and Lady Benyon: 154 (bottom), 175
Mr Graham Parlour: 155, 179, 186 (bottom), 187, 195 (top).
Mr John Green: 161, 191 (bottom), 197, 199 (bottom).
British Red Cross: 168 (top), 183 (bottom).
Mrs M Franklin /*Reading Evening Post*: 168 (bottom).
Mrs Joan Dunn: 203 (top).
The Directors of Windsor Homes PLC: 206.
Mrs Barbara Pires: 253, 257.
Mrs Margaret Pilgrim: 272, 276.
Reading Museum Service: 279, 283 (top), 312 (top). (Copyright Reading Museum Service, Reading Borough Council. All rights reserved.)
Mr Dennis Petty: 283 (bottom).

PART I

READING UNION WORKHOUSE

by

MARGARET RAILTON

Workhouse nurse *c*1890

BATTLE
WORKHOUSE AND HOSPITAL
1867–2005

INTRODUCTION

During the first week of August 1867 groups of men, women and children made their way along Oxford Road, Reading on foot and by cart clutching their meagre belongings. These were the first of several groups who, over the next two months, were to be moved from the old parish Workhouses to the newly built Reading Union institution on the western boundary of the town. This, it was hoped, would be the beginning of a new era for the paupers of Reading.

Until the 20th century there were no state pensions for the elderly and no sick pay or unemployment benefit for those unable to work. For the poor, dependent upon their health to maintain themselves and their families, unemployment caused great hardship and distress. There was no safety net for hard times except the Poor Law system.

Since the 16th century a series of Poor Laws had determined how the poor should be cared for, including those in need of medical treatment. Until 1834 these Poor Laws were administered at parish level through officials called 'Overseers of the Poor' and funded by a parish poor rate. 'Poor Relief' was given to those in need either within the community as 'outdoor relief' in the form of small sums of money, food or medical attention, or in the parish workhouse as 'indoor relief' where the inmates were provided with their basic needs and medical treatment if necessary.

In Reading the three parishes, St Giles, St Lawrence[1] and St Mary, each had their own workhouse and overseers of the poor. St Giles' Workhouse was an old building opposite the church in Horn Street, St Lawrence's a group of old cottages in Thorn Street and St Mary's a building in Pinkney's Lane built in the 1790s. The overseers in each parish were appointed annually at the Easter Vestry meeting. Their duties

3

included collecting the poor rate within the parish, allocating the funds to those in need, providing medical treatment for the sick and keeping accounts of all transactions including the administration and maintenance of the parish workhouse.

For some 200 years this system worked relatively well but by the 1830s parishes throughout the country were experiencing problems. All too often those in receipt of poor relief never came off the list and many of those paying the poor rate were crippled by its size. In 1833 a Royal Commission was appointed with instructions to examine every aspect of the Poor Law system. Information was gathered from all parts of the country on behalf of the Poor Law Commissioners and following this in 1834 the Poor Law Amendment Act was passed by Parliament.

The New Poor Law, as it came to be called, set out to remedy the ills of the old system and in particular to cut the cost of poor relief. Central administration from London was introduced, headed by three Poor Law Commissioners. Parishes were grouped into Poor Law Unions managed by Boards of Guardians elected by local ratepayers who still financed the system. These Boards could also include local magistrates as ex-officio guardians. Those eligible for poor relief would be strictly limited with every union appointing a Relieving Officer to question all applicants. Medical practitioners would be contracted to attend the sick within the parishes of the union and also in the workhouse. No outdoor relief would be given to the able-bodied and, unless destitute, none would be admitted to the workhouse. Indoor relief was now primarily for the old, the sick, the infirm, orphaned and abandoned children and cases of mental illness not severe enough to be sent to an asylum. The emphasis was now to be on economy, with the harshness of the workhouse, the humiliation of its uniform and the stigma of pauperism acting as powerful deterrents for those reluctant to support themselves.

The Reading Poor Law Union was officially formed on August 10th 1835 and consisted of the three parishes, St Giles, St Lawrence and St Mary, with Southcote and Whitley. It covered an area of eight square miles with a population of 16,042. A Board of 15 Guardians (five elected annually from each parish) would administer the Poor Law within the Union. All important decisions had to be referred to the Poor Law Commissioners[2] in London and Inspectors would visit the Union at regular intervals to check that all was in order. The Guardians would not be paid but the officials such as the clerk, auditor, relieving officer, workhouse master and matron and medical officers would receive salaries determined by the Board. Every effort was to be made to reduce the poor rate through improved administration and strict control of all expenditure.

At their first meeting on August 12th 1835 the Guardians decided that St Giles' parish Workhouse in Horn Street would be closed. The other two Workhouses, St Lawrence's in Thorn Street and St Mary's in Pinkney's Lane, would be retained. With some alterations these two Workhouses would be able to accommodate all paupers eligible for indoor relief.

Medical practitioners were appointed to attend the sick in each parish with separate contracts for the two Workhouses.

These arrangements proved adequate for some years but by 1861 the population of Reading had risen to 25,876, an increase of over one third since the Union was formed in 1835. This had resulted in further demands upon the Union's resources. Complaints were made that the Workhouses were overcrowded and the facilities were inadequate. It was noted that at St Mary's Workhouse some of the men were having to sleep two in a bed. After visiting the Workhouses in October 1863 Mr R B Cane, the Poor Law Inspector, wrote to the Guardians: 'I was struck with the highly unfavourable appearance which these houses present when contrasted with the more modern and complete establishments which are to be found elsewhere. I cannot think that these houses are consistent with the importance of the Reading Union and I hope that the day is not distant when the Guardians will adopt what appears to be the only effectual remedy and the only real means for providing satisfactory arrangements for the maintenance and care of the In-door Poor.'

Mr Cane's comments fell on deaf ears and six months later in April 1864 he wrote again in more forceful tones: 'The only remedy for the most defective state of the accommodation ... is the erection of a workhouse which will remove the discredit which the existing buildings bring upon so important a Union as that of Reading.' The Guardians' Minutes recorded nothing further on the subject until the following month when a short sentence noted simply: 'Resolved that the Clerk do make enquiries as to the cost of about a dozen workhouses each capable of accommodating 400 inmates.' The wheels had now been set in motion for a new workhouse to be built.

NOTES

1 St Lawrence can also be spelt St Laurence but as the contemporary records used 'w' this spelling will be adopted here.
2 In 1848 the Poor Law Commission was replaced by the Poor Law Board responsible to a Government minister.

Outline Plan of New Workhouse, Ordnance Survey 1877

1

THE NEW WORKHOUSE

Within a few years of their formation in 1835 eight of the twelve Berkshire Poor Law Unions had built new central workhouses. Several different architects had been employed and the buildings varied considerably in size and design. The smallest, Cookham Workhouse, was built for 200 occupants and the largest, Abingdon Workhouse, was built for 500. It was to be almost 30 years later before the Reading Guardians agreed to replace their old buildings.

The Poor Law Board did not have the power to order unions to build new workhouses but they were able, as a last resort, to order the closure of substandard buildings, thereby forcing guardians to take action. In May 1864, following censure from Mr Cane, a Poor Law Inspector, the Reading Guardians avoided such measures when they reluctantly agreed to contact several unions, including Abingdon, Hungerford and Bradfield, regarding the cost of their buildings. A special committee was then set up to consider the matter and another to find and negotiate the purchase of a site.

The Search for a Site
Several possible sites were inspected and the most suitable proved to be an eight and a half acre plot along the Oxford Road belonging to Mr G V Jones. This land had at one time belonged to the Abbot of Battle Abbey in Sussex. It straddled the Borough boundary with some six acres in Tilehurst parish and two acres in St Mary's parish. It included six houses called Battle Terrace and three others called Battle Place. The price of the whole was £5,000. At the end of August 1865 the Guardians agreed to purchase the site subject to the necessary approval of the Poor Law Board. This was obtained a few weeks later provided 'a sufficient supply of good water' and 'proper drainage' could be obtained. It was to be several months before the sale was completed.

The Guardians then asked if a lunatic asylum could be built in connection with the proposed new workhouse. At that time dangerous mental patients were sent to Littlemore Asylum near Oxford at a cost of 10s 6d (52p) each per week. About 40 patients from the Reading Union were being cared for there and the Guardians were keen that this expenditure should be reduced. Permission was not granted as, by law, dangerous cases had to be sent to asylums but 'idiots and harmless and chronic lunatics' could be maintained in separate wards within the workhouse[1].

Designs and Estimates

In the meantime the committee formed to 'consider the proposal of erecting a new Workhouse' had not made much progress. The original idea of a building suitable for 400 inmates was soon abandoned. In past years the number of paupers in the two old Workhouses had always been under 200, even in the winter months. It was agreed that a building large enough for 250 inmates would be adequate.

Deciding upon the design was more difficult. Since the first union workhouses were built in the 1830s and 1840s much had changed. The former courtyard style, as architect Kempthorne had employed for the Newbury Union Workhouse, and other designs with radiating wings as at the Bradfield Union Workhouse, were no longer popular. Ventilation and sanitation had now become matters of great importance. The concept of separate parallel buildings, as the East Grinstead Union had adopted in the construction of their new Workhouse in 1859, appealed to the Reading Guardians and Mr Cane arranged for copies of the plans to be sent to them early in November 1865.

The Guardians immediately invited local architects to enter a competition to provide plans for the new Workhouse, entries to be submitted by January 8th 1866. The architect of the second best plan would be employed to alter St Lawrence's Workhouse to provide a Board Room for the Guardians, a residence for the Relieving Officer, vagrants' wards and accommodation for 'such other purposes as may hereafter be deemed necessary'.

Even before the Guardians had turned their attention to the design of the new Workhouse they had decided that the cost should not exceed £6,700. This plus the cost of the land would mean expenditure of £11,700. In October 1865 the Poor Law Board was asked for approval to borrow this amount secured by a charge on the poor rates. In December authority was obtained to borrow this sum.

Six local architects agreed to enter the competition and each was sent instructions. The East Grinstead Workhouse plans were to provide a basic model, the buildings to be three storeys and built as far as possible in St Mary's parish and to comply with the Poor Law regulations. There should be three separate parallel blocks, one for the main building, one for an infirmary and a third for fever cases. They should accommodate 250 inmates and cost not more than £6,700.

The plans submitted by Messrs Cooper and Goulding, W and J T Brown, Mr Woodman, Mr Joseph Morris, Mr C Smith and Mr J S Dodd were carefully scrutinised. At a meeting held on January 11th attended by Mr Cane, the Poor Law Inspector, it was decided that the architect whose plans were accepted should enter into an agreement that the Board would reserve the power to reject the plans and could employ any other architect who might have competed, if the lowest tender for the work exceeded £7,000. A short list of two was agreed. The plans of Messrs Brown and Mr Woodman would be submitted to an Extraordinary Meeting of the Guardians to be held on January 18th when the final selection would be made.

After much discussion at the Extraordinary Meeting, the Guardians made the final decision by a written vote. Messrs Brown's plans obtained four votes and Mr Woodman's eight votes. Mr Woodman was asked to provide detailed specifications to be forwarded with his plans to the Poor Law Board for approval. In the meantime all the plans entered in the competition would be exhibited at the Town Rooms in Friar Street for inspection by the public.

It was to be supposed that once the decision had been made that Mr Woodman's plans would be used for the new Workhouse and Messrs Brown would carry out the alterations to St Lawrence's Workhouse, everything would proceed smoothly and quickly. Unfortunately this was not to be the case and no sooner had the vote been taken than complaints were made that the wrong plans had been chosen. Up to this time there had been little general interest in the subject and the local papers seldom recorded anything about the Workhouse apart from the number of inmates and the cost of their maintenance per head per week. Indignant letters were now published in the *Reading Mercury* and the *Berkshire Chronicle*. Handbills were distributed round the town to the same effect. It was believed that Messrs Brown's plans had been better than those of Mr Woodman, they followed more closely those of the East Grinstead Workhouse, they gave more space for the inmates and the buildings were better placed on the site.

One of the competitors wrote at length to the *Reading Mercury* and among his many complaints about Mr Woodman's plans he noted that baths had been placed under staircases, there was no provision for married couples, the dining hall was too small and the infirmary space so cramped that 'all the occupants may be quickly infected with the same disease'. The letter ended by saying that if professional assistance had been called in and the designs judged by the instructions given to the architects, the result would have been different and 'the labour of weeks not sacrificed in such an unsatisfactory manner'.

This letter was followed by another which was sent directly to the Poor Law Board and signed by two of the Guardians, Mr Phillips and Mr Ivey, who had proposed and seconded Messrs Brown's plans at the vital meeting. They believed the vote had not been 'in accordance with the merits of the plans submitted'. Mr Cane, the Poor Law Inspector who had attended the meeting but had no vote, had favoured Messrs Brown's plans. Although the estimates of both sets of plans were the same, those of Messrs Brown provided more accommodation. The infirmary was at least 25% larger, it was better ventilated and had received the commendation of the

Inspector. Furthermore the fever wards were nearly double the extent and situated further from the infirmary. They believed that Mr Woodman's plans were the only ones 'not in accordance with those of East Grinstead'.

At this time Mr Woodman was probably better known locally than Messrs Brown. In the mid-1850s he had become Borough Surveyor for Reading and had been involved with the restoration of the old Town Hall. In 1863 he had carried out the complete restoration of Greyfriars Church and in 1865 he was the architect and surveyor to the Reading Industrial Exhibition.

The Guardians stood their ground and forwarded Mr Woodman's plans and specifications to the Poor Law Board for approval. Any previous criticism was nothing compared to what was to follow from the Poor Law Board. There were numerous defects in the plans and the specifications were inadequate. The main building, outbuildings and fever wards were all criticised but the infirmary plans were damned as 'ill-adapted for the accommodation of the sick'. To all intents and purposes the Guardians were being informed that Mr Woodman should be asked to redraw these plans. Unfortunately none of the original plans of any of the competitors have survived and it is to be wondered if the Guardians had chosen Mr Woodman's plans for the external appearance of the buildings rather than their internal layout.

Since 1834 the Poor Law had demanded that all inmates of workhouses should be classified and separated into various groups according to sex, age and state of health. These criteria were fundamental in planning the new Reading Union Workhouse. Mr Woodman's plans were to provide accommodation for a total of 250 paupers. Of these 201 would be in the main building – 106 men and 95 women. The men and women would be on separate sides and divided into five categories, as shown below.

Aged and infirm	males 51	females 51
Able-bodied single	20	20
Able-bodied married	23	13
Children in nursery	7	6
Imbeciles and epileptics	5	5

In the infirmary provision was made for 43 patients with the men and women on separate sides of the building and divided into four categories.

Sick wards	male 13	female 13
Itch wards	4	3
Four dirty case rooms	2	2
Lying-in ward	3 mothers and 3 infants	

The detached fever ward would take six patients, three male and three female.

Mr Woodman's plans were amended to rectify the problems identified by the Poor Law Board, such as better accommodation in the main building. Criticism of inadequate heating was answered by adding extra fireplaces but there was endless debate regarding the positioning of windows and whether the sashes should be made of metal or wood. Imbecile cases were to be housed in the main building and a padded room was required for use if necessary. The Poor Law Board asked that the lighting in this room should be able to be dimmed or turned off at night and this was agreed. However the Guardians would not agree to altering the position of the building as they wanted it to be as far as possible in St Mary's parish and not encroach upon Tilehurst.

The problems concerning the infirmary were more significant. The Guardians were prepared to agree that the mortuary and wash-house should not be under the same roof as the sick wards but they were adamant that no extra wards for dirty cases should be built as they could easily be added later. The amended plans altered the layout so that the men's and women's wards were separated by the nurse's room and bathroom with a staircase in the centre. By the middle of March the Poor Law Board announced that, apart from ventilation and minor details, they 'generally approved' the plans.

By now the price of labour and materials was rising and it was believed that the whole building would cost considerably more than £7,000. Builders resident in the Union area were invited to submit tenders for the main building and separate ones for the infirmary and fever wards. Ten tenders were obtained and that of Mr John Grover of Great Knollys Street was accepted. The main building would cost £5,975 and the infirmary and fever wards £1,365 – a total of £7,340. With the cost of the site added, over £12,000 would be required. The £10,000 loan at 5% arranged with the Mutual Life Assurance office, secured upon the poor rates, to be paid off in 40 half-yearly instalments of £398 7s 2d, would no longer be sufficient.

In April 1866 the annual elections within the three Reading parishes were held to select the Guardians for the year ahead. The new Board of Guardians announced that they would not be responsible for the decisions of the previous Board regarding the new Workhouse building. Nevertheless a Workhouse Building Committee was formed consisting of the Chairman, Mr William Briant, and four other Guardians and a month later a Clerk of Works was appointed to supervise the building work. Mr Jonathan Leaver of Greyfriars Road, Reading would be paid £2 per week, with one week's notice on either side. He would submit weekly reports and when not supervising the building of the new Workhouse he would be concerned with other works undertaken by the Guardians.

Problems with the Plans
By the end of the year (1866) the building was progressing well and it was believed that the new Workhouse would be completed and ready for

occupation in June 1867. This was in spite of a short bricklayers' strike in July and delay in obtaining possession of the garden of 1, Battle Place needed for the new entrance lodge.

This optimism was short-lived when, at their meeting on January 3rd 1867, the Guardians were informed that the floor space at the new Workhouse was less than that in the two old Workhouses. Furthermore there were now 54 patients in the old Workhouse infirmaries and the new infirmary at best could only accommodate 55 patients. With a rapidly increasing population it appeared that the new infirmary would be far too small.

Mr Woodman was consulted and, as the infirmary was still in the course of construction, he suggested that an additional floor could be added. This would cost £430 and the infirmary could then accommodate some 100 patients. Four days later he produced the necessary plans. A special committee was formed to confer with Mr Walford, the Medical Officer for St Lawrence's parish, and Mr Workman, the Medical Officer for St Mary's parish. Dr Edward Smith FRS, who had been appointed an Inspector for the Poor Law Board in 1865 and was also its Medical Officer, would also be consulted.

Dr Smith was an authority on workhouse infirmaries. In 1866, at the request of the Poor Law Board, he and Mr Farnal, a Poor Law Inspector for the Metropolitan District, had published the results of their inquiries into these infirmaries and he was now investigating conditions in provincial workhouse infirmaries. He informed the Reading Guardians that the space that was now required in workhouse infirmaries was 75% more than had been allowed for in Mr Woodman's plans.

On January 10th he attended the meeting of the Reading Guardians and explained that ordinary cases of illness should be three feet apart, each with 850 cubic feet of space, offensive cases should have 1,200 cubic feet and fever cases 2,000 cubic feet with beds six feet apart. It was believed that this recommendation would be included in a bill to be introduced at the next session of Parliament and would become law. Dr Smith suggested that the Guardians should construct the infirmary 'with these facts in mind'.

The Committee reported that if the beds were rearranged 62 patients could be accommodated. The Medical Officers thought extensions were needed in the long term though Mr Walford did not think that they were absolutely necessary at present. A majority of the Committee believed extensions should be made now when it would be cheaper and less inconvenient than if proceeded with when the building was occupied.

At the several adjourned meetings that followed it became obvious that the infirmary would have to be enlarged to comply with the new requirements of the Poor Law Board. A letter from Mr Woodman noted: 'Since the building has been in the course of erection an entire revolution has taken place in the views of the Poor Law Board and there can be little doubt that in future such buildings will be constructed as hospitals.'

It was eventually agreed that an additional storey would be built over the centre portion of the infirmary. This, combined with alterations to the external walls of the bathrooms and water-closets, and by adding the nurse's rooms on the ground floor to the adjoining wards, would provide accommodation for 75 patients. By the end of January these alterations had been approved by Dr Smith and the Poor Law Board. It was estimated that that a further £2,300 would be needed to meet the cost of these alterations and to furnish and equip the new Workhouse. The final cost would now be £14,000 and a further loan on top of the original one for £10,000 would be needed.

The New Tramp Wards
Messrs Brown, the architects whose plans for the new Workhouse had come second in the competition, were now asked to submit plans for the alteration of St Lawrence's Workhouse. A board room for the Guardians' weekly meetings, a residence for the Relieving Officer and accommodation for tramps were required. It was the duty of the Guardians to provide overnight shelter for the 'wayfaring and vagrant poor'. Since 1847 the Guardians had maintained these 'casual wards' in an old granary in the Forbury belonging to Reading Corporation. It had been adapted to provide four wards, one for each sex, a third which was used as an infirmary and a fourth for the employment of the vagrants.

Applicants to the casual or tramp wards would be admitted if they had obtained a ticket from the Relieving Officer at St Lawrence's Workhouse. Food, consisting of bread and water, and shelter for one night were provided free. The next morning, before being escorted by the police to the edge of the town, the tramps, if physically fit, would be required to pick one quarter of a pound of oakum. The Medical Officer of St Lawrence's parish was paid £20 per year to attend the sick at this additional workhouse and a member of the Reading police was paid £26 per year to assist the workhouse officials in these casual wards. When the casual wards at St Lawrence's Workhouse had been completed the building at the Forbury would be closed.

Furnishing and Equipping the New Workhouse
Elections to appoint the Guardians for the year ahead were held in the three Reading parishes in April 1867. Mr William Briant, a Guardian for some 30 years and Chairman for the past seven, had indicated that he would not be standing for re-election. At its first meeting the new Board appointed Mr John Okey Taylor as its Chairman and Mr Rowland Charles Hurley the Vice-Chairman. Members for the Assessment Committee, the Workhouse Visiting Committee, the Finance Committee and the Building Committee were chosen. A fifth committee, the New Workhouse Furnishing Committee, was formed consisting of the Chairman and three other Guardians 'with power to adopt such measures as they may deem

necessary for fitting up the workhouse for the reception of paupers'. Over the next few months this Committee would be fully occupied.

Once again the need to keep costs down was all important. A new range costing £98 was approved for the scullery. It had a strong iron boiler and would be able to warm the dining hall. This estimate included the cost of installation and maintenance for one year. Bedsteads were a different matter. Many now in the old Workhouses could be used in the new building. Double beds and large single beds could be reduced in size and painted a dark stone colour. Estimates would be obtained for this work.

Dr Smith attended one meeting and offered the Furnishing Committee helpful suggestions about articles that were 'desirable to be used in the new Workhouse'. His advice that an entirely new stock of beds should be obtained was not taken but the Committee did accept his offer to go to London to see the other items that had been suggested. These included woollen rugs with a red stripe, mackintosh sheets, chairs to be placed between the beds, lockers, screens for the infirmary and flock beds to replace the existing straw beds. Some items, including water beds, were 'left for consideration' but 50 new beds costing 14s each were ordered and later 50 flock beds with bolsters and pillows at 14s per set were added to the list.

On June 12th 1867 the Guardians visited the new Workhouse. The building work, which should have been finished by June 1st, was still not completed. Mr Grover's request for an extension of two months was agreed but with a £100 penalty if the work failed to be completed by August 12th. Mr Woodman was asked to get the main building finished 'forthwith' so preparations could be made for the transfer of paupers from the old Workhouses. In the meantime much remained to be done.

In addition to the main building work, stables and a coach house were to be built behind the Porter's Lodge and a separate building erected for fumigating clothes. Old piggeries in the grounds were to be repaired and two paupers, Beedel and Wheeler, were directed to do this work. Very little in the way of fixtures and fittings from the old Workhouses could be reused in the new Workhouse apart from some benches which were to be fixed up in the dining room.

The Appointment of Workhouse Staff

Although most of the daily tasks in the Workhouse, such as cleaning, cooking, laundry and gardening, would be undertaken by the paupers themselves, paid staff had to be employed to take charge and organise the routine on behalf of the Guardians. The most important position was that of the Master who, with his wife acting as the Matron or housekeeper, would direct the daily lives of the inmates and supervise the work of the other staff. This was a most responsible and onerous job and entailed keeping numerous books and records which had to be presented to the Guardians at their weekly meetings. On May 2nd 1867 the positions of Master and Matron for the new Reading Union Workhouse were advertised in the local papers and also in *Knight's Official Circular*. The Guardians stipulated that the candidates must be competent at their jobs and that they should be aged between 35 and 45 years. The Master would be paid a salary of £65 per year and the Matron £35 per year. They would be provided with an unfurnished apartment, rations, gas, coals and washing.

There were 48 replies to the advertisement. All the applicants were couples who had held positions as Master and Matron or Schoolmaster and Matron at other Poor Law unions and were therefore familiar with the demands of the jobs and the requirements of the Poor Law Board. They came from as far away as Cambridge, London and Stoke-on-Trent as well as places nearer such as Basingstoke and Chippenham. The Matron of St Lawrence's Reading and the Master and Matron of St Mary's Reading also applied. A short list of 14 couples was later reduced to eight whose references as to 'general capabilities and moral character' were required from their previous unions. A final six couples were interviewed and on June 13th Mr and Mrs Pocock from the Melksham Union, Trowbridge were appointed to take up their posts on June 24th. Mr Pocock was asked to supply a personal security of £100 and he and his wife were each required to provide bonds of £150.

Mr and Mrs Pocock had four children and the Poor Law Board stipulated that £5 a year should be charged for every child over three years of age. It was usual for this charge to be paid by the guardians of a union but in this case the Reading Guardians decided that Mr Pocock should pay this himself and for every child over two years of age. As Mr Pocock's youngest child was 18 months old and the others four, six and eight years, a total of £15 would be deducted from his salary each year. The Guardians did agree to furnish the two sitting rooms in his apartment in the main Workhouse building, leaving him to furnish the bedrooms. A small room was also made available for his use as an office.

The job of Porter was also advertised in the local papers and in *Knight's Official Circular*. Candidates should be unmarried or widowed, 'without encumbrances' and not older than 45 years. They should be competent in baking and able to superintend the garden work. The salary would be £25 per year with a furnished apartment, rations, gas, coal and washing. There were five applicants but only one, Francis Talbot, was considered suitable. He was aged 43 and was the Porter at Newhaven Workhouse. He was asked to attend an interview but only if he felt he was 'thoroughly competent to undertake the baking'. Unfortunately Talbot felt he had only 'limited experience' at baking so another candidate was required.

Mr Henry Smith and his wife Sophia, who had been employed at the District School at Wargrave for eight years, were asked to attend an interview. Mrs Smith had references from Mr Cheeseman, the Superintendent of the school, as she had been in charge of the steam cooking apparatus at the school for that time and had managed it satisfactorily. The Guardians appointed the Smiths – Mr Smith as the

Porter and Superintendent of the Baking and Gardening at £25 per year and Mrs Smith as Assistant Matron or Storekeeper and Superintendent of the Steam Cooking Apparatus at £15 a year with lodgings, rations and washing. They would take up their posts on July 8th and work under and by the direction of the Master and Matron. The Porter would take charge of the keys, superintend the men at work and the removal of the altered bedsteads. Mrs Smith would arrange for pauper women to alter the sacking to fit the bedsteads and supervise the work.

The Appointment of a Chaplain

There was no chapel in the new Workhouse and services would be held in the dining room. The Revd G T Tubbs, the senior Chaplain to the Reading Union, was offered the appointment of Chaplain with a salary of £60 per year. He would be required to take a short service on Sunday mornings between 9.30 am and 10.30 am, a full service on Sunday afternoons and possibly services on Wednesday and Friday mornings. Mr Tubbs accepted the position but remarked that he felt the salary to be somewhat lower than it should be in view of the work entailed. The provision of a new surplice, Bible and prayer book was later altered when it was found that a surplice and Bible at the old St Mary's Workhouse could still be used and only a new prayer book was needed.

The Appointment of a Medical Officer

When the Reading Union was formed in 1835 one Medical Officer was appointed to attend all the Poor Law patients including those in the Union Workhouses. The appointment was made by advertising for tenders and the contract lasted for one year only. This system caused much resentment and the following year the Guardians agreed to appoint three Medical Officers, one for each parish, with those for St Mary's and St Lawrence's parishes to include the Workhouses in their districts. These appointments were still to be made through tenders and for one year only. This system was changed in 1842 when a Medical Order of the Poor Law Commissioners directed that medical appointments should be advertised with a fixed salary and for life unless otherwise stipulated and could only be terminated by resignation, legal disqualification or dismissal.

In June 1867, with the building almost completed, the Guardians had to appoint a Medical Officer to attend the paupers in the new Workhouse and Mr J L Walford, the senior Medical Officer in the Union, was offered the position. Mr Walford had been the Medical Officer for St Lawrence's parish and Workhouse since 1840. When the Guardians offered him the position of Medical Officer to the new Workhouse at a salary of £120 a year (£110 for the Workhouse and £10 for the Tramp Wards) he accepted but said the salary was less than he had expected but hoped it might be increased should the Board feel his experience justified it. In view of his other medical commitments he decided he would now resign his appointment as Medical Officer for St Lawrence's parish.

Mr Walford was born in Essex in 1812 and held the dual qualifications in medicine and surgery required by the Poor Law Board – LSA (Licentiate of the Society of Apothecaries) in 1833 and MRCS (Member of the Royal College of Surgeons) in 1837. He set up practice in Reading and was also appointed an Honorary Surgeon at the Reading Dispensary. In addition to his Union work he became a member of the Town Council in 1850, Mayor in 1855 and later an Alderman and JP. In 1866 he was appointed Medical Officer for the District of Reading under the Prevention of Diseases Act. His duties required him to inspect the streets, courts, alleys and other areas in the District and to report on the sanitary conditions to the local Board of Health from time to time. He was a Director of the Reading Cemetery Company and a member

Mr Walford, Workhouse Medical Officer 1867–82

of the Reading Pathological Society which had been founded in 1841 (one of the oldest medical societies in the country), where he was a regular contributor to their meetings.

It was Mr Walford's suggestion in 1867 that the Guardians should subscribe to the Royal Berkshire Hospital. The infirmaries at the two old Workhouses had no operating theatres and the facilities at the new Workhouse infirmary would not be any better. Relations between the Hospital and the Reading Guardians had always been strained. The Hospital, built and maintained by voluntary subscriptions and donations, had opened in May 1839 amid much celebration and acclaim. The handsome building, on the four-acre site given by Lord Sidmouth, was the only hospital in the county and its opening had filled a great need in the community. Patients were admitted by ticket on the recommendation of a subscriber, the number of patients allowed being in proportion to the size of the subscription. Only those deemed to be 'worthy objects of charity' were eligible for admission and the cost of the treatment was covered by the annual subscription or donation. Accident and emergency cases were admitted without a ticket but, if able, these patients were asked to contribute towards the cost of their treatment.

In many instances the Reading Guardians had become involved as often those who met with accidents had technically made themselves casual paupers and thereby became the responsibility of the parish in which they

17

had gained settlement. On these occasions the Hospital asked the Guardians to pay 7s (35p) per week for the maintenance of each patient. They refused to pay and declined to subscribe to the Hospital as they believed their Medical Officers had been contracted to attend all paupers in the Union regardless of the circumstances.

Since 1839 there had been great advances in surgery. The advent of anaesthetics in 1847 made operations easier to perform and since 1866 the benefits of antiseptic treatment were shown in the improved recovery rate of patients. The Poor Law Board had always recommended that unions should subscribe to their local hospitals to enable them to send the most serious cases of accident or illness there. By 1867 Reading was the only Union for many miles that did not subscribe. It was only in the middle of that year, when Mr Walford reported that an inmate at one of the Workhouse infirmaries was likely to need his leg amputated and there was no convenient place in which to perform the operation, that the Guardians changed their minds. It was arranged that the Union would make an annual subscription of six guineas (£6 6s or £6 30p) which would enable the Guardians to send three in-patients to the Hospital each year and to have four out-patients always on the books.

Preparing the Move to the New Workhouse

By the time the Poor Law Board had officially sanctioned the Union's subscription to the Royal Berkshire Hospital the new Workhouse was well on the way to completion. As soon as Mr Pocock, the Master, took over on July 20th he started to make arrangements for the transfer of paupers from the old Workhouses to the new. Two women had been hired to clean the premises. They had been supplied with soap and soda and were paid 2s 6d (12p) per week. The main building now had to be furnished as quickly as possible. St Lawrence's Workhouse would be cleared first to enable Messrs Brown to start work on the apartment for the Relieving Officer, the Board Room and Tramp Wards. From August 1st all infirmary cases would be transferred from St Lawrence's Workhouse to St Mary's to which all new paupers and maternity cases would also be admitted.

Within a week Mr Pocock was able to report that the steam cooking apparatus had been installed and tested and all spare articles like forms, tables and fenders, had been removed from the old Workhouses. There were still a considerable number of items at St Lawrence's Workhouse which could be adapted for the new and the clock in the kitchen could be repaired and reused. Various things like mats, door scrapers, dusters, scales, brushes and a bell were still required and also cabbage seeds and 500 celery plants for the garden.

The Appointment of a Nurse

During the first week in August 41 paupers were transferred from St Lawrence's Workhouse to the new Workhouse. There was still much to be done at the new building. The laundry had not yet been completed and the infirmary was far from ready and unlikely to be fit for occupation by August 12th. The roof had sunk in two or three places, in some wards lime whiting had been used instead of size whiting and the painting and glazing work was behind schedule. Nevertheless that week advertisements were placed in the newspapers for the position of Nurse at the new Workhouse infirmary. Applicants should be female, single or widowed, aged not less than 25 years. The salary would be £20 per year with rations, washing and a furnished apartment. Candidates should apply in their own handwriting giving details of previous and present employment with testimonials as to character and qualifications. All applications were to be received by August 21st. The election would take place on August 29th by which time the infirmary should have been completed and ready for occupation.

The building and staffing of the infirmary had come at a time when such buildings and the standards of nursing within them were subject to much criticism. The Guardians had already seen this when Dr Smith noted the unsuitability of the original infirmary plans. As the Medical Officer for the Poor Law Board he had written a circular letter in May 1865 about nursing in the sick wards of workhouses. Little had changed since 1847 when the duties of a nurse were 'to attend the sick in sick and lying-in wards and to administer to them all medicines and medical applications according to the direction of the medical officer, to inform the medical officer of any defects which may be observed in the arrangements of the sick or lying-in ward, and to take care that a light is kept on at night in the sick ward'. To these directions had been added the requirement that a nurse should be able to read but there was no reference as to hours or conditions and nothing about training. At this time most unions used paupers as nurses and it was at the discretion of the guardians whether they should receive any pay, and most did not. In many respects Dr Smith's letter of 1865 was disappointing. The directions of 1847 were repeated, adding that nurses should be suitable and experienced and carefully vetted before being appointed. As they held positions of great responsibility they should be adequately remunerated. If necessary a paid assistant could be employed. The subject of training was not mentioned.

Trained nurses were only just beginning to be required by hospitals and few workhouse infirmaries considered employing them. Until 1866 no trained nurses were employed at the Royal Berkshire Hospital. By that time the Hospital had expanded from 50 to 120 beds. The staff still consisted of the Matron / Housekeeper, whose salary was £70 per year, and four nurses, each of whom was paid £20 a year. In 1866 the Hospital's Board of Management decided that trained nurses were now essential and following advice from Florence Nightingale and others an agreement was made with the Bath Home for Trained Nurses that a trained Superintendent Nurse (salary £70) and three trained nurses (one at £30 and two at £20) would be supplied. Probationers would also be taken for training and if later engaged as nurses they would be paid £20 a year. Within a short time the nursing staff had been increased to ten.

By comparison the Workhouse infirmary was but a poor relation. The Nurse would be expected to look after 75 patients in the main infirmary as well as up to six cases in the fever wards. The backgrounds of the eight applicants bore witness to the type of 'nurse' one might expect. Mr Walford had recommended that someone who 'understood midwifery' should be appointed but the non-medical Guardians had no other guidance than their own judgement. One of the applicants had been the housekeeper at Reading Borough Police Station and a female searcher, one had been a needlewoman, another had been a nurse in private families, four had been nurses in workhouses at St Margaret's Westminster, Birmingham, Cruddington in Salop and Dover.

Mrs Bloxsom, aged 38, late Matron of Linton Union Workhouse in Cambridgeshire, appeared to be the most promising, although as a matron it is doubtful if she had much experience in nursing. She was asked to attend an interview and would be allowed £1 8s 3d (£1.41p) for the cost of her second class railway ticket. Mrs Bloxsom made a good impression. She 'produced original testimonials which were satisfactory' and had 'attended midwifery cases'. Her two dependent children aged 10 and 11 years would not be living at the Workhouse. She was appointed to the job and would start work on September 11th.

On August 26th members of the Board of Guardians inspected the new Workhouse accompanied by Mr Woodman, the architect. He reported that the Workhouse was now complete except for the Porter's Lodge and Committee Room which still had to be painted. He pointed out various defects in the work but none was believed to 'affect the stability of the structure'. The Guardians officially resolved they would now take possession of the building and Mr Grover, the contractor, agreed to make good all the defects by December 26th. He expressed his gratitude that the Guardians had not demanded the £100 penalty for late completion.

Diets and Tenders

In May 1867 Dr Smith had reported to the Poor Law Board the results of his study of workhouse diets and offered guidelines on the diets that should be used in these institutions. The Reading Guardians sent for a copy of the report. Dr Smith believed that food should be 'plain and wholesome, the quantity sufficient without being excessive and the composition and cooking such as to render it palatable so that waste can be avoided either from the food being more than the inmates require or from the food being distasteful to them'. In September the Chairman and Vice-Chairman, with the assistance of Mr Walford, prepared diet tables for the new Workhouse inmates, no doubt bearing in mind Dr Smith's guidelines. Mr Walford would decide on the diets of infirmary patients and beer would only be given on his direction. The suggestion that tea should be 'milked as well as sugared' was not adopted.

Prices had risen considerably over the two years it had taken to plan and build the new Workhouse. In October 1865 the weekly cost of maintenance for each indoor pauper had been 3s 1d (about 15p). By December that year it had risen to 3s 9d (about 18p) and by June 1867 it had almost doubled to 5s 10d (28p) per week. It was therefore important that the best prices should be obtained when placing the six-monthly orders for provisions and drapery in the middle of September.

There were several replies to the advertisements for tenders and the following were accepted:

From Mr Charles Moss of Broad Street: Bread (best seconds) at 7d per 4lb loaf, flour at 4s 4d per sack.

From Mr Charles Willson also of Broad Street: Meat at 6d per lb, suet at 5d per lb, shins of beef at 1s 9d each. Joints for the Master and Officers at 7½d per lb.

Mr R W Randall would supply milk at 10d per gallon.

Other grocery items included tea at 1s 8d per lb, coffee at 1s 2d per lb, tea for the officers at 2s 5d per lb, sugar at 3½d per lb, butter at 10½d per lb, bacon at 70s (£3.50) per cwt, yellow soap at 36s (£1.80) per cwt, candles at 5s 4d per dozen lb.

Tenders for drapery were accepted from Messrs J W Hopkins:

Dowlas (a type of strong linen) at 9½d per yard, stout calico at 6d per yard, grogram (a coarse mixture of silk, mohair and wool) 1s 3½d per yard, flannel at 11½d per yard, check linen at 8½d per yard, sheeting at 3½d per yard; Women's bonnets at 6s 11d per dozen, girls' bonnets at 5s 11d per dozen, stays at 1s 9d per pair, men's and women's neckerchiefs at 6s 6d per dozen.

Messrs Simmonds, the Bridge Street brewers, would supply ale at 1s per gallon and table beer at 9d per gallon.

Over the following weeks a variety of practical matters had to be attended to. Frederick J Brown was appointed to be the Workhouse barber. He would shave the men twice a week and cut their hair when necessary. His salary of £20 a year would be paid quarterly.

Inevitably there would be several deaths each month among the inmates. Many were old, frail and suffered chronic diseases while others were admitted with fatal illnesses. Arrangements had to be made for these funerals. Mr Dunn's quotation for funerals for indoor paupers was accepted.

For those aged 8 weeks and under............................... 15s 0d
2 months to 12 months...................... 18s 0d
1 year to 5 years £1 1s 6d
5 years to under 10 years............... £1 5s 6d
10 years to 15 years...................... £1 12s 0d
15 years and upwards................... £1 17s 0d

It was agreed that Mr Dunn would buy the old workhouse hearse for £4.

Mr Pocock, the Master, would allow leave to any pauper 'who might desire to follow a deceased inmate to the grave'. On such occasions it was customary to allow each man attending a funeral to have bread and cheese and be given 3d.

Arrangements were also made for the paupers to cultivate the workhouse grounds. Messrs Suttons had given a quantity of evergreens and shrubs to be planted in front of the main building. At the back the piggeries had been renovated and during September were stocked with eight store pigs costing 12s 6d each and six others at 32s each. A land produce and farm account would now be kept.

During September the paupers remaining in the old Workhouses were gradually transferred to the new building and new paupers admitted directly. Owing to delays in completing the building work, the infirmary and Nurse's room were the last to be furnished. A few days before Mrs Bloxsom was due to start work the Guardians authorised that furniture 'considered actually necessary' should now be obtained for this building. By the end of September the whole Workhouse, including the infirmary, was occupied and the old Workhouses were declared empty. The total cost had come to £13,747 18s 6d which included the price of the site, the building and furnishing costs and the architect's fees.

The New Workhouse

The new Workhouse was described by one observer as more like a large public school than a Poor Law institution. Built of red brick with slate roofs, the architecture was said to be 'plain Elizabethan style'. All agreed it had been built 'in a very healthy situation where there is the advantage of plenty of pure air'.

The entrance from the Oxford Road was between Battle Terrace and Battle Place, some yards further down the road than in later years. Iron gates by the road led to massive doors inside a lofty archway. On the left of the entrance was the Porter's Lodge and on the right a Committee Room. Behind these on either side were the men's and women's Receiving Wards, bathrooms and lavatories. It was to these buildings that the paupers came when the Relieving Officer, based at the old St Lawrence's Workhouse in Thorn Street, gave them tickets of admission. When they were first admitted the paupers were examined by the Medical Officer who decided how they should be classified and to which part of the Workhouse they should be admitted.

The Porter's Lodge, Committee Room and Receiving Wards were all single storey buildings. The main Workhouse building was directly behind the Receiving Wards and separated from them by airing (or exercise) yards. It was an imposing two-storey building, constructed so that the various categories of paupers were housed completely separately as required by the Poor Law Board. The men and women were on different sides, the men on the left (west) and the women on the right (east). Each side was subdivided into four categories, aged and infirm, married, unmarried and imbeciles. The two sides were identical in plan with day rooms on the ground floor and dormitories above. There was a main staircase but, as every section was self-contained, each had its own staircase with its own dormitory, bathroom and lavatory. Only the imbecile wards had their dormitories on the ground floor adjoining their bathrooms and day rooms. A long corridor ran the width of the building, at each end of which was a door to the grounds. A third door on the south side, facing the Receiving Wards, formed the main entrance to the building, on either side of which were the Master's rooms.

In the front rooms, facing Oxford Road, were day wards for the aged and infirm and day wards and dormitories for the imbeciles. Behind these wards was the main corridor with day rooms for married and unmarried paupers. There was no accommodation for married couples, a fact that caused distress and gave rise to much criticism. On the women's side there was also a nursery for young children. Older children were not accommodated in the Workhouse and since 1850 had been sent to the District School in Wargrave where pauper children from both the Reading and Wokingham Unions were cared for[2].

The kitchen, scullery, larder and storage areas were situated centrally behind the day wards and adjoining the airing yards for the single and married paupers. The dining-room cum chapel was behind the kitchen area and was accessible by a short corridor. The rows of chairs had been designed so that the backs could be turned up to form narrow tables. Thus the needs of both a chapel and dining-room had been met. There were more airing yards on either side of the dining-room with workshops at the back of those on the men's side and the laundry, wash-house and drying ground at the back of those on the women's side.

The rooms in this main building were described as light and airy with whitewashed walls. The ground floor rooms had brick floors. All were heated with open coal fires (the larger rooms had two fireplaces) and each room had ventilators. The requirements of the Poor Law Board in this respect had been acknowledged. The rooms were uniformly furnished, the dormitories with two rows of beds and the day rooms with benches and tables.

The infirmary was situated well behind the main building and was very similar in design. Once again the men's and women's wards were in different parts of the building – men to the left and women to the right. There were seven wards on each side including convalescent wards. There was also a lying-in or maternity ward on the ground floor. On each side of the building there was a padded room. There were airing yards at the front and back. At the back of the men's airing yard behind the infirmary there was a mortuary and on the women's side the wash-house and a storage area. The Nurse had her own bedroom and kitchen but there was no operating theatre or surgeon's room. At the back of the infirmary, between the men's and women's airing yards was a small single-storey building with two wards for 'dirty' cases. It came to be known as 'The

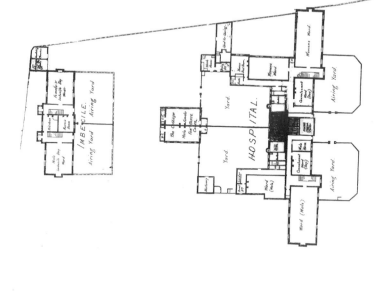

Reading Union Workhouse

This is the only known ground plan of the Workhouse which shows the original layout. Dating from 1889 the only significant difference from the 1867 plan is the change of use of the building behind the infirmary/hospital from fever wards to imbecile wards.

Reading Union Workhouse

Cottage' and was where infectious and contagious cases were placed. The fever wards were in a separate one-storey building behind the infirmary.

Over the next three months a regular routine was gradually established. Complaint notices, as used at the Bradfield Union, were hung up in each room. These informed the paupers that those with complaints should write to the Clerk of the Union or make the complaint in person before the Visiting Committee.

In October the Lancet Commission notified the Guardians that they would probably be visiting the Reading Workhouse to make a report. This Commission, composed of three doctors, had been set up by the Lancet in 1865 to enquire into conditions in the Metropolitan District workhouses. Their enquiries were made about the same time as those carried out by Dr Smith and Mr Farnal on behalf of the Poor Law Board. Both had then turned their attention to provincial workhouses and in this capacity the new Workhouse at Reading was of interest.

The Lancet doctors asked if the Reading Guardians had provided any means of occupying the aged and infirm and suggested that suitable publications and periodicals should be obtained. Without waiting for the visit the Guardians agreed that the Chairman should purchase 'such a quantity of publications and periodicals as he might deem suitable for the aged and infirm'. Some weeks later a visitor noted that in the aged and infirm men's and women's day rooms there were shelves with books, which 'seemed dry and uninteresting'. As well as Bibles there were periodicals such as *Sunday at Home, Cassell's Magazine, The British Workman, Old*

Jonathan, The Quiver, and *The Cottager and Artisan.* There were a few copies of local newspapers which were much appreciated. There were also some pictures on the walls depicting scenes from the Scriptures and in the dormitories texts 'printed in bold type'.

Additional items were found to be necessary. Messrs Rood and Co. of London were asked to supply 5 cwt of seaweed for beds at 16s a cwt. Some invalid chairs and bed rests were needed for the infirmary and also a 'hot water apparatus' to hold 12 dinners. As the weather got colder six dozen woollen bed rugs at 6s 8d each and woollen Witney blankets at 3s 11d a pair were ordered.

Problems also appeared. The heating and hot water system was declared to be 'absolutely useless', the chimney in the Nurse's kitchen smoked so badly the room was 'uninhabitable' and the drying apparatus in the laundry was 'defective'. Some inmates said they had been warmer and more comfortable in the old Workhouses.

Christmas Celebrations

When Christmas came special celebrations were arranged for the paupers. The dining-room was decorated with holly and ivy, banners carried the messages 'Glory to God in the Highest' and 'I wish you a Happy New Year and a Merry Christmas'. Three arches of evergreens were placed over the aisle leading from the entrance to the rostrum at the end of the room. At one o'clock the inmates assembled and were served a meal of beef followed by plum pudding and, as a treat, beer and tobacco. A visitor noted the paupers' great enjoyment of the meal. This was followed by an address by Mr Taylor, the Chairman of the Board of Guardians, who said he was glad to see the inmates appreciated the kindness that had been shown to them and he was sure it was the earnest wish of the Guardians to make them as happy and comfortable as possible. The paupers rose to their feet and 'cheered him lustily for two or three minutes' and then 'gave hearty cheers for the Guardians and the Master and Matron'. Benevolence and gratitude had been shown in abundance.

NOTES

1 The Berkshire County Mental Hospital, also known as the Moulsford Asylum or Fair Mile Hospital, was opened in 1870 in the parish of Cholsey, near Wallingford to receive patients from Berkshire. All patients from that county previously admitted to the Littlemore Asylum near Oxford were then transferred to the new hospital.
2 This school had been opened in 1850 in the former Wargrave parish workhouse in Victoria Road (now the site of the Doctors' Surgery) when a new workhouse had been built in Wokingham to cater for paupers in the Wokingham Union which included the parish of Wargrave.

2
THE EARLY YEARS
1868–1872

The first few years of the new Workhouse proved a testing time for the Board of Guardians. It was inevitable that there would be problems as the new institution was larger and more complex in its management than the two former Workhouses. It was also a time when the Poor Law Board became increasingly concerned about the standard of treatment and facilities in workhouse infirmaries.

The Death of George Wheeler
The year 1868 started badly. The day before, December 31st 1867, an inmate, George Wheeler, had burnt to death. The inquest held on January 1st and the subsequent enquiries drew attention to various shortcomings and did little to enhance the reputation of the Workhouse. George Wheeler, aged 47, was a shoemaker and relief rural postman of St Mary's parish. He had been admitted to the Workhouse on December 28th on a certificate issued by Mr Frank Workman, the Medical Officer for that parish. Mr Walford, the Workhouse Medical Officer, saw him the following day and confirmed Mr Workman's diagnosis that he was 'a person of unsound mind'. He was put in a ward in the imbecile section and left in the charge of two pauper inmates. While left unattended he threw himself on the open fire and set himself alight. He died of his burns on December 31st.

The inquest was held at the Workhouse the following day before Mr Weedon (the Coroner) and a jury. Evidence was taken from Mr Walford, Mrs Bloxsom (the Nurse), and the two pauper inmates who had been left in charge. It transpired that George Wheeler was depressed, in a feeble state, ate little, was restless but did not seem suicidal. On the Monday afternoon, while unattended, he suddenly rushed to the fireplace, which was protected only by a low fender, and attempted to get up the chimney. His screams brought the Nurse and two paupers who found him with his clothes on fire. In spite of treatment, George Wheeler died of his burns the following day. The jury returned a verdict that he had committed suicide 'by setting fire to himself while in an unsound state of mind'.

The Lunacy Commission Board sent a member, Mr Charles Palmer Phillips, to report on the circumstances of George Wheeler's death. His report coincided with one submitted by Mr Wilkes, one of the Visiting Lunacy Commissioners. These reports are most revealing and describe in some detail the workhouse system regarding those classified as imbeciles, idiots and of feeble mind.

Mr Phillips reported that it had been a grave error to send a patient in Wheeler's state to the Workhouse where there were no proper means of treating such cases. He should have been sent straight to the Asylum, although it was usual in that area for all insane patients to be sent first to the Workhouse. The Relieving Officer had not complied with certain regulations which required notice to be given within three days to a Justice of the Peace of every lunatic coming under his observation. In future the Relieving Officer should send all insane patients whenever practical straight to the Asylum without admitting them to the Workhouse.

Mr Wilkes' report stated that on either side of the main Workhouse building there were wards for six or eight insane patients of each sex. The patients were under the charge of pauper inmates to whom the Guardians were considering giving small allowances for their work. The wards had cheerful day rooms and dormitories with bathrooms and lavatories. At the time of his report Mr Wilkes found there were a total of 22 inmates of unsound mind in the Workhouse. Of these 8 were men and 14 were women, half of whom were in the imbecile wards and the remainder either in the infirmary or in the main building. He found that two of those in the infirmary should probably have been in the Asylum as their 'dirty habits' caused great annoyance and trouble. All the patients were clean and well-clothed, the rooms were clean and well-ventilated and the beds 'in good order'. The diet was tea with bread and butter for breakfast and supper, and for dinner meat and beer.

Mr Wilkes made several recommendations including that high fenders should be put in the wards for insane inmates. He noted that a belt for confining the hands was hanging up in the male imbecile room. This should be removed and never used without the sanction of the Master or Medical Officer. He drew attention to the fact that there was no hot water in the bathroom and there was no Visiting Committee book. In the infirmary the Nurse should have a book in which to enter the names of all patients placed in the padded cells with the date and length of time they were secluded. The Guardians acknowledged these reports and stated that some points had already been rectified and others were being considered by the Visiting Committee.

A visitor to the Workhouse soon after George Wheeler's death described the male imbecile ward and the infirmary. There were five patients in the male imbecile ward, three men and two boys with a male pauper in charge. As noted by Mr Wilkes, the ward and dormitory were clean and cheerful. The infirmary was different. It was almost full and the women's side was particularly crowded with the beds far too close together. In one ward, full of very ill patients, 'the heated atmosphere combined with the effluvia rising from so many sick persons was almost intolerable …

and how a sick person could live there was a mystery'. The visitor made one very telling observation that, with the increasing population of the Union, it was almost inevitable that the Workhouse would before long prove to be too small and the infirmary inadequate. 'This was a question which, sooner or later, the Guardians would have to consider.' The Workhouse at this time had been open for less than six months.

The Poor Law Board in its Report for 1867–68 had drawn attention to the fact that the sick wards of the workhouses were originally provided for paupers in the workhouse who might become ill and 'not as State hospitals into which all the sick poor of the country might be received for medical treatment and care'. However there can be no doubt that many paupers receiving outdoor relief were admitted to their union workhouse infirmaries when they became ill and could not be looked after at home.

Problems of Sanitation

Even while enquiries were being made into George Wheeler's death a most difficult and persistent problem arose. Mr Woodman, the architect, had warned the Guardians when the Workhouse was being built that there would probably be problems with the lavatories and drainage. When the Vachel Almshouses in Castle Street had been rebuilt a few years earlier the residents, unaccustomed to the then modern conveniences, had put bricks, rags, bones and sticks down the drains. Mr Woodman's prediction came true and in January 1868, when the Workhouse cesspits were found to be overflowing, it was discovered that all the taps were full on in the upper bathrooms of the main building as well as one in the wash-house and two in the infirmary. All sorts of items such as cloths were discovered in the cesspits. Notices were put up in all the bathrooms warning that if these offences continued those responsible would be punished. Various inmates were told to see that the taps were turned off and the able-bodied were directed to dig out an extra cesspit and channels to take the water into the drains.

In spite of these measures the following month Mr Woodman described the cesspool system as 'utterly useless' and recommended that an additional piece of land should be purchased to enable ditches in the area to take the sewage outfall. Unfortunately the land in question was not available for purchase at that time. It was then suggested that the lavatories could be adapted to earth closets, although this would not solve the problem of disposing of the waste water from the wash-house.

Nothing was decided and within months there were complaints that offensive overflows were injurious to the health of the inhabitants of Battle Place and Battle Terrace. The Guardians considered connecting the drains to the main sewer but when the lowest tender proved to be £1,225 the idea was dropped. Instead the system of earth closets would be adopted with waste water used to irrigate the lower ground. Advertisements for tenders appeared in the papers and that of Mr Beard of Brighton for £325 was accepted as being the lowest.

By this time it was September and when Mr Beard's tender was sent to the Poor Law Board for approval the Guardians were told they could proceed as the matter was urgent but the system did not appear to be satisfactory and would be regarded as an experiment. The plan, by today's standards, was appalling. Solid matter would be mixed with earth and spread on the garden adjoining the Workhouse. Liquids of all kinds would be distributed directly through open channels over the remaining Workhouse property 'in the manner pursued when irrigating farming land'.

In January 1869 a separate building was erected for preparing the dry earth for the closets and the following September it was noted that the system was working satisfactorily. It had been nearly two years since the problem had arisen and even then the so-called solution was by no means ideal.

Inmates' Complaints
No sooner had the drainage problem become apparent in January 1868 than another was brought to the attention of the Guardians. The Poor Law Board had received an anonymous letter from some inmates complaining that their diet was 'contrary to the rules of the Poor Law Board'. The letter also stated that: 'There are a class of people going out day after day and getting drunk and we don't dare look or speak about it ... if we make any complaint it is not took any notice of it so we took and wrote to the headquarters about it.' The letter also stated that a pauper was doing the Porter's work which he paid for and the pauper was carried in drunk at night. Furthermore there were 16 beds in one room not 2 feet apart. The letter ended: 'Gentlemen, I hope you will see into it for the poor inmates of the Reading new Workhouse.' It was signed: 'From the inmates of the Reading Union.'

The Guardians acknowledged receipt of the letter and instructed the Visiting Committee to make enquiries. They reported that all the paupers questioned denied any knowledge of the letter and said they were well satisfied with the diet and general management of the Workhouse. Whether there was any truth behind the allegations will never be known but no doubt it encouraged the Guardians to keep a stricter eye on the running of the institution.

The New Tramp Wards
Meanwhile it had been decided that the former St Mary's Workhouse should be sold as it was no longer of use to the Union. The Churchwardens of that parish agreed that a proportion of the proceeds of the sale, estimated to be about £800, would be used towards the cost of the new Workhouse. The Poor Law Board had suggested that the Guardians should buy the former St Lawrence's Workhouse which belonged to St Lawrence's parish. As only a portion of the building was now required for a Board Room, accommodation for the Relieving Officer and new Tramp Wards, it was decided to rent that part of the building now needed by

Union for 30s (£1.50p) per month. The remaining part of the building was sold by the parish in 1870.

Messrs Brown's alterations to the old St Lawrence's Workhouse had been proceeding steadily. The Relieving Officer's accommodation and the Board Room had already been finished and by the end of March 1868 the new Tramp Wards had been completed, fitted out and were ready for occupation. The wards in the Forbury could now be closed.

The entrance to the Tramp Wards was in Thorn Street and on each side of the door were notices informing the tramps of the terms upon which they would be admitted. Immediately inside there was a room for the Porter on one side and a bathroom and lavatory on the other. Beyond were the wards with men on one side of the building and women on the other. These ground floor wards were equipped only with benches and straw on the floor for bedding. The floor above was to be used by vagrants who were not in good health and the wards were furnished with some of the old iron bedsteads from the former Workhouses. There were two rooms for each sex, one to be used as an infirmary and the other as a sleeping room.

Tramps requiring overnight accommodation had to obtain a ticket from the Superintendent of the Borough Police and take it to the Tramp Wards to obtain admission from Mr Bonner, the Superintendent of Vagrancy, who was also the Relieving Officer. He was assisted by the Porter and, if necessary, the police. Mr Bonner was authorised to direct any or all the tramps to take a bath on admission. In some unions the tramps' clothing was fumigated but at this time the Reading Union did not have the necessary equipment. This was to lead to complaints of filthy, verminous bedding.

In return for overnight accommodation with supper and breakfast of 6 ounces of bread and water, those tramps who were fit enough had to perform various tasks. The men had to pick 1lb of oakum or break 1 bushel of stones and the women had to pick ½lb of oakum or do housework, no task to last longer than four hours. The workrooms for the oakum picking and stone breaking were at the back of the building. Sometimes the tramps were too ill to leave the next morning and remained in the infirmary wards until they were able to move on. Here they were attended by Mr Walford, the Medical Officer, and nursed and cooked for by Mrs Bonner who received £7 7s a year for this work. Tramps who became very ill were transferred to the Workhouse infirmary.

A few weeks after the new Tramp Wards were opened there were complaints that a policeman had admitted a tramp who appeared to be drunk and had put him in one of the beds in the men's upper ward instead of on a straw bed on the ground floor. When the tramp left the following morning his bed was found 'in a filthy condition'. It transpired that the man was 'a foreigner' who had walked from Maidenhead. He had been found by the policeman between 2am and 3am wet through and exhausted but not drunk and had been treated accordingly.

Poor Law Unions had a statutory obligation to provide overnight accommodation for tramps passing through their area. Reading, situated on the main roads between London and Bath, Southampton and Oxford, attracted many travellers on foot who could not afford to pay for lodgings. Many undertook their journeys in search of work and were not tramps in the usual sense of the word and were considered to be 'a better class of tramp'. Others were proper vagrants who used tramp wards in order to get from one place to another as a way of life. During its first year some 4,366 tramps were accommodated at the new Tramp Wards in Reading.

Development of the Land

Back at the Workhouse great strides were being made in developing the land. The pigs had proved to be a profitable undertaking and in February 1868 £47 10s was raised by their sale. It was decided to expand the farming side and in April a Garden and Farm Committee was formed consisting of three Guardians who would 'superintend the management of the garden and farm'. Inmates who were fit enough provided the labour. Six more pigs were bought at £1 3s each. Two cows costing £37 10s were also purchased and a dairy was then set up complete with a churn, butter tub and a print with which to decorate the butter.

The Porter, who had been managing the garden, was now working under the direction of the new Committee. The garden was most productive with fruit, including strawberries, cherries and rhubarb, and a variety of vegetables (including asparagus) available for sale. At first the Master sent various inmates into the town to sell the produce but later it was sold direct to greengrocers and market traders. In the autumn a hedge was planted round the Workhouse garden using 1,500 hornbeam plants costing 6s (30p) per hundred. A successful market garden had now been established in conjunction with the Workhouse.

There had always been a problem with seasonal unemployment when able-bodied men were laid off work and had to receive poor relief. Many became inmates of the Workhouse. In November 1869 the Guardians formed a Labour Committee to find out if employment could be obtained for these men to enable 'the labour of the paupers to be made productive'. The Committee advised that the gravel on the south-west side of the Workhouse grounds should be dug and sold from time to time. This would provide not only employment but also a profitable sideline. A shed near the farm buildings would be necessary. As this would be behind the public house belonging to Messrs Blandy and Hawkins, a boundary wall, estimated to cost between £140 and £160, would have to be built. A Superintendent of Labour should be employed, candidates to be between 30 and 40 years of age and competent to undertake the supervision of able-bodied paupers. They should 'thoroughly understand garden operations and the management of cattle and pigs'. The salary would be £25 per year with rations, lodgings and washing.

Demands upon the Staff

By this time the Workhouse building, unlike the grounds, had undergone little change but the work of the staff had become more demanding. When the Chaplain, Mr Tubbs, was criticised for not giving a sermon at the Sunday morning services, he replied that with 200 inmates there was a great deal of work. It was agreed that he would take a short service at 9.15am on Sundays with a full service at 3pm. On Wednesdays at 10am he would take the usual service consisting of the Litany and give a half-hour sermon. He pointed out that this was in addition to visiting the sick and infirm and, as he had to give a large stipend to his curate, he suggested his salary should be increased from £60 to £100 per year. The Guardians were unmoved and it was not until June 1869, some 17 months later, that they agreed to increase his salary by £20 to £80 per year. This was about the same time as the Poor Law Board required all unions to allow Roman Catholic priests to visit inmates of that faith in the workhouses.

Mr Walford, the Medical Officer, also felt his work deserved a higher salary. In December 1868 he pointed out to the Guardians that his duties at the Workhouse had turned out to be 'more onerous than expected' and it was often difficult to find room for the different types of patients. He was in sole charge of the patients at the Workhouse and Tramp Wards and, in the case of lunatics, he had to run the risk of 'coming into collision with the Lunacy Commission'. He had to pay £30 a year for a dispenser and this, plus the cost of drugs and horse hire, left him with about £30 out of his annual salary of £120. His request for a rise in salary was not granted until April 1870 when the Guardians agreed to an increase of £20 which gave him a salary of £140 a year.

In the case of Mrs Bloxsom, the Nurse, the Guardians were more considerate. Within six months of her appointment her salary had been raised from £20 to £25 per year 'on account of the heavy duties she had to perform'. When this rise was queried by the Poor Law Board the Guardians replied that they believed £20 was not an adequate remuneration for her services. The Guardians had also arranged for two paupers to help her: Mary Walden to act as an additional nurse in the infirmary with a salary of £1 6s per year and Mary Ann Allen to take charge of the idiots and imbeciles with a salary of £2 12s per year. Both would be allowed accommodation, rations and washing.

Mrs Bloxsom was so highly regarded that she was allowed to have her two children lodged at Battle Terrace and visit her each day. However, when the children developed scarlet fever and the Poor Law Inspector found them living at the Workhouse, Mrs Bloxsom was told they must leave and in future could only visit her with permission from the Master. Many poor widows with children took jobs in workhouses to enable their children to be looked after privately and avoid the stigma of pauperism. Before trained nurses were employed at the Royal Berkshire Hospital, several 'nurses' were pauper widows who were anxious to keep their children out of the workhouse.

The Need to Enlarge the Infirmary

The prediction made in January 1868 that before long the Workhouse would prove to be too small and the infirmary inadequate, became true all too soon. Overcrowded wards with not enough room to separate patients properly, overworked staff and the dropping of standards became apparent and were commented on in the regular reports of the Poor Law Inspector and the Inspector for the Commission in Lunacy. Minor details, such as the lack of bedpans and mackintosh sheets for the infirmary, were easily put right. A stretcher, similar to the one used at the Royal Berkshire Hospital, was acquired, also invalid chairs and bed rests. A badly-needed drying closet was built in the infirmary yard adjoining the wash-room. But the most critical problem was a lack of space and this crisis came at a time when the Poor Law Board was giving much attention to improving the conditions of workhouse infirmaries.

Poor Law Unions had always been encouraged to subscribe to local hospitals to enable paupers who were very ill to have the benefit of the medical expertise and facilities which only hospitals could supply. While acknowledging that the workhouse infirmaries did not bear comparison with the local hospitals, the Poor Law Board emphasised that it was highly important that they 'should be supplied with all reasonable and proper appliances for the treatment of diseases of all kinds'. Furthermore it was essential that they should be clean, have sufficient space, provide good nursing and do 'everything which may tend to promote a cure or alleviate suffering'.

In the middle of 1868 the Poor Law Board issued two memoranda specifying the 'Points to be attended to in the Construction of Workhouses' and 'Points to be attended to as regards Fittings and Medical Appliances'. The first was of particular interest to architects planning new workhouses or adapting old ones. The importance of designing buildings suitable for the various categories of inmates was stressed and also the necessity for proper spacing of beds. 'The length of wards should be calculated according to the following minimum wall space for each bed: for dormitories only 4 feet, for ordinary sick wards 6 feet, for lying-in, fever and small-pox wards 7 to 8 feet.'

The second memorandum, 'Points to be attended to as regards Fittings and Medical Appliances', included details on every conceivable aspect of workhouse fittings including crockery, furniture and size of beds. Under 'Lavatories and Baths' it stated: 'Roller towels on rollers should be supplied at least twice a week, and in the proportion of not less than one to six inmates. The towels should be dried after the morning's use and the lavatory kept dry and clean.' Under 'Sick Wards' it noted that the fittings should be similar to those provided in general hospitals and described in detail the size of beds, the type of mattresses, the need for two sheets and two or three blankets and a cheerful rug for each bed. There should be a sufficient supply of brushes and combs in each ward and they must be kept clean and in good order. Among the items listed were medicine glasses, feeding bottles, spittoons, urinals, mackintosh sheets, square and round mackintosh cushions with a depression in the centre to prevent bedsores, mackintosh urinals to be worn by men 'who pass urine involuntarily', one small towel 'to each person who is usually washed in bed' and 'a sufficient number of roller towels'. One of the last items was 'jackets with long sleeves for lunatics' (straitjackets).

To the Guardians these 'Memoranda' must have seemed almost incidental when compared with their immediate problems. Following his visit in September 1868, Mr Henley, the new Poor Law Inspector, reported that Joseph Wright aged 70 and his wife complained of being separated as there was no accommodation for married couples. The Guardians agreed to make arrangements for such couples to be together. Nothing was discussed about the lack of space both in the main building and in the infirmary until the following April when a Building Committee was formed 'to consider matters connected with the internal arrangements at the Workhouse'. Nothing was decided and in November 1869 the Inspector for the Commission in Lunacy drew attention once again to the lack of space. There were 21 inmates of unsound mind, one of whom had to remain in the Tramp Wards for lack of space in the Workhouse. The rest were dispersed round the building and three were in the infirmary. Here the Inspector found conditions to be unsatisfactory with crowded wards and advised that the number of beds should be reduced. The Building Committee agreed that there should be alterations to provide a further 15 to 18 beds but once again no further action was taken.

It took the Poor Law Inspector's visit in February 1870 to get things moving. Once again he drew attention to the lack of infirmary accommodation and the need to make better provision for fever cases. The following month a meeting of the Building Committee was attended by Mr Walford, the Medical Officer, who pointed out that there had been a great increase in the number of patients over the past six months and more beds were now occupied in the Tramp Wards by patients who should have been moved to the infirmary. At last the Building Committee took action and agreed unanimously to enlarge the infirmary and build new fever wards. Mr Thomas Fulkes, a Reading architect, would be asked to prepare plans. He had been one of the architects who had entered the competition for plans for the proposed Royal Berkshire Hospital in 1837. His plans had been commended and had come eighth out of 55 entries.

Within weeks Mr Fulkes had prepared plans which were sent to the Poor Law Board for approval. As if inspired at the prospect of an enlarged infirmary, the Guardians immediately ordered special blue serge jackets and trousers for the paupers who acted as male infirmary attendants. The two-storey extension to the infirmary would provide 30 additional beds which would bring the total number of beds to 100. The new fever wards, with accommodation for 24 patients, would be built on the site of the present one-storey fever wards behind the infirmary. There would be four wards, each 24 feet long and 20 feet wide, with the male and female patients on separate sides. There would also be a bathroom, kitchen and accommodation for a nurse. On the south side there would be enclosed airing yards. These extensions would, it was believed, provide ample accommodation for many years to come.

Three months later, when the Guardians formally approved the plans, they asked Mr Fulkes to produce plans for the southern boundary wall with gates and also for a boundary wall on the east side of the Workhouse, a water tank and a bakehouse. The boundary wall would provide employment for the able-bodied paupers although it was considered to be only 'a partial work' as paupers could still escape from other parts of the Workhouse property.

The erection of a bakehouse was regarded as a cost-effective measure. At that time the indoor and outdoor poor of the Union required on average about 1,100 x 4lb loaves of bread each week. As it was believed that this would increase yearly, it would be more economical to bake the bread on the premises. The initial outlay in establishing the bakery would soon be paid off and the whole operation would become profitable.

The Poor Law Board approved the plans with certain minor altera- tions. The infirmary extensions, the fever wards and bakehouse would cost about £4,000 and a further loan would be required. When the Guardians advertised for tenders there were only two replies: Messrs Wheeler quoted £3,486 and Mr James Matthews £3,100. Mr Matthews' tender was accepted and in September, by the time the building work was under way, his tender of £224 16s 6d for building the eastern boundary wall was accepted. It would appear that this wall would not now be built by the paupers.

Changes in the Nursing Staff
Most of the work entailed in the day-to-day running of the Workhouse was carried out by the inmates themselves under the supervision of the small number of paid staff. By the middle of 1870, with the enlargement of the infirmary, the building of new fever wards, ambitious plans for the farm and garden and the establishment of a bakery, additional paid staff were now required. It was particularly unfortunate that it was at this point that Mrs Bloxsom, the Nurse, tendered her resignation.

Mrs Bloxsom had been the Nurse since the infirmary had opened in September 1867 and had proved to be hard-working and diligent. No reason was given for her resignation. The advertisement for her replacement stated that candidates should not be under 35 years of age. The salary would be £20 per year. Applications would be considered on July 7th 1870.

There were two candidates for the position of Nurse and the choice of Mrs E Young, a widow aged 40 from Liverpool, was unfortunate. Within days she had resigned without giving a reason. The Guardians then advertised for a man and wife, the man to be Superintendent of Labour and the wife the Nurse. The salary of each would be £25 per year with accommodation, rations and washing. No suitable couple was found so the position of Nurse was re-advertised and Mrs C Parkin from the Chard Union was appointed to start work at the end of September.

Mrs Parkin was a disastrous choice. By January 1871 Mr Pocock, the Master, and Mr Walford, the Medical Officer were both complaining of her inefficiency. Mistakes were being made daily. All too often patients were given the wrong medicines while others did not receive what had been prescribed. She had also 'exhibited great violence of temper and used disrespectful language'. Mr Walford believed the job was beyond her capabilities and she herself had said that there were more sick cases than she had been accustomed to looking after.

The Guardians also consulted the Matron, the Cook, the pauper nurse in charge of the infants and the pauper nurse in charge of the imbeciles. All confirmed the opinions of the Master and Medical Officer and Mrs Parkin was asked to resign. Mrs Parkin challenged the Guardians' decision and wrote to the Poor Law Board complaining that nothing had been proved 'against her character and ability', but to no avail. The Guardians magnanimously gave her a testimonial stating that she had been 'a sober and steady officer' and her midwifery duties had been 'uniformly good'. Once again the post was advertised. Candidates, to be aged between 30 and 45 years, should supply not more than four testimonials.

Meantime the Biggleswade Union had requested a testimonial for former Nurse Young and had been sent an extract from the Workhouse Punishment Book relating to Mrs Young's conduct with an inmate called Thomas Dell. This provoked a furious response from Mrs Young who believed it had all come about because she had complained that the Porter, Henry Smith, had insulted her in her bedroom on August 30th, the night before she had left the Workhouse. Upon investigating the complaint the Guardians found that Mrs Young had resigned on August 4th and had left on August 31st. The Master, Mr Pocock, said that no formal complaint had been made against her although there had been 'rumours of occasional intemperance'. With regard to cohabiting with Dell, an inmate, on the night of August 30th, the Master said he had not been told about this until after Mrs Young had left. Thomas Dell had admitted to this behaviour and had been punished.

The next Nurse to be appointed was Mrs Annie Barker, but only after she had assured the Board that within a month she would have qualified herself to undertake midwifery cases. By this time, March 1871, the infirmary extensions had been finished and Mr Henley, the Poor Law Inspector, recommended the appointment of a paid Assistant Nurse. The 100-bed infirmary was more than one nurse could look after. Mrs Fanny Williams from Battersea was appointed in September with a salary of £15 a year and the usual rations, washing and accommodation.

The Superintendent of Labour

The position of Superintendent of Labour had remained unfilled until the end of September 1870 when there were five applicants in reply to the

Guardians' advertisement. Charles Thacker, aged 39 of Spring Gardens, Reading, was appointed with a salary of £20 per year and the usual allowances. It was arranged that two rooms would be built for him next to the new bakery. At the same time an additional storey would be added to the adjoining building for storage, and repairs would be carried out to the cattle sheds which had recently been damaged by fire. This work would cost £152.

Over a year later, in December 1871, the Farm Committee introduced measures to regulate the running of the farm and garden. The duties of the Superintendent of Labour were to be undertaken under the supervision of the Master. Decisions relating to the cropping of the garden, the purchase of articles required for the garden, the purchase of cattle, the sale of cattle and produce, were to be made under the direction of the Committee.

The Master would organise the male inmates able to undertake daily labour, see that they were 'satisfactorily employed' by the Superintendent of Labour in the garden or on the farm, and report weekly to the Board of Guardians. He would order, in writing, the quantity of vegetables or other produce required for use in the Workhouse, to be supplied daily by the Superintendent of Labour.

The Superintendent of Labour would keep a Day Book for entry of the produce of the farm, livestock, vegetables, gravel and any other products, with the date of sale and to whom the sale was made. He would supply what was required by the Master each day for the Workhouse. He would take his instructions from the Committee and keep accounts of the purchase and sale of all items. The Day Book would be shown to the Master every Monday morning.

At the same time as these new regulations were being introduced, John Smith from Holyport was appointed Gardener at a weekly wage of £1. The following year he was promoted to become Superintendent of Labour and Gardener. His weekly wage was increased to £1 3s and he was given accommodation at Battle Terrace, for which he would pay 5s (25p) per week.

The New Bakehouse
By the end of 1870 the new bakehouse had been completed and the Porter said he would undertake the baking with the help of the paupers if an experienced man could be engaged for a week or two. During this time bread would be baked for the inmates only. The necessary equipment was obtained and by the end of January 1871 the bakery was able to undertake the baking for the whole Union. As thrift was of the essence at the Workhouse, a 'practical baker' was engaged to see how many loaves could be obtained from a sack of flour. Some time later a handcart was bought to take bread from the bakery to the Relieving Offices in Thorn Street.

It soon became apparent that a full-time baker should be employed. The successful applicant would be paid £1 a week and have rented accommodation in one of the cottages at Battle Terrace. He would be supplied with two assistants from among the Workhouse inmates. Henry Somers' appointment was of short duration and within two weeks he was dismissed when found 'in a state of intoxication'. Once again Henry Smith, the Porter, took over until another baker was appointed and Henry Bushell was taken on as the Assistant Baker at 16s (80p) per week. At the end of 1871 he was promoted to Baker and given the rooms formerly occupied by the Superintendent of Labour in the Workhouse, with the usual allowances but a reduced wage of 8s (40p) per week.

Consumption of Beer and Spirits
The supply and consumption of beer and spirits at the Workhouse was kept under constant review. The Poor Law Board issued guidelines but it was up to the Medical Officer to decide how much should be given to the various categories of paupers in addition to prescribing for medicinal purposes to the patients in the infirmary. Beer was particularly important and was consumed by inmates and staff alike. If the price and quality were not approved, the supplier was changed. When Dymore Brown's beer was pronounced to be 'indifferent' the Guardians removed their order to Messrs Harris and Hewett. Spirits and stout were purchased from Mr Lewis Cooper and included Strongest Raw Gin at 13s 6d per gallon, Betts British Brandy at 3s per bottle and Single Stout 1s 3d per gallon. When it was discovered that the landlord of the New Inn was handing beer over the wall to inmates working on the land, the Guardians were understandably furious and threatened dire consequences.

Attempts were made by the Guardians to see if the consumption of beer and porter could be reduced, but without much success. It was then found that the Reading Union spent more on beer than any other union in Berkshire. In 1870 some £294 6s was spent on beer alone and this worked out at £1 4s 3d per head. The Cookham Union was the next highest spender at 19s 6d per head and the Wallingford Union was the lowest at 7s 6d per head. The Master and Medical Officer were asked to make certain that a reduction was achieved. Their efforts, however, produced many complaints but little success.

The Guardians then turned their attention to the prices they were being charged and found that for certain items Mr Lewis Cooper was charging the Union more than he was charging the Royal Berkshire Hospital. It was agreed that Mr Cooper would supply spirits and Messrs Simmonds would supply beer and porter at the same price as to the Hospital. For example brandy would now be 18s a gallon rather than £1 a gallon.

By 1873 the amount spent on beer was still believed to be too high. It was calculated that, on the instructions of the Medical Officer, almost 50% was consumed by patients in the infirmary and 14% by the aged and infirm in the main building. A further 30% was supplied to inmates who were 'engaged in daily labour' such as laundry and domestic work, preparing the earth closets and work on the farm and garden. The remaining 6% was waste. No account in the calculations was made for consumption by the staff who undoubtedly had their full ration. In future no beer was to be issued to those engaged in daily labour unless sanctioned by the Board of Guardians. The quantities to be issued would be recorded in a book to be kept by the Master and produced at the weekly Board meetings. No other beer would be given unless ordered by the Medical Officer. These new regulations appear to have been satisfactory and no further complaints about consumption were made by the Guardians. No doubt the inmates, especially those working on the land, felt very differently.

The Workhouse Diet
Workhouse diets had to be generally approved by the Poor Law Board and in this matter, as with everything else, the Guardians had their eye on economy. Half-yearly tenders made certain that there was no undue expenditure. Produce from the farm and garden was of considerable help but additional means of saving were always looked for.

The purchase of tins of Australian meat appeared to be one such saving. In January 1870 one dozen 4lb tins of Australian boiled mutton were purchased at $5\frac{1}{2}$d per pound – a saving of some $\frac{1}{2}$d per pound compared with local butcher's meat. This meat was given first to patients in the infirmary and a few weeks later was used on Wednesdays throughout the Workhouse. Infirmary patients were then given 3oz of this meat and 12oz of potatoes on Saturdays instead of their usual meat.

The meat was not popular and the following year when the Master wrote to various unions about their diets, he also asked about Australian meat and the method in which it was used. The Master of the City of London Union, which had three workhouses, did not mince his words. This meat had been supplied to all three workhouses and 'none could face it again'. Out of 144lb of meat only about 12lb were eaten. He believed it to be most unsuitable for workhouses and frequently the meat was found to have gone bad.

The Reading Guardians had enquired about diets in general as well as Australian meat and were surprised to find that 'although the Union was liberal in the dietary to the Workhouse inmates, it was not so liberal as many people had imagined'. Furthermore the diet appeared to be below the average of the other unions consulted. Nevertheless it was believed there was no reason for complaints. If any alterations were made there would be no great saving and it would not be worth the expense of getting them organised. The usual diet, including the use of Australian meat, was retained and it was not until 1875, when Mr Walford pointed out the waste from Australian meat, that the Guardians agreed to 'discontinue its purchase'.

The Emigration of Children to Canada
By 1870 the District School in Wargrave, which had opened in 1850 to take pauper children from the Reading and Wokingham Unions, looked after

95 children from the Reading Union, 48 boys and 47 girls. The cost to the Reading Union was between £800 and £1,000 each year. At that time groups of children were being sent from England to Canada where, it was thought, they would have more opportunities than if they had remained in their workhouse schools. The initial cost of sending the children abroad would be offset by the longer-term saving to the unions in supporting them.

In June 1870 the possibility of sending children to Canada was discussed by the Reading Guardians and a list of suitable pauper children, aged between seven and twelve years, was drawn up. Parties of children to go to Canada were being organised on a fairly regular basis by Miss Rye from the House of Industry in Commercial Road, Spitalfields, London. She explained that orphaned or abandoned children would be placed in an industrial establishment in Canada with the view of getting them into service or adopted by families. The charge would be £6 5s per child to cover an outfit and expenses.

The Poor Law Board was consulted and agreed to the proposition provided each child gave its consent before two Justices of the Peace. The Guardians then held a special meeting on October 24th 1870 to consider a letter from Miss Rye to Miss Hodson, a female missionary in Reading. Ten children from the Reading Union could be taken to Canada the following month. The Superintendent of the District School produced a list of 10 girls between the ages of 9 and 13 years for the approval of the Guardians.

Three days later the matter was discussed further. Although the Poor Law Board had authorised the expenditure, difficulties had arisen over three of the girls. One mother, who had deserted her child, objected to her daughter going to Canada. These objections were over-ruled when the Guardians found that the mother was cohabiting with a man and had five illegitimate children. Another girl, Matilda Gregory, had changed her mind and said she would live with her sister in Reading and be taught to make bonnets. The Guardians agreed and directed she should be given clothing to the value of £1. Ellen Perdue also withdrew on the instigation of her aunt, Mrs Dowling of West Street Reading, who offered her niece a home. The Guardians agreed and a set of clothing was also provided for her. Two other girls were selected in their place. Within days the ten children, all named in the Guardians' Minutes, sailed for Canada and nothing further is known about them.

A second group of ten boys was sent to Canada in June 1871. They were aged between 9 and 14 years and all were either orphans or had been deserted. Their departure had been delayed by an outbreak of measles at the District school. This group was sent via the Training House at Hampton and was accompanied by a Mr Joseph Merry, brother-in-law of Miss Macpherson who had organised that particular sailing. The cost was nearly £11 per boy and included all expenses from the base in London to the Home in Canada. Here the boys would be looked after until proper situations could be found for them. If they became ill they would be cared for and if one should die 'the death would be reported to the Guardians and friends (if any) of the child'. If a boy did not suit a master or a master suit a boy, the Home would take him back and find another placement for him. The Guardians had to pay for two light suits for hot summer wear in Canada and one warm suit of cloth. Instead of boxes each boy was provided with a canvas travelling bag which was specially made and cost 2s 6d. The total outlay was £10 14s 6d per boy of which £8 went to Miss Macpherson and £2 14s 6d covered the cost of the outfit. Mr Brice Bennet, the Headmaster of the District School, took the ten boys to the Training House at Hampton on June 1st 1871. Two wrote back to the

Mr and Mrs Bennett, Superintendent and Matron of Wargrave District School

school saying they were quite happy and were very kindly treated. In mid-June they sailed for Canada.

Nothing further is recorded about these children except that in September Miss Rye sent the Guardians a photograph of the Children's Home in Niagara and another of a group from her last party of children when they arrived there. When she offered to take more children with a group leaving in March 1872, the Guardians wrote saying they would not have any more children to send to Canada. What prompted this decision is not known. Perhaps the Guardians had second thoughts about sending young children so far from their own country and friends. Perhaps they were anxious that they had abrogated their responsibility as 'Guardians' to these children. The possibility that the children might be exploited was never openly considered. In 1873 new buildings were erected at the District School which was then able to accommodate 200 children. The facilities were described as being particularly good and offered every opportunity to the pauper inmates. It was to be some time before further groups of children from the Union were sent to Canada.

General Improvements

As the running of the Workhouse became established various improvements were gradually introduced. In 1868 the half-yearly contracts included many items in addition to the usual provisions and drapery. Men's coats were purchased at 15s 6d each, suits at 24s 6d each and boys' suits at 12s 6d each. Hats for men cost 18s 6d per dozen and caps 8s 11d.

Women's shawls were 6s 11d each, bonnets 5s 11d each and stays 13s 6d per dozen. Girls' bonnets cost 13s 6d per dozen.

John Lee, the Porter at the Tramp Wards, agreed to make boots and shoes for the Workhouse inmates and was provided with the necessary equipment and leather. He was paid 3s 6d per pair for men's strong boots, 3s per pair for light boots, 2s 9d per pair for shoes and 2s 6d per pair for women's boots.

When Mr Silver of Duke Street offered to donate a supply of mourning cloaks, the Guardians accepted with gratitude. The cloaks would be used by paupers who acted as bearers at the funerals of their Workhouse friends.

In 1868 the Guardians increased their annual subscription to the Royal Berkshire Hospital from 6 guineas to 10 guineas which enabled five in-patients to be admitted to the Hospital each year and a further five to be on the out-patient lists. This measure was not as altruistic as might first appear as the Guardians also notified the Medical Officers of the three parishes that the additional payment of £5, which they had been receiving for every fracture case, would no longer be paid. These patients and all emergency cases in future would be sent straight to the Hospital.

The system of additional payments for fractures, dislocations, amputations and difficult midwifery cases had always been a subject of contention between the Guardians and the Medical Officers, as were their frequent requests for increases in salary. When Mr Walford was notified that he should examine all lunatic, feeble-minded and imbecile cases upon admission to the Workhouse and again when leaving and that he should attend the Workhouse daily, he felt an increase in salary was more than justified, particularly as he now had to give up his work at the Reading Dispensary. Reluctantly, in 1873, the Guardians agreed to give him a gratuity of £15 'in view of the increased number of patients in his charge'.

Various practical measures were introduced. In 1870 pass tickets, issued by the Master, became necessary for any inmate leaving the Workhouse on errands or for any other purpose. The Porter was instructed see that everyone leaving the building had one. The following year friends were allowed to visit inmates once a fortnight instead of once a month. A list was drawn up of relatives who might be able to contribute towards the maintenance of inmates but with what success, if any, is not known.

Improvements to the wards in the main building gradually took place. Brick floors were replaced by wooden floors. These would be warmer for the inmates and generally more comfortable. Firewood was delivered to be chopped up by the able-bodied for use on the ward fires. Items such as clocks and more books and pictures were purchased to make the wards more homely. A stove was installed to heat the dining room. However it was not until 1872 that a hot water system for the baths in the main building and the probationary wards was considered. In this respect the infirmary had better facilities than the rest of the Workhouse.

At the same time as the hot water system was being installed a complete renewal of the farm buildings was taking place. The Farm Committee had recommended that all the old buildings should be pulled down and replaced with a carpenter's shop, a tool shed, a cow stall for three cows and a shed for hay and straw. The whole yard would be fenced and the boundary wall between the Workhouse and the New Inn raised to 6½ feet. Mr Fuller, a surveyor, had produced plans and Mr Wells' tender of £480 had been accepted.

In 1870 the new Berkshire Lunatic Asylum at Moulsford near Wallingford was opened and gradually patients were transferred from the Littlemore Asylum near Oxford. This was more convenient for all concerned and by July 1871 all the Reading patients had been transferred and all future admissions were sent there.

The following year a carriage costing £12 was purchased from Mr Lewington of Bridge Street for the conveyance of invalid or infectious cases to the Workhouse infirmary. Mr Henry Bowler of Watlington Street was engaged to provide horse hire. Ordinary cases from any part of the Borough to the Workhouse would cost 1s 6d and infectious cases 2s 6d. The journey to the Asylum at Moulsford would cost 8s 6d for a horse and man and other journeys would be charged 9d per mile.

There were few special occasions for the paupers apart from the Christmas dinner each year and possibly an entertainment. On January 15th 1872 Miss Barker, the Head Nurse, decided to give the convalescent patients a treat. Through the generosity of some friends she provided tea and afterwards 12 musicians entertained the patients until 11.40pm. What should have been a happy occasion ended with an enquiry by the Board of Guardians and implications that the Master, Mr Pocock, was not in full control of his staff.

The Master had heard of the proposed tea and entertainment and believed the Nurse had obtained permission from the Guardians but he had not been told the date. When he discovered the entertainment in full swing, he decided not to interfere to avoid unpleasantness but to mention it later to the Visiting Committee. The Visiting Committee raised the subject as a complaint at the Board meeting three days later. It transpired that the Nurse had not obtained the necessary permission. Mr Pocock then sent the Board a letter of resignation.

After consulting Mr Henley, the Poor Law Inspector, a special meeting of the Board of Guardians looked into the matter. Mr Pocock had written a second letter withdrawing his resignation and asked the Board for their support. He said he and his wife bore no ill feeling towards the Nurse. When asked if there was a lack of harmony between the members of staff, he said there were no problems except between the Nurse and the Porter, Henry Smith. The Nurse, when questioned, said the Porter interfered with her work in the infirmary. She had not spoken to him for four months nor would she do so in her present situation for 20 years.

It was necessary to restore the authority of the Master and the Guardians made the Nurse agree 'to act under the direction of the Master and Matron'. Mr and Mrs Pocock in their turn were asked 'to endeavour to restore harmony among the officers of the establishment'.

The following week the Guardians confirmed the withdrawal of Mr Pocock's letter of resignation as they felt that the conduct of the officers was sufficiently satisfactory to justify him remaining as Master. They also discussed a suggestion made by Mr Pocock that it would 'exert a most beneficial influence both on the officers and the inmates if the Guardians could occasionally hold their meetings at the Workhouse rather than at Thorn Street'. Mr Pocock believed that there was a feeling of isolation between the staff and the Guardians whose instructions they had to carry out.

This feeling was almost inevitable. The weekly meetings of the Board of Guardians were held some distance from the Workhouse at the old St Lawrence's Workhouse which had been adapted to provide a Board Room and offices for the Relieving Officer, his assistant and the Union Clerk. It was conveniently placed for the Guardians whose responsibilities were the administration of the Poor Law throughout the Union. As well as some 200 Workhouse inmates they were also responsible for three times that number who were receiving outdoor relief. They were bombarded with orders and directives from the Poor Law Board and their weekly meetings were fully occupied with keeping abreast of the myriad of detail which was now required. For their part the Workhouse staff, particularly the Master and Medical Officer, had to keep numerous books and accounts of all aspects of the administration of the institution, all of which had to be produced for the weekly meetings of the Board of Guardians.

At first the Guardians agreed to hold their weekly meetings at the Workhouse once a month but one week later they changed their minds. The Board of Guardians would hold their meetings quarterly at the Workhouse 'for the purpose of making a general inspection'.

Three months later Miss Barker resigned and Mrs H Seward from Kensington Hall, Fulham, was appointed Head Nurse with a salary of £30 a year.

The End of the Poor Law Board

The Poor Law Board, which had been formed in 1848 to take the place of the Poor Law Commission, was dissolved in 1871 with the passing of the Local Government Board Act. The Act established an entirely new Government Department, the Local Government Board, to combine the responsibilities of the former Poor Law Board and those of the Medical Department of the Privy Council. The latter had been formed in 1858 when the earlier Board of Health was disbanded.

By this time it was becoming increasingly acknowledged that overcrowding, poor sanitary conditions and bad water supplies were the cause of a large proportion of ill-health and disease, particularly cholera and typhoid. It was believed that by combining the two branches in one Government Department much more could be accomplished in bringing about better sanitary conditions and improved public health.

The Reading Board of Guardians noted that in August 1871 they would now be answerable to the Local Government Board but their duties and powers would not be altered and there would be no change in their proceedings. The regular inspections would continue but the inspectors would now be employed by the Local Government Board rather than the former Poor Law Board.

Other Acts of Parliament at that time concerned the new Local Government Board in its medical capacity and added to the responsibilities of the Guardians. Under the Vaccination Act of 1871 the Local Government Board required the Reading Guardians to appoint a Vaccination Officer whose expenses would be paid out of the local Poor Rate. Free vaccination under the Poor Law had been available since 1841 and in 1853 had been made compulsory. Until 1871 the Reading Guardians had paid their three parish Medical Officers to vaccinate within their parishes. In future the one Vaccination Officer would carry out these duties. Mr Lousley, the Medical Officer of St Giles' parish, was appointed. A

Mr Lousley, Vaccination Offcer 1871

Vaccination Station was set up in the centrally placed Reading Dispensary premises in Chain Street where a room and waiting room were made available to Mr Lousley one afternoon each week. The annual rent of £10 was paid by the Guardians.

In December 1871 another Act came into force which concerned the Reading Tramp Wards. Mr Bonner, the Superintendent, was required to keep additional records of the admission and discharge of tramps and details of their work and diet. His salary and that of his wife were increased. The Board of Guardians now had to provide adequate bathing facilities for the tramps, to have serge shirts or sleeping garments available for them and to obtain the necessary means for disinfecting and drying the tramps' clothes.

Using the earlier Diseases Prevention Act the Local Government Board asked the Guardians to obtain reports of the prevalence of disease in the Union. The three Medical Officers pointed out that overcrowding, poor sanitary conditions and general poverty were at the root of the problem. The following year the Public Health Act of 1872 provided a framework for improving sanitary conditions. The whole country, with the exception of London, was divided into sanitary districts, each of which was placed under a single authority responsible for administering sanitary law. Each district was to appoint a Medical Officer of Health and a Sanitary Inspector.

In Reading the Town Council, which had been constituted as a Local Board of Health in 1850, now became an Urban Sanitary Authority. Dr John Shea was appointed its first Medical Officer of Health with a salary of £300 per year. He also held the position of Assistant Physician at the Royal Berkshire Hospital. He and Mr Walford, the Inspector of Nuisances and also the Workhouse Medical Officer, would play an important role in the implementation of sanitary reform and public health in the Borough. For their part the Board of Guardians were now required to send the Medical Officer of Health weekly returns of sickness and mortality within the Workhouse. More attention would now have to be paid to its sanitary conditions and the health of the inmates.

In the five years since the new Workhouse had opened much had been achieved. The buildings had been enlarged, better facilities had been provided and the number of staff, both inside and out, had been increased. During the same period the number of inmates had risen by nearly one hundred. In September 1867 there were 153 inmates: 12 able-bodied, 123 who were infirm or disabled, 11 children and 7 imbeciles or idiots. The weekly cost of those receiving indoor relief was 5s 10d per head. In addition there were 47 lunatics at the Littlemore Asylum and 77 children at the District School.

Five years later, in September 1873, there were 247 Workhouse inmates: 9 able-bodied, 189 infirm or disabled, 22 children and 27 imbeciles or idiots. The weekly cost of those receiving indoor relief had now been reduced to 5s 8¼d per head, which was now shown as 5s 1¼d for food and 7d for clothes. In addition the Guardians were responsible for 52 lunatics at the Berkshire Asylum and 87 children at the District School.

At that time, apart from those directly involved, little was known about the Reading Poor Law Guardians and the Union Workhouse. Although weekly reports of the number of inmates and the cost of their maintenance were given to the local newspapers, the public had little further information. In August 1873 a new weekly paper was launched in Reading called the *Reading Observer*. The editor contacted the Guardians and asked if a reporter could attend the meetings of the Board and report the proceedings in his paper. This was agreed and regular reports began to be included in the weekly papers. Members of the public gradually became aware of the work of the Guardians and the life of the Workhouse inmates. This, combined with the recent legislation, was to influence the development of the Reading Workhouse in the years ahead.

3

WIDER HORIZONS
1873–1889

By far the largest proportion of the Workhouse inmates were those classified as infirm or disabled. Of the 189 in this category in 1873 more than half were being treated in the infirmary. Even before the Local Government Act had been passed consideration was being given to whether sick paupers should be sent to workhouse infirmaries or treated in their homes. The earlier concept that only workhouse inmates who had become sick were eligible for admission to union infirmaries, had been found to be impractical. Medical officers were asked to inform the Poor Law Board of the circumstances that led them to decide when a sick pauper should be admitted to the workhouse. Was it the nature of the disease, the wishes of the patient and family, the home circumstances or 'the character and extent of infirmary accommodation'?

The medical officer's opinion was not final, as it was the relieving officer of a union who advised the guardians whether a pauper should be admitted to the workhouse infirmary or remain at home. The Poor Law Board asked to what extent were the decisions of the relieving officers influenced by the medical officers' opinions. In most cases it was found that the report of the relieving officer was based on the recommendation of the medical officer.

Information was gradually being assembled and statistics prepared to show the number and ages of paupers on the medical officers' books, both inside and outside the workhouses, with a classification of their diseases. By the time the Local Government Board was established a vast amount of information had been collected and collated from across the country and a further, but rhetorical, question had been asked. How far was it advisable 'in a sanitary or social point of view to extend gratuitous medical relief beyond the actual pauper class'? Would this be an additional public burden, might it have a pauperising tendency and diminish self-reliance and would it be competing with those organisations for the thrifty to make provision for sickness?

By the 1870s many organisations had been established in Reading to help the poor in times of sickness. The Royal Berkshire Hospital was available to 'those worthy of charity' provided they could obtain a ticket of admission from a subscriber. The Reading Dispensary, founded in 1802, offered similar facilities to out-patients and had also introduced a provident scheme. Friendly Societies and Benefit Clubs had been established and these offered provident schemes to their members. Medical treatment was now available to many who would otherwise be unable to afford it. Nevertheless there were still a large number of people on the brink of pauperism and in times of sickness only Poor Law medical relief was available to them.

The Establishment of the Union Dispensary
The establishment of union dispensaries had been recommended by the Poor Law Board for some years. They believed that by providing a dispensary in a central location where sick paupers could obtain out-patient advice, medicines and, if necessary, medical appliances, there would be a reduction in the number of paupers admitted to workhouse infirmaries. There would also be 'more efficient control over the whole administration of outdoor medical relief'. It was not until the end of 1872 that the Reading Guardians considered the proposition.

By April 1873 it had been agreed that a Dispensary should be provided at the Union's Thorn Street premises and Mr Fulkes was asked to prepare a plan and specifications. When these were sent to the Local Government Board for approval the layout of the rooms was criticised. The waiting room was between the consulting room and the dispensary and would result in the doctor having no direct communication with the dispenser. Furthermore, after seeing the doctor, the patients would have to cross the waiting room to get their medicines from the dispenser.

Once this matter had been resolved the Guardians invited tenders from nine builders and that of Mr Searle of Kings Road for £217 was accepted. The Guardians arranged to buy the stock of Mr Eginton, apothecary and chemist of Queens Road, and Mr Walford was asked to prepare a list of the drugs that would be required. Advertisements were placed in the local papers for a Dispenser to start work when the Dispensary opened on September 29th.

The qualifications of the Dispenser and the duties he would be required to undertake were described in detail. 'The person elected must devote sufficient time daily for the efficient discharge of his duties and conform to all regulations of the Local Government Board. The hours of attendance to be regulated and sanctioned by the Board of Guardians. Candidates must be Licentiates of the Apothecaries Company in London or duly registered under the Pharmacy Act of 1868 or some other authority of Law on that behalf. Preference to be given to persons who have passed either a minor or major examination of the Pharmaceutical Society of Great Britain.' The salary would be £60 per year.

There were three candidates and Mr Nutt from Gainsborough was appointed. He had provided three testimonials and was registered under the Pharmacy Act of 1868. His times of attendance at the Dispensary would be every morning at 9am and every afternoon at 4pm and he was required 'to continue his attendance on each occasion until his work is completed and the books made up'. Drugs would be obtained from Messrs Bradley and Bliss in Market Place for one year. Mr and Mrs Griffin were appointed Porter and Portress of the Dispensary and Tramp Wards with wages of £1 per week and accommodation, coal and gas.

The Medical Officers of the three parishes were detailed to attend the Dispensary at fixed times in rotation. Their salaries were then reviewed. Although their duties had increased, they no longer had to pay for the drugs they prescribed nor would they have the expense of employing a dispenser. Mr Walford's salary was adjusted from £140 to £130 per year for the Workhouse and Tramp Wards, Mr Lousley's became £105 for St Giles' parish, Mr Vines' £30 for St Lawrence's parish and Mr Moore's £90 for St Mary's parish. Mr Walford expressed his great appreciation that he no longer had these additional expenses.

The Dispensary was a success and the following year Mr Nutt's salary was raised from £60 to £75 per year. By 1877 his work had increased to such an extent that a salary of £85 per year was agreed. When an assistant dispenser was required at the Royal Berkshire Hospital it was arranged that Mr Nutt would attend the Hospital three times a week for £30 per year.

The link with the Hospital continued when Mr Nutt resigned in 1878 and Mr Chick, a Dispenser at the Hospital, was appointed in his place. When he resigned a few months later he was replaced by Mr John Eaton from East Molesey. The link with the Hospital was re-established in 1883 with the appointment of Mr W R Hadwin who had been the Hospital's Dispenser for many years. In spite of excellent references the Local Government Board queried Mr Hadwin's qualifications as his certificate from the Apothecaries Company of London only allowed him to be appointed as an assistant to an apothecary. After much debate and reassurance by the Guardians that Mr Hadwin was 'regarded by the whole medical profession of the town as a most able and efficient Dispenser', the Local Government Board relented and Mr Hadwin's appointment was confirmed. Mr Hadwin was the Union's Dispenser until 1888 when he moved from Reading and was replaced by Mr Thomas Willis Smart of Reading.

The Tramp Wards
With the establishment of the Dispensary the Union premises in Thorn Street were fully occupied. In the following years the demands upon the Tramp Wards steadily increased. In January 1874 it was decided that no tramps would be admitted after 10pm. However when the Guardians found that most other unions would admit tramps at any hour, the regulation was altered to enable tramps needing shelter after 10pm to apply at the Police Station. Here they would be searched and any items retained would be returned on application the next morning. They would then be taken to Thorn Street where the tool room at the Tramp Wards

was adapted to receive these late arrivals. It was noted that there was a tendency for tramps to arrive late to avoid having a bath.

When Mr and Mrs Griffin, the Porter and Portress, resigned in June 1874 the Guardians decided 'a better type of couple' should be employed. It was necessary to have someone able to keep control and an increased wage of £1 5s per week was advertised with unfurnished rooms and an allowance for coal and gas. A suitable uniform would be provided for the man and his duties would include supervising the admission, bathing and discharge of the vagrants and to assist the Relieving Officer. His wife would act as the female searcher, do the vagrant ward washing and work under the supervision of Mrs Bonner.

The appointment of Mr and Mrs Bursland was short-lived and within months Mr and Mrs William Ryland took these posts. When Mr Bonner, the Relieving Officer and Superintendent of the Tramp Wards, resigned in 1876 through ill health, Mr William Heavingham was appointed in his place with a salary of £100 per year and his wife was made Matron of the Tramp Wards with a salary of £20 per year.

There was a great increase in vagrancy during the winter of 1876–7 and the Clerk of the Peace informed the Guardians that the Court of Quarter Sessions proposed to reintroduce the ticket system for vagrants. The requirement that all vagrants had to obtain a ticket from the police before admission to the Tramp Wards had gradually fallen into disuse. Its reintroduction would bring more control to the admission of vagrants.

The position of Assistant Relieving Officer was abolished in 1879 when Mr and Mrs Henry Holt were appointed Porter and Portress with a salary of £1 10s a week. Strict times of admission between 6pm and 10pm were introduced and the police were allowed to inspect the wards at any time to 'apprehend, if necessary, notorious characters charged with committing any criminal offence'. A more rigorous regime had become necessary.

Stricter rules were introduced in 1882 with the passing of the Casual Poor Act. This described the tasks vagrants were expected to perform in return for accommodation in tramp wards. Over a century later it is difficult to imagine how such work could be required of people fed only on bread and water. Then, however, it was believed imperative that no one should take advantage of the Poor Law and all those who were able should have to work.

The Casual Poor Act of 1882 divided tramps into two classes, those who remained in tramp wards for one night and those who remained longer. It described in detail the tasks the tramps had to perform:

Class 1. Casual Paupers who remained for one night.

Males should break 2cwt of stones or such other quantity but not less than 1½cwt nor more than 3cwt as the Guardians might prescribe, having regard to the nature of the stone, or pick 1lb unbeaten or 2lb of beaten oakum, or tie up 80 bundles of firewood, or chop 10 bushels of firewood.

Females should pick ½lb of unbeaten oakum or 1lb of beaten oakum, or do not less than three hours' work washing or scrubbing and cleaning

CLASS 2.   Casual Paupers who remained for more than one night.

Males for each entire day of detention should break 7cwt of stones but not less than 5cwt and not more than 10cwt according to the type of stone, or pick 4lb of unbeaten or 8lb of beaten oakum, or tie up 200 bundles of firewood, or chop 30 bushels of firewood.

Females for each entire day of detention should pick 2lb of unbeaten oakum or 4lb of beaten oakum, or do not less than nine hours work in washing, scrubbing and cleaning or needlework.

This hard regime was designed to deter tramps from seeking accommodation and to ensure that the tasks performed by those who were admitted would go some way towards paying for their keep. Once the tasks had been completed the tramps could leave as this would give them a better chance of obtaining employment that day. The suggestion that money found on the tramps should be returned and not confiscated as had become customary, was turned down. This too would deter those seeking overnight shelter.

The new Act was effective and the number of tramps seeking accommodation was reduced. In 1882, before the new Act came into operation, 5,753 tramps were admitted (4,822 men, 593 women and 338 children) and the following year, when the new regulations were in operation, only 2,449 were admitted (1,976 men, 301 women and 174 children).

In spite of these measures the number of admissions slowly began to rise and by the winter of 1886 far more vagrants were being admitted than the facilities could cope with. The Local Government Board Inspector, Mr Jenner-Fust, and the Guardians agreed that alterations to the first floor rooms would provide more accommodation. One was used for storing old Union documents and papers. These would be sorted to see what could be destroyed. In the meantime sick vagrants who the Medical Officer believed would be ill for longer than one day and two nights would be sent to the Workhouse infirmary and those who arrived seriously ill would be sent there directly. It was to be several months before these alterations were completed and even then the accommodation left much to be desired.

In 1889 the number of tramps admitted had risen to 5,605, which was almost as many as in 1882 before the new Act came into force. Most of these were men (5,037) but the number of women had halved to 318 and only 251 were children. One economy introduced in 1888 had been not to keep any tramp in on Sundays, but against this there had been an increase in the cost of the new system which had risen from £35 per year in 1882 to £63 in 1889. The diet however had been improved and the men now had

$1\frac{1}{2}$ oz of cheese with their 8oz of bread and water for midday dinner and the women had gruel. Bread and water only remained the diet for breakfast and supper. The sale of firewood chopped up by the tramps raised £176 in 1889. The labour of the tramps had been profitable even if the tramps themselves had seen little improvement in their lives.

Able-bodied Paupers

The Poor Law regulations stipulated that no able-bodied pauper should obtain relief except within the workhouse. There were usually only a small number of inmates in this category in the Reading Workhouse as indoor relief for the able-bodied was regarded as a last resort only for the desperate. Those who were admitted were employed in the laundry, in cleaning and on the farm. A special shed was provided for the wood chopped up by the tramps and sent from the Tramp Wards up to the Workhouse. Here it was made into bundles by the able-bodied and sold for 4s 6d per 100 bundles or 5s if delivered within the Borough.

Seasonal unemployment was a different matter and frequently it was not possible to provide sufficient accommodation in the Workhouse for men laid off work in the winter months. In January 1873 work on the public drainage system was suddenly stopped and 130 men employed by Messrs Vickers and Crane had no work and became dependent on the Poor Law to maintain themselves and their families. The Guardians determined to take whatever steps were necessary to help them. It was agreed with the Urban Sanitary Authority that gravel should be dug from the Workhouse grounds and payment of 1s per cubic foot would be made. The Master and the Farm Committee would obtain the necessary shovels, pickaxes and wheelbarrows. The scheme appears to have been a success but in August the Guardians complained to the Borough Surveyor that $\frac{1}{2}$ acre of the Workhouse grounds could not be cultivated as it was covered in gravel and screenings. Nevertheless a principle had been established that the able-bodied could obtain relief outside the Workhouse in return for labour.

The following winter (1874) the Guardians attempted to provide work on the Workhouse premises for the unemployed but once again there were more applicants than could be accommodated within the Workhouse. The problem recurred each winter and in October 1875 the Guardians decided that in future able-bodied men should be employed in stone breaking. In January 1879 arrangements were made to provide labour for the unemployed in the Tramp Wards as well as in the Workhouse. The Guardians applied to the Local Government Board to bring in the Outdoor Labour Test. This provided set tasks to be performed by the able-bodied in return for outdoor relief and did not require them to be admitted to the Workhouse. The request was not sanctioned. As long as there was any room in the Workhouse the regulations should apply and the Wokingham Union should be asked to take male paupers if there was space in their Workhouse.

Weeks later the Local Government Board sanctioned the introduction of the Outdoor Labour Test. It was only needed for a few weeks but in December that year the Test had to be used again to cope with the increased number applying for outdoor relief. The tasks required to be performed were now noted in detail.

Males had to pick 3lb of unbeaten oakum or chop 20 bushels of firewood, or tie up 150 bundles of firewood, or dig out and wheel away three yards of gravel from the gravel pit.

Females had to pick 1½lb of unbeaten oakum.

The hours of work to be from 8am to 4pm.

Specific tasks were made compulsory the following year (1880) for the able-bodied who had been admitted to the Workhouse, provided they were not suffering from 'any temporary or permanent infirmity of the body'. The tasks should be 'suitable for age, strength and capability'.

Males had to break from 7 to 10 bushels of granite per day and remove both unbroken and broken stones to any part of the Workhouse premises if required, or pick 6lb of unbeaten oakum.

Females had to pick 2lb of unbeaten oakum or do any other work that might be considered necessary.

A stone yard and shed were provided adjoining the farm buildings and sheds for oakum picking erected beside the male and female airing yards. Conditions were now much harder for the able-bodied seeking relief whether inside or outside the Workhouse.

The Outdoor Labour Test was introduced again in the winter of 1880–1. It was then arranged with the Urban Sanitary Authority that they would supply the Guardians with stones. These were to be broken to a uniform size and not larger than would pass through a ring $2\frac{1}{4}$ inches in diameter. The Sanitary Authority would pay 1s 3d per cubic yard for the broken stones.

In December 1882 the Guardians sent a deputation to the Mayor to ask if the Urban Sanitary Authority could provide work for the unemployed and noted that by doing so there would be a saving in the amount expended on outdoor relief which in turn would benefit the poor rate. The Mayor was sympathetic and agreed that in severe weather when men were 'thrown out of employment' he and the Borough Surveyor would 'make such arrangements as they may deem expedient for the employment of unemployed labour'. This was a great advance and would take the pressure off the Workhouse accommodation in the winter months.

Over the next few years these conditions remained in force with the Outdoor Labour Test being used when necessary and the indoor able-bodied required to undertake the various tasks of work in exchange for their keep. By the end of 1887, however, the Guardians were complaining that the able-bodied paupers in the Workhouse 'were in the habit of obtaining frequent admission and discharging themselves two or three days later'. It was believed that the Workhouse had become 'an encouragement to an idle life and not a deterrent from it'.

A communication was sent to the Local Government Board on the subject suggesting that rules should be adopted that required the able-bodied paupers to remain in the Workhouse for a fixed time, possibly seven days on the first admission, and if admitted again within a certain period they should remain for 14 days, and on their third admission for 21 days. The Guardians felt so strongly that they suggested a Bill should be introduced into Parliament to give them the authority to detain paupers for these fixed periods. The Local Government Board acknowledged the communication and said it would receive their attention. Although the Guardians had resolved to adopt these measures, it is not known if indeed they did so. In any event the life of the able-bodied pauper was not going to be made any easier.

Infectious Diseases

When the Poor Law Union was formed in 1835 the population of Reading was 16,042. By the 1870s it had doubled and in 1871 was recorded as 32,314 and rising rapidly. The Reading Urban Sanitary Authority, formed after the passing of the Public Health Act of 1872, held its first meeting on May 9th 1873. Its remit was 'to transact and have charge of all matters relating to the health of the District and the duties of the Medical Officer of Health and the Inspector of Nuisances'. It was noted that the Guardians of the Reading Union would provide returns of sickness and instruct the Registrars of the District to furnish the Medical Officer of Health with the returns of mortality within the Borough. They would also be in communication with the Inspector of Nuisances.

So began a new era in the Public Health of the Borough as Dr Shea, the Medical Officer of Health, began to collect a wide range of local information, particularly in regard to infectious diseases. He reported in 1873 that the returns of sickness and mortality were hampered by the 'imperfect manner' in which the books of the charitable Reading Dispensary were kept. Nevertheless in his first Annual Report he was able to record that in 1873 there were 32 deaths in the Union Workhouse and 17 in the Royal Berkshire Hospital. The total deaths in the Borough were 18.4 per 1,000. The age of statistics had arrived.

Sanitary reform was desperately needed in the poorer and more crowded parts of the town. These were the areas from which the Workhouse would be most likely to receive its inmates. Any improvements in these places would be to the advantage of both the paupers and the Guardians. Dr Shea reported that cleansing, disinfecting and whitewashing of premises was being carried out, accumulations of refuse were being removed, cesspools and drains were being disinfected. In addition a supply of pure water was now being provided and 'a liberal and free distribution of disinfectants by men sent round daily through the town for that purpose'. It was hoped that these measures would help to prevent and retard the spread of disease.

The Guardians were fully aware of the problems associated with infectious diseases. When the Workhouse was built in 1867 a small detached building was erected for fever cases and in 1870 this had been enlarged to take and isolate 24 patients. Disinfecting apparatus had been obtained in 1871 and the occasional smallpox cases were closely monitored with vaccination and revaccination carried out on all contacts.

In 1874 Dr Shea drew the attention of the Sanitary Authority to the lack of facilities in the Borough for disinfecting the bedding and clothing of infectious cases. The Guardians alone had such equipment and were asked if this could be made available to the Sanitary Authority. It was arranged that men from the Workhouse would be sent to the town to collect items of clothing and bedding to be disinfected. These would be placed in boxes provided by the Sanitary Authority and the disinfecting and washing would be undertaken at the Workhouse. A charge of 15s (75p) would be made for each box to include collection, disinfecting, washing and return. No Workhouse inmate would be used to return the boxes.

By the time the Public Health Act of 1875 was passed the population of Reading had reached 35,500. This Act, also known as 'The Great Public Health Act', gave sanitary authorities greater powers to improve every aspect of public health and sanitary reform. It covered sewerage, nuisances, infectious diseases, prevention of epidemics, paving and lighting of streets, the purchase of land for amenities, the inspection of markets and slaughterhouses and also the imposition of sanitary laws through bye-laws.

It was in the area of infectious diseases and the prevention of epidemics that the Reading Guardians became most involved with the Sanitary Authority. In 1875 the Local Government Board asked what facilities were available in the District for the isolation of infectious cases. Dr Shea had to reply that at that time 'no such means were at their disposal'. The only place where infectious cases could be taken was the Workhouse. The Guardians were asked if they would accept non-pauper infectious cases if necessary. They were unable to help as the Local Government Board would only sanction the admission of pauper cases. An infectious hospital was urgently needed in the town and Dr Shea informed the Sanitary Authority that sooner or later steps would have to be taken to provide these necessary facilities.

In January 1876 the Guardians notified the Sanitary Authority that two cases of fever from the town had been admitted into the Workhouse, one of which was not a pauper. The Local Government Board in their turn urged the Sanitary Authority to provide a suitable fever hospital for non-pauper cases. Not only would this be in the interests of public health but the advantages would compensate the expense involved. Furthermore arrangements might also be made whereby the Guardians would be entitled to send pauper patients to such a hospital at a mutually agreed rate of payment. No action was taken by the Sanitary Authority apart from agreeing that the Guardians would now be paid £1 1s per box for disinfecting clothing and bedding.

The problem of non-pauper admissions continued and later that year two further cases prompted further complaints from the Guardians. On September 2nd one of Admiral Layton's servants was admitted suffering from scarlet fever. On September 13th a man was admitted with typhoid fever. It transpired that he had a weekly wage of £1 10s and during his illness his provident club paid him £1 5s. Such non-pauper cases should not have been sent to the Workhouse.

Mr Walford suggested that the Guardians should consider accepting such cases if the patients agreed to pay double the average cost of maintenance and, in addition, give a 'modest fee' to the Medical Officer for his attendance. He believed the Guardians would be right in admitting such cases 'where the accommodation is acceptable to those applying'. The Guardians disagreed and the Relieving Officer was directed not to give orders for such admissions. The Mayor, on behalf of the Sanitary Authority, explained they could not afford the expense of building and maintaining a fever hospital nor were they bound by law to do so. The Guardians relented and agreed to admit fever cases as long as they had room but should an epidemic arise only paupers would be admitted to the Workhouse fever wards. When Dr Shea suggested that two or three huts might be erected in the Workhouse grounds for non-pauper infectious cases, the Guardians considered the idea. When it transpired that the Sanitary Authority wanted 'to avail themselves of the Workhouse appliances and nursing staff' the Guardians were unable to agree.

Additional difficulties arose for the Sanitary Authority when non-pauper patients refused to go to the Workhouse. One such case was a domestic servant girl aged 25 who contracted smallpox in London and returned to her parents' home in Reading. They refused to have her removed to the Workhouse as they did not want her to be considered a pauper. The girl implied that she would have been willing to go to an infectious hospital had one existed. As it was she remained at home with her parents and ten brothers and sisters, several of whom later developed the disease. The stigma of the Workhouse was very powerful.

In the meantime the Local Government Board informed the Guardians that they should stop disinfecting the clothing and bedding of non-paupers. It was 'irregular, objectionable and likely to introduce infection into the Workhouse'. The Sanitary Authority was given three months in which to make other arrangements. At the same time the Reading Dispensary asked the Guardians to find other premises for their vaccination station as the rooms were needed for an additional surgeon. Alternative accommodation was found at the Bridge Street School.

It was at this point that the Royal Berkshire Hospital built its own fever wards. The Hospital had never admitted patients with infectious diseases but when cases arose within the building they were isolated as far as possible. In 1878 a special single-storey building, designed by Joseph Morris, was erected on the boundary with Redlands Road. This was to be used by Hospital patients only. Cases of enteric fever, however, were admitted and the Sanitary Authority expressed their appreciation in 1880 when several cases had been treated there.

The problem of isolating and treating non-pauper smallpox and scarlet fever cases remained. It was not until 1877 that the Sanitary Authority seriously considered premises for isolating and treating cases of infectious diseases and even then it was widely believed that the expense was not justified. Having considered adapting Whitley Tank Cottage, on the Sanitary Authority's Waterworks Undertaking near Spring Gardens, it was eventually only used periodically. However in 1880, following an outbreak of smallpox, a temporary hospital was erected on a site on the west side of Bridge Street on a portion of the wharf belonging to the Sanitary Authority, between the River Kennett and St Giles Mill Stream. Later a disinfecting chamber, ambulance shed and mortuary were added. The 'temporary' hospital remained in use for over a quarter of a century.

By 1881 the population of Reading had risen to over 42,000, an increase of 10,000 in the last decade. Although the Bridge Street fever hospital had helped to ease the pressure on the Workhouse accommodation, it was becoming increasingly difficult to find room to isolate infectious cases. Mr Joseph Greenaway, the Reading architect, was instructed to prepare plans for a suitable building to be erected in the north west part of the Workhouse grounds, away from the other buildings, where infectious cases could be isolated and treated. It was anticipated that the cost would be paid out of the rates and no loan would be needed. Dr Shea and the Local Government Board were consulted and in June 1881 the plans were approved. Thirteen tenders were submitted and that of Messrs Pilgrim and Son for £454 15s was accepted. This was the same firm that had built the infectious hospital in Bridge Street.

The 'Infectious Hut Hospital' was completed in December 1881. It was a single-storey, wooden building and consisted of two 24 x 14ft wards separated by a nurse's room. Each ward had three beds and its own bathroom and lavatory. A covered way led to a smaller building in which were a kitchen, stores and wash-house. The Wokingham Union had offered to sell the Guardians surplus furniture from their temporary infectious hospital in Swallowfield at a reduced price, but the Guardians declined the offer and bought their own furniture at a cost of £15 5s 3d. A fence, 3ft 8in and 360ft long, was erected to enclose the building. When the patients were moved to the new building, the imbecile inmates were moved to the former fever wards. Some much needed accommodation in the main building had been provided.

The Sanitary Authority now found they needed accommodation for scarlet fever cases. In 1884 Dr Shea, the Medical Officer of Health,

SOUTH ELEVATION

Infectious Hut Hospital. View from South

submitted plans for a two-storey building to be erected on land adjoining the smallpox building. The Sanitary Authority agreed to the plans and also a mortuary and ambulance shed. The project was delayed by objections raised by Messrs H and G Simmonds whose Bridge Street premises included part of the wharf required for the new hospital. By 1885, when non-pauper scarlet fever cases were being admitted to the Workhouse, the need to get the new hospital under way became urgent. Messrs Simmonds' objections were over-ruled, plans and specifications were agreed and Messrs Pilgrim's tender of £360 12s was accepted.

The new scarlet fever hospital was completed and furnished in September 1885. Patients would be charged for the use of the hospital and they would be expected to provide their own medical attendants. In special cases the charge could be modified. Like the smallpox hospital, this hospital was to remain in use for many years. These hospitals for infectious diseases were the first to provide municipal accommodation for the inhabitants of the Borough and filled the gap between those able to obtain charitable help and those who were supported by the poor rates.

Workhouse Changes

The only building work undertaken at the Workhouse, apart from the new fever wards, was the enlargement of the laundry in 1873 at a cost of £320, the building of an ambulance shed ten years later and a new mortuary in 1884.

Until 1883 it had been customary to hire transport to take paupers to the Workhouse and the asylum at Moulsford but that year it was decided the Reading Union should have its own ambulance. The Royal Berkshire Hospital had obtained its first horse-drawn ambulance the year before when Dr Howard's model, with sliding shutters on the sides, was purchased at a cost of 60 guineas. The Guardians obtained four tenders ranging in price from £37 10s to £45 and decided to buy the cheapest, which was Richard Hadgood's ambulance. An ambulance shed, costing £11 10s, was built at the north-east corner of the Workhouse grounds adjoining the imbecile wards.

The new mortuary was built the following year. Made of brick and measuring 8ft 6in long and 7ft 6in wide, it cost £12 10s and was built at the north-west corner of the men's airing yard. Arrangements for pauper funerals had changed since Mr Dunn's original tender in 1867 and in 1876 the cost of adult pauper funerals from the Workhouse had risen by 2s if the inmates did not act as bearers. Two years later it was agreed that the cost of outdoor pauper funerals would be the same as that for the inmates and the charges were altered to:

Children 8 weeks and under	17s 6d
2 months to 12 months	£1 0s 6d
1 year to 5 years	£1 4s 0d
5 years to 10 years	£1 8s 0d
10 years to 15 years.............	£1 15s 0d
over 15 years	£2 2s 0d

For an additional 1s the name and age of the deceased would be painted on the coffin. In 1881 it was arranged that the Porter would attend all pauper burials and would be paid 1s each time. Mr Dunn's contract was terminated in 1889 and Mr Lovegrove's simpler tender was accepted. The cost of funerals for paupers under 10 years of age would be £1 7s and for those over 10 years the charge would be £1 15s.

By 1889 all the original Workhouse staff had left and for some situations the changes had been frequent. Mr Henry Smith had been appointed Porter in 1867 and Mrs Smith, his wife, had been appointed Cook at the same time. Both resigned in 1875. There were several different Porters appointed between 1875 and 1889 and the salary remained unchanged until 1889 when it was raised from £20 to £24 a year with the usual allowances. After 1876 the Porter's wife was required to superintend the laundry work and assist the Matron and after 1889 her salary was raised from £15 to £19 per year.

Mrs Smith's successor as Cook in 1875 was Edward Smith, a discharged inmate who was appointed with a wage of 10s per week with accommodation, rations and washing. As part of his contract he was required to pay the Guardians 4s 6d each week towards the maintenance of his children at the District School. His wage was increased to 12s per week in 1878 and he remained at the Workhouse until he resigned in 1885. His successors were appointed with a reduced wage of 10s per week.

From January 1876 the Workhouse officers were given fixed weekly allowances of certain provisions. Each was given 8lb of bread, 7lb of meat, 12oz of butter, 10oz of cheese, 3oz of tea, 3oz of coffee, 1lb of sugar, 1½ quarts of milk, 1lb of flour and 3oz of suet. At the same time money allowances were introduced in lieu of the beer ration. The Master and Matron were each allowed 2s per week and all other officers 1s 4d each per week, which probably corresponded to some 1½ pints of beer each day. At the Royal Berkshire Hospital similar steps were taken in 1877 when £3 per year was offered to the nurses and servants in lieu of their daily beer ration and within one year all had accepted the offer.

Mr Swadling remained the Gardener and Superintendent of Labour until 1883 when he resigned through ill health. Walter Hicks, his assistant, took over with a wage of 25s per week and his hours were set at 8am to 6.30pm in winter and 7am to 6.30pm in summer. In 1888 when it was decided that cows would no longer be kept at the Workhouse and therefore the wage would be reduced to 21s per week, Hicks resigned. His successors were appointed with a salary of £25 a year with accommodation and allowances.

There were also changes at the bakery and by 1889 the weekly wage of the Baker had increased from 8s to 13s with accommodation as before in the Workhouse. The Assistant Baker's wages were increased from 6s to 7s per week in the same period.

The resignation of Mr and Mrs Pocock, the Master and Matron, in 1878 was a great blow to the Guardians. The Pococks had been at the Workhouse for 11½ years, since the building had opened in 1867, and had served the Union well. Mr Pocock's health had broken down and he could no longer continue his arduous work. He would be allowed superannuation of £90 a year.

The post was advertised in the local papers, the *Local Government Chronicle* and *The Daily Telegraph*. Candidates were to be man and wife, not under 35 years of age and must have experience in a joint capacity of Master and Matron in a workhouse. The Master must be competent at keeping books and accounts and able to undertake all the duties required by the Local Government Board regulations. He must be able to keep discipline and superintend the employment of the paupers. A bond of £200 was required. The Matron would be in charge of all the domestic arrangements at the Workhouse and the employment of the female paupers. The salary of the Master would be £75 per year and that of the Matron £45 per year with furnished accommodation and allowances. Five couples were interviewed in the presence of the Local Government Board Inspector and Mr and Mrs Pope, Master and Matron of the Sudbury Union, were appointed.

One resignation, that of the Union Clerk, Mr Howlett, came about through unforeseen circumstances. In 1879 a new auditor, Mr Household, had pointed out irregularities in the Union's accounts and had refused to certify them. The problem concerned an order for 500lb of beef which had been obtained for the inmates' Christmas dinner in 1878, from which 43lb had been given to officials. The auditor reported this to the Local Government Board who then instructed their Inspector, Mr Henley, to carry out an official investigation. Various witnesses were called including the butcher, members of the Visiting Committee, the Chairmen of the Board of Guardians, the Clerk of the Union, the Relieving Officer and the auditor.

It transpired that the 500lb of beef had cost £27 10s 3d and the four joints weighing 43lb, which had been given to officials, were valued at £1 19s 5d. In the Master's books all had been paid for by the Union. It was

Mr Pope, Workhouse Master 1878–97

Mrs Pope, Workhouse Matron 1878–97

against the rules that meat paid for by the ratepayers for consumption by the inmates should be consumed by officials. Although this had been the custom for several years, it had never been queried before. Following the enquiry the Local Government Board notified the Guardians that there was no legal authority for their action and it had brought 'grave discredit' to all concerned. The Guardians would be surcharged and the Clerk, who was declared to be unfit for the position, must resign. They would not require the Master to resign on this occasion.

The Guardians were understandably horrified and felt the criticism was not deserved. For several years at Christmas, on their instructions, joints had been sent to the Clerk, his Assistant, the Relieving Officer and the Superintendent of the Tramp Wards. If this had been incorrect, it should have been noticed by the auditor. Now it had been declared unlawful, the Guardians had been surcharged and the Clerk asked for his resignation.

Mr Howlett, the Clerk, sent the Guardians a letter of resignation which they refused to accept. He then explained that he wished to resign as the worry of the enquiry had brought back a medical affliction of the head. When Mr Walford confirmed that he was unable to undertake any mental work at present the Guardians accepted his resignation. Mr Kift, the Assistant Clerk, was asked to take over temporarily and in November 1879 he was officially elected Clerk with a salary of £165 per year.

The 'Meat Enquiry' was reported in detail in the local papers and produced an outburst of indignation against the Local Government Board and what was felt to be their bureaucratic behaviour. The Clerk had been made the scapegoat for the action of the Guardians who, the papers stated, could rest assured would have the sympathy of the public. Mr William Palmer of Kendrick House wrote to the papers and criticised the Local Government Board. Their action towards Mr Howlett had been 'arbitrary and unjustified' and 'even cruel'. He ended: 'I certainly think we had better sometimes go wrong than be judicially ruled by an irresponsible and secret tribunal.' New light had been thrown on the working of the Poor Law and the relations between the Guardians and the Local Government Board.

Mr Kift, Union Clerk 1879–1907

Mr Walford, the Medical Officer, resigned in 1882. He had not been well for several years and had given up his appointment as Inspector of Nuisances and sold his private practice in 1880. He had been appointed Medical Officer to St Lawrence's parish and Workhouse in 1839 and to the new Workhouse when it opened in 1867. The Guardians expressed their gratitude for all Mr Walford's work for the Union over the years. Before his request for superannuation of £87 per year was agreed, the Local Government Board insisted he should be examined by their Inspector to 'ascertain whether he was permanently impaired'. His appointment under Poor Law regulations had been for life unless disability or any disciplinary matter intervened. Mr Henley reported that Mr Walford had resigned 'by reason of old age and permanent infirmity of body' which made him 'incapable of discharging efficiently the duties of his office'. Superannuation was therefore agreed.

The position of Medical Officer to the Workhouse and Tramp Wards was advertised with a salary of £120 per year. The election would take place on August 17th 1882. There were two candidates: Mr William Richardson LRCP, of Oxford Road, Reading, who also held a qualification from the College of Surgeons of Edinburgh, and Mr H G Armstrong of Friar Street, Reading, who was an Assistant Surgeon at the Royal Berkshire Hospital. Mr Richardson was elected by nine votes to three votes and was notified he should attend the Workhouse daily before 1pm.

The Medical Officer was required to keep records of all patients admitted to the infirmary, the fever wards, the dirty wards, the imbecile wards and the Tramp Wards, with details of their treatment and the medicines he prescribed. These books had to be presented to the Board of Guardians for regular inspection. Unfortunately none of these records have survived and only the Minutes of the Board of Guardians remain which give no details about patients or their treatment. The only glimpse of the work of the Medical Officer is to be found among the records of the Reading Pathological Society where Mr Walford's occasional contributions are noted. As all very serious cases were sent to the Royal Berkshire Hospital and as there were no facilities for operations to be carried out at the Workhouse, the cases tended to be either associated with difficult labour, cancer or were 'of an unusual nature'.

There were more changes among the nursing staff than in any other department of the Workhouse. The work was extremely hard and all too often the health of the nurses was unequal to the demands of the job. With a nursing staff of only two, the Head Nurse and the Assistant Nurse, and with patients in the infirmary, the Cottage, the fever wards and the imbecile wards, it was necessary to have the assistance of pauper inmates. Their help with watching patients and performing simple menial tasks was essential. In 1873 seven male pauper 'nurses' asked the Guardians if they might be given an extra allowance of bread, cheese and beer on the nights when they were sitting up with patients. By agreeing to this the Guardians were probably assured of a ready supply of pauper assistants.

Between 1873 and 1889 there were eight different Head Nurses. When Miss Bailey became seriously ill in 1875 a temporary nurse was employed to help the Assistant Nurse. Mrs Emily Wiggins of Castle Street was a trained nurse from Guy's Hospital and her short term at the Workhouse was the first time that a professional nurse had been employed there. It is doubtful whether the next Head Nurse, Miss Sutcliffe from the Chorlton Union Hospital, near Manchester, was fully trained but her testimonials were stated to be 'very satisfactory'.

In 1877 when Miss Sutcliffe resigned through ill health, the Guardians decided to advertise for a man and wife to be paid a salary of £22 10s each with accommodation and allowances. Mr and Mrs John Walker, from the Prescott Union, were appointed. Mr Walker would be the male Nurse and Superintendent of the imbecile wards and Mrs Walker would be the Nurse and midwife. The Assistant Nurse was given a month's notice as 'the recent arrangements had made her services unnecessary'.

Mr and Mrs Walker's tenure lasted for one year when an incident involving an alleged lunatic admitted to the Workhouse led to an enquiry by the Guardians. The patient had become very violent and had torn Mrs Walker's clothes. She demanded to be paid £1 5s compensation by the patient's sister. When the Guardians heard about this the money was repaid but Mrs Walker was told the situation was regarded as a serious dereliction of duty and if repeated would result in instant dismissal. The Walkers resigned the following month.

The Guardians reverted to appointing a Head Nurse with a salary of £30 and an Assistant Nurse with a salary of £15 per year. When their first appointed Head Nurse arrived intoxicated and had to leave, the Assistant Nurse was appointed in her place with a salary of £20 and a male Nurse was engaged with a salary of £10 10s. Not surprisingly this proved to be unsatisfactory and the arrangement lasted only a few months.

It was not until December 1880 that the Guardians appointed a trained Head Nurse. Miss Susan Pinnington from the Nurses Home and Training Institution in Sheffield was engaged with a salary of £25 per year (later increased to £30) with accommodation and allowances. At the same time the salary of the male Nurse was increased to £20. In 1882 when he died suddenly on the premises, the Local Government Board suggested that the Guardians might 'more readily obtain the services of a properly qualified person if they were to elect a female'. The Guardians took no notice and once again appointed a male Nurse but with an increased salary of £25 per year. Male nurses continued to be employed, though few stayed any length of time, and by 1889 the salary had been increased to £30 per year.

The Local Government Board suggested in 1884 that an Assistant Nurse should be appointed to take charge of the imbecile wards, which by this time had been moved to the former fever wards behind the infirmary. When not needed there she could attend at the fever wards. Miss Sarah Collins was appointed in reply to the advertisement for 'a strong, active woman' with a salary of £15 per year, accommodation and allowances.

By 1889 the nursing staff had increased from two to three and the total salaries from £45 to £75 per year. But of most importance was the fact that the Board of Guardians had at last appointed a trained nurse and a higher standard of nursing had been introduced to the Workhouse.

Treatment for Patients Elsewhere

The treatment available to the patients in the Workhouse was limited and by subscribing to the Royal Berkshire Hospital it was possible to send severely ill patients there. But even the Hospital had limitations and the Board of Guardians began to subscribe to a variety of institutions to enable paupers to obtain more specialised treatment.

In 1875 a pauper patient was sent to the Royal Sea Bathing Institution at Margate for treatment for tuberculosis. An annual subscription of £2 2s was paid and in 1877 this was raised to £5 each year. The Royal Berkshire Hospital also subscribed to this institution for their patients.

In 1879 a subscription of £2 2s was sent to the Bath Mineral Water Hospital when it was pointed out that 15 patients had been admitted from the parishes of the Reading Union and their average stay of two months had cost the institution £7 for each. By 1882 a further 13 pauper patients had been sent and the Bath Hospital wrote saying all had brought certificates notifying poverty signed by the Guardians. Once again it was noted that each patient had stayed on average two months and had cost the Hospital a total of £91. Frugality raised its head and the Guardians only increased their annual subscription to £5 5s.

Henshaw's Blind Asylum in Manchester was added to the list of subscriptions in 1879 when a blind pauper, Alfred Pearcy 21 years old, had asked if he could be sent to a blind asylum. The usual charge for such institutions was 4s or 5s per week, on top of which was the cost of clothing and travel expenses. A subscription of £2 2s was agreed and it was hoped Alfred Pearcy would learn a trade or occupation. Unfortunately this was not to be the case and in 1881 he was sent back to the Workhouse as he had been found to be mentally incapable of learning a trade and, although he had done his best, he had failed to learn basket and mat making.

In 1883 an annual subscription of £3 3s was sent to the Royal London Ophthalmic Hospital in Moorfields and over the years patients were sent there for advice and treatment. In 1888 the British Hospital for Diseases of the Skin, in London, was asked to admit a pauper patient and 10s 6d was paid towards her maintenance. All too often the Guardians were glad to make use of the charitable status of these institutions and avoid paying the full cost of their paupers' treatment.

A different case was that of the Association for Promoting Trained Nursing in Workhouses, also known as the Workhouse Nursing Association. In 1886 the Guardians were asked to subscribe towards this fairly recently established Association whose President was HRH Princess Mary Duchess of Teck, later to become Queen Mary. The Association paid for the nurses to be trained, provided their uniforms and afterwards obtained work for them in workhouse infirmaries. The Guardians agreed it was 'worthy of support' and subscribed £1 1s.

In 1889 the Guardians increased their annual subscription to the Royal Berkshire Hospital from 10 guineas to 15 guineas to enable them to obtain additional in-patient tickets. For many years their annual subscription had allowed the Guardians to vote when medical staff were to be appointed at the Hospital. On these occasions, after full discussions, the Board of Guardians delegated their Chairman to vote for the candidate they had agreed to support. Another link with the Hospital had been established.

Public Support

The public gradually became more aware of the life of the Workhouse inmates and two incidents brought this to the fore in 1873. In January that year a four-week old baby boy was found abandoned in a basket in the garden of 76, Oxford Road after midnight and was brought to the Workhouse by a policeman. The Guardians instructed handbills to be printed and circulated in the town offering a reward of £5 for information that might lead to the discovery of the person who had deserted the baby. Incidents like these were not uncommon and the number of abandoned or deserted children in the District School bore witness to the desperation of poverty and the stigma of illegitimacy.

Later the same year another baby, only 24 hours old, was found on the lawn of Lexdon House. Once again the police took the baby to the Workhouse and handbills, offering a reward of £5, were distributed. Nothing further is known about these babies and in all probability, if they survived, they remained in the Workhouse until they were old enough to be sent to the District School, after which some job would be found for them.

Originally the only special occasions provided for the inmates were the Christmas dinner and entertainment arranged by the Guardians each year. Gradually additional 'treats' were arranged by members of the public. Although they were not frequent they were much appreciated and relieved the monotony of Workhouse life. Sometimes inmates were entertained for tea in private houses, or taken to the circus and the pantomime. In 1880 Messrs Dann and Lewis, the photographers, gave an entertainment of 'dissolving views'. There were also concerts given by groups like the Band of Hope and Temperance Choir and St Mary's Chapel Choir. The Reading Hand Bell Ringers also gave a performance. The Mayor's 'treats' were always popular but one which was particularly appreciated was provided by voluntary subscription. It consisted of a special tea with bread and butter, buns, tea, oranges, sweets, tobacco and snuff. Afterwards there was a magic lantern show and a minstrel show. It was declared to have been 'an excellent treat' as most of the items of food were never provided by the Union and were not allowed to be given to the inmates by visitors.

To most of the inmates the Workhouse was a refuge where they were looked after in their old age and treated free when they were ill. Although the daily life of the inmates gradually became less harsh and their diets were slightly improved, there were complaints. When it was believed there was not enough meat in the pies and stews, the helpings were weighed to make sure everyone obtained their full ration. Inmates were allowed to ask for leave of absence once a month if permission was obtained from the Master. Men could go out on Monday afternoons and women on Friday afternoons. It was also agreed that the elderly and infirm would be allowed to take a walk on Sundays on the gravel paths of the Workhouse grounds.

Mental Patients

Until the new fever wards were built in 1881 inmates classified as harmless lunatics, imbeciles and the feeble minded were looked after in the main building. Included in this category were those suffering from epilepsy. With today's medical knowledge, the inclusion of these patients with the mentally ill was a great mistake but in the 19th century there were no other means of looking after them and their fits must have caused alarm and fear. As soon as the new fever wards were completed the mentally ill patients were moved to the former fever wards behind the infirmary. These were well adapted for the mentally ill and provided much needed extra space in the main building.

To some the Workhouse was more like a prison and a different light is thrown on the life of the inmates with the letters of complaint which were sent by patients to the Local Government Board. In 1876 Thomas Crown, diagnosed as a harmless lunatic, wrote that he had been removed to the Workhouse on an order signed by Mr Royds, a surgeon of London Street, saying he was suffering from delirium tremens. Crown said this was not true. He was being held against his will and had been deprived of his liberty. Furthermore he had been made to pay 5s 6d per week for his diet. Enquiries revealed that the Medical Officer believed Crown had got better and would be released. Whether he should have ever been admitted or if he would have been released without the letter of complaint, will never be known.

Ten years later Thomas Crown was again in the Workhouse and again he wrote to the Local Government Board. He complained that he had been removed from his ward by the Medical Officer and placed in the Cottage which was set apart for 'loathsome and foul' diseases and he was not properly treated. The Board of Guardians investigated the allegation and reported that Crown should be removed from the Cottage immediately and the Medical Officer should attend the next Board meeting. Mr Richardson, the Medical Officer, explained that Crown had used insolent language and he had moved him to the Cottage which at the time contained no 'foul or loathsome' cases. The Medical Officer was reprimanded and told never to put Crown in the Cottage again. The Local Government Board was informed.

Another incident was brought to light in 1876 following an inspection by the Local Government Board Inspector. He had received a complaint from a patient who said he had been detained for 16 days as an alleged lunatic. The Inspector reported that from the Poor Law point of view three rules had been broken. The Relieving Officer had failed to notify a Justice of the Peace within the statuary three days that an alleged lunatic had been detained, the Medical Officer had not complied with the rule to examine the patient and the Master should have obtained a certificate from the Medical Officer to enable the man to be detained. It was also pointed out that the patient was wearing his own clothes.

Mr Walford said the patient was a lunatic but need not be moved to Moulsford Asylum. He regretted not filling in the forms. The Master and Relieving Officer also expressed their regret. The Guardians said that such incidents must not recur. All necessary paperwork must be completed before these patients were admitted. The patient was not released.

During the 1880s several patients were sent to the Workhouse by the Army under the Army Act of 1881. They had all been born in Reading and when they became unfit for military service they were discharged from the Army and returned to their place of settlement. All had become mentally ill and were put into the imbecile wards. In 1886 Pte F Wiggins, suffering from dementia, was removed from the Royal Victoria Hospital, Netley with three 'guides' to escort him. The same year Pte Harry Cripps, 'a lunatic suffering from mania' was also sent to the Workhouse from Netley under escort. The following year Pte William Ellis, 'a harmless lunatic' was discharged from the Army at Aldershot and admitted to the imbecile wards.

At the same time twelve patients who had been admitted to the Moulsford Asylum were declared fit enough to be discharged and admitted to the imbecile wards at the Workhouse. Sometimes it was possible for patients to leave the Workhouse if there was someone prepared to look after them. One such case was a youth called Herbert Rollinson who was able to leave when the Revd D G Brown agreed he could take proper care of him.

Bodies for Dissection

A request made in March 1886 posed a dilemma for the Guardians. Dr J B Sanderson, from the Schools of Anatomy at Oxford University, asked if he might be allowed to remove any 'unclaimed' bodies of paupers dying in the Workhouse to be used for dissection by anatomy students at the University. Under the Anatomy Act the Guardians were authorised to release the bodies of paupers who died in the Workhouse or within the Union who had no relations and no one responsible for them.

The Guardians discussed the matter at length and eventually voted by seven votes to four votes to reject the request. Dr Saunderson was greatly disappointed and asked if he might discuss the subject in person. This was put to the vote and, with the Chairman's casting vote, Dr Saunderson was asked to attend a Board meeting. Yet another vote was taken to see if the former decision should be overturned but, by a majority of only one vote, the answer remained 'no'.

The next election for Guardians was held in April 1887 and the following month Dr Saunderson put his case to the new Board. He emphasised the great need for bodies for dissection. The days were over when bodies were obtained by grave robbers. It was extremely difficult for the Guardians to come to a final decision on such a sensitive subject and eventually they agreed it would be raised again 'at a later date'. That date turned out to be six years later, in 1892.

The Chaplain

The Revd G I Tubbs, the incumbent at St Mary's Chapel, had been Chaplain to the Workhouse since it was opened in 1867. From time to time he had asked for an increase in salary and the Guardians on their part complained he was not always attending sufficiently to his duties. In 1880, by which time there had been a significant increase in the number of inmates and a larger number of sick and infirm to be visited, the Guardians agreed that his salary should be raised from £80 to £100 per year.

In November 1888 Mr Tubbs sent the Guardians a letter of resignation. He was now in his 76th year and had been seriously ill. He wished to give up his Workhouse duties at Christmas. His request for superannuation was turned down. When the Guardians advertised the post with a salary of £80 a year, little did they anticipate that one of the most controversial periods in the history of the Workhouse was about to begin, one in which public opinion would be involved as never before.

There were five applicants for the post of Chaplain from local clergymen. A letter was also received from the Nonconformist Ministers of the town offering to undertake the religious duties at the Workhouse on a voluntary basis. Calling themselves the 'Ministers Fraternal', they wanted 'neither fee or reward of any description' and 'considered it a privilege to administer the consolation of religion to the inmates of the Union'. They suggested, if their offer were accepted, a term of 6 months or 13 months should be agreed.

The offer was tempting. The Union would save the expense of the £80 salary and, as it was pointed out, there were 150 unions in the country without a paid chaplain, nor were the Guardians obliged to appoint a member of the Episcopal Church. Although Nonconformist ministers were 'not all at one' on sectarian matters, they were agreed upon the great point of teaching the Gospel of Christ and the truths of the Scriptures. One Guardian suggested the Church of England clergy should be offered the opportunity of meeting the Nonconformists on the same terms. If there could be united services 'it would be a great thing'. It was agreed the offer would be considered further.

The matter was discussed and debated over the following weeks without any decision being taken. Eventually on January 17th 1889 the Revd H Brooker, who had succeeded Mr Tubbs at St Mary's Chapel, was appointed with a salary of £80 a year. Within weeks the appointment was declared invalid by the Local Government Board. It transpired that the Chairman of the Guardians, who favoured the appointment of a Church of England clergyman, had refused to put to the vote an amendment which had been seconded, that the offer of the Ministers Fraternal should be accepted. The appointment of Mr Brooker was then rescinded and a committee was formed to consider the appointment further.

The annual election of Guardians by the ratepayers of the Reading parishes always took place in April. The election in 1889 took an unexpected turn when the appointment of a paid chaplain or the acceptance of the offer of voluntary help from the Nonconformists became an issue. The result was that 11 of the 15 Guardians were elected on the Nonconformist 'ticket'. The Chairman, Mr Hayward, remained committed to support the view that a paid chaplain should be appointed.

By this time the Rural Dean had become involved and was sent particulars of the Nonconformists' offer. He consulted the clergy of the town and all were agreed that: 'The interests of the inmates of the Workhouse, especially of the sick and aged, would be seriously imperilled by the divided responsibility in religious instruction.' Furthermore the clergy would not be willing to co-operate with the

Nonconformists and suggested that a Church of England clergyman should be appointed.

There was one reply when the Guardians asked if any Church of England clergy would be prepared to co-operate with the Nonconformists on a voluntary basis. The Revd B Body, of Eldon Square, Chaplain at the Wokingham Union, agreed to share the work with the Ministers Fraternal. A timetable of services and visiting was drawn up for the consideration of the Board. It was also decided that a musical instrument should be obtained 'with the view to making the religious services at the Workhouse of a more bright and cheerful nature'. As had been usual before, a list was drawn up of laymen who would be able to take services on Sundays if necessary.

By the autumn of 1889 Mr Wright, a staunch supporter of the Nonconformists, had become Chairman of the Board of Guardians when Mr Hayward died. Although the new system was working well and the inmates were being visited frequently, the Local Government Board expressed concern that the services taken by Mr Body were inadequate. Once again the local clergy were approached to see if they would co-operate on a voluntary basis. None would agree.

It was suggested that inmates should be allowed to leave the Workhouse on Sundays, as had been allowed previously, to attend services of their own religious persuasion in the town. This was agreed provided the service being

Mr Wright, Chairman of Board of Guardians 1889

held at the Workhouse was 'contrary to the religious feeling of such inmates'. By the time the period agreed for the Nonconformists to attend at the Workhouse came to an end Mr Body was only visiting the inmates and no Church of England services were being taken. As most of the paupers were Church of England, the Guardians, under pressure from the Local Government Board, agreed to advertise for a Church of England Chaplain whose salary would be £100 a year.

This caused fury among the ratepayers who had elected the Guardians to support the Nonconformists' offer. A deputation was sent to complain to the Board. This was followed by two public meetings held at the Victoria and West Street Halls at which, by a large majority, it was resolved that the appointment of a paid chaplain was contrary to the wishes of the majority of the ratepayers at the last election. The voluntary system should be continued until the ratepayers had a chance to consider the question again and vote on it.

The Guardians now decided the inmates should be asked if they found the religious services conducted by the Nonconformist Ministers to be satisfactory. The result of their enquiry was not made known. The issue of the appointment remained unresolved until eventually the Local Government Board insisted a paid Church of England Chaplain must be appointed. In February 1890 the Revd C W H Henrick, Vicar of Holy Trinity Church, was appointed temporarily. He would take a service once every Sunday, visit the sick at least twice a week and more often in cases of dangerous illness and administer Holy Communion 'as often as necessary'. He would be paid 1½ guineas per week.

In April the elections were held for the new Board of Guardians. It was then agreed to advertise for a permanent Chaplain whose salary would be £100 per year. In May the Revd A N Halpin from Newcastle was elected. The Nonconformists' offer to continue taking services at the Workhouse in co-operation with the Church of England was accepted, provided their services did not interfere with those conducted by the Chaplain. After 18 months of acrimony, agreement had at last been reached and the original intention that there should be co-operation between the Church of England and the Nonconformists had eventually come about.

Overcrowding and Boundary Extensions

The new fever wards temporarily relieved the pressure on accommodation in the main building but by 1884 the Workhouse once again was overcrowded, particularly in the winter months. The Wokingham Union Guardians were asked if some male paupers from the Reading Union could be admitted to their Workhouse. This was not possible as the Wokingham Workhouse only had space available for 'old women of good health'. In 1887 Mr Richardson, the Medical Officer, drew the attention of the Guardians to the lack of space in the infirmary. Accommodation in the Tramp Wards was also proving inadequate. The lack of space was now affecting all departments.

Although 1887 started with an overcrowded Workhouse, one innovation was made which was to greatly assist the Guardians and officers of the Union. It would now be possible to have a telephone installed. The Royal Berkshire Hospital had been connected to the Reading Exchange in 1886. However, when the Local Government Board were asked to approve the idea for the Workhouse they immediately asked what expenditure would be entailed. By May it was agreed that the South of England Telephone Company would connect the Workhouse to the Reading Exchange for £6 and the total cost per year would be £18. The Guardians' letter-heads then displayed the fact that they were now on the telephone and the number was 67.

The following month Queen Victoria's Golden Jubilee was celebrated throughout the country on June 21st. All inmates who were able attended

CHARLES KIFT,
CLERK AND SUPERINTENDENT
REGISTRAR.

—

National Telephone No. 67.

a special dinner given to the aged poor of the town and the others were provided with 'a suitable dinner' at the Workhouse.

By this time discussions were taking place about extending the boundaries of Reading Borough. The town had increased in size rapidly over the past decade and by 1887 some 25% of the county's population of quarter of a million now lived there. A map of the proposed extensions had been sent to the Guardians for their consideration. The Reading Corporation Act, passed by Parliament in 1888, granted County Borough status to Reading and almost doubled the size of the Borough.

Parts of some of the parishes of the adjoining Wokingham and Bradfield Unions were now incorporated within the extended Borough but technically were outside the area of the Reading Union. The Reading Guardians asked the Local Government Board if an enquiry could be held to enable the area of the Reading Union to be made co-terminous for Poor Law and Registration purposes with that of the extended Borough of Reading.

The implications of an enlarged Reading Union were great. The Workhouse was already stretched for accommodation and any enlargement of the catchment area would put a strain on the Union's resources. The Bradfield and Wokingham Guardians were consulted as theirs were the adjoining Unions affected. The Bradfield Guardians pointed out that there were no paupers, either indoor or outdoor, in that part of their Union transferred to Reading Borough. If it became part of the Reading Union for Poor Law purposes it would result in 'a serious pecuniary loss' to the Bradfield Union.

The Wokingham Guardians also objected. About one eighth of the total value of their Union was now within the Borough of Reading and if this was withdrawn the Wokingham Union could not make any reductions in overheads like officers' salaries and workhouse expenses and furthermore they would lose the poor rates for the area. They believed there would be no advantage in any transfer especially as the Reading Workhouse would not be able to accommodate any more inmates.

Although nothing had been decided on extending the area of the Reading Union, in May 1888 one Guardian suggested that, in anticipating such an event, a committee should be formed to consider enlarging or altering the Workhouse and also to removing the Tramp Wards from Thorn Street to the main Workhouse site. When put to the vote the proposition was not agreed.

The enquiry asked for by the Reading Guardians was eventually authorised by the Local Government Board to be held on October 24th 1888. Messrs Blandy and Witherington, solicitors, were instructed to represent the Guardians. The enquiry found in favour of the Reading Guardians and in December the Local Government Board issued an Order transferring the portion of the affected parishes to the Reading Union for both Poor Law and Registration purposes. Compensation asked for by the Wokingham and Bradfield Guardians in respect of their loss in the poor rate was not allowed. The enlargement of the Reading Union would take effect on March 24th 1889.

The Local Government Act of 1888 enabled improved grants to be made to Poor Law unions from central funds. These would include paying the salaries, remuneration and superannuation allowances of union officers and those employed in the District Schools. It also included the payment of drugs and medical appliances. A proportion of the salaries of the medical officers and the drugs they supplied had been paid from central funds for some years, but under the new Act almost half the annual expenditure of the Union would now be paid from that source and not from the poor rates. This would be of considerable help to the Reading Guardians, especially at a time when the Union was to be increased in size.

The proposal made in May 1888 that a committee should be formed to consider enlarging or altering the Workhouse was raised again in January 1889 and this time it was agreed that a Building and Repairs Committee should be formed. When the Committee submitted its first report within weeks of the enlargement of the Union, it was decided to postpone any consideration for enlarging the Workhouse until after the election of the new Board of Guardians in April. This would be almost one month after the Union had been officially enlarged.

On March 24th 1889, when the Reading Union was made coterminous with the Borough of Reading, parts of the parishes of Burghfield and Tilehurst from the Bradfield Union, and Earley and Shinfield from the Wokingham Union, were transferred for Poor Law and Registration purposes. It was now necessary to establish how many paupers from these areas would have to be moved to the Reading Workhouse and how many children at the District School in Wargrave would now be paid for by the Reading Union rather than the Wokingham Union.

The extended Union also affected the areas attended by the District Medical Officers and they now asked for additional remuneration for this extra work. St Giles' District now included parts of Earley and Shinfield and had a population of 31,000. Mr Little, the Medical Officer, had his salary increased from £105 to £140. St Mary's District now included parts of Tilehurst and Burghfield with a population of 22,000. Mr Moore's salary was increased from £105 to £120. He was also the Medical Officer for St Lawrence's District which had not increased in size and remained at 5,120, so his salary for this work was unaltered at £30 per year.

Until now in April each year five Guardians had been elected by the ratepayers of each of the three Districts to form the Reading Union Board of Guardians. With the enlarged area of the Union the members of St Giles' Vestry suggested that there should be additional representation for the population which was now nearly 60,000. They believed there should be 21 Guardians rather than the present 15 and that they should represent municipal wards rather than parishes. St Giles', with five municipal wards, should have 10 representatives, St Mary's, with four municipal wards, should have eight, and St Lawrence's, with only one ward, should have three representatives. Copies of this suggestion were sent to the Local Government Board for their consideration.

The Local Government Board had no time to make a decision on the subject before the elections for Guardians were held in April 1889 and as usual 15 representatives were returned. Mr William Hayward was made Chairman but had to resign in May through ill health. Mr Wright was made Chairman in his place. He had been a Guardian for many years and had been notable for his support for the Nonconformist Ministers. He had also been the Guardian who suggested in May 1888 that a committee should be formed to consider enlarging or altering the Workhouse.

By now overcrowding in the Workhouse had become acute and the Local Government Board informed the Guardians that their Inspector had reported that additional accommodation was 'much required'. They asked what decisions had been made by the Guardians on the subject. Now under pressure, the Guardians referred the matter to the Building and Repairs Committee.

The Building and Repairs Committee, with Mr Wright as their Chairman, had met several times and decided that an architect must be consulted. Their choice was Mr Charles Smith FRIBA of Friar Street. He was well known in the area and had carried out a considerable amount of work in Reading and beyond since 1857. He also took a keen interest in local affairs. He was a JP, was Mayor of Reading in 1874–5 and 1875–6 besides holding other offices. He had taken his son into partnership in 1882.

When consulted about superintending and carrying out the work of altering and enlarging the Workhouse, Messrs Charles Smith and Son wrote to the Guardians giving the terms on which they should be appointed. They should be paid commission of 5% on the cost of the work. For this they would prepare designs, working plans, specifications and sets of duplicate copies. They would also make plans of the existing buildings. They would submit plans to the Local Government Board and prepare tracings for the Local Sanitary Authority. They would visit 'such modern workhouse buildings as necessary'. They would superintend all the building work. All plans and tracings would belong to the Guardians.

In August 1889 the Guardians approved these terms and officially appointed Messrs Charles Smith and Son the architects for the alterations and extensions. All was now ready for the next important stage in the development of the Reading Union Workhouse.

4

EXPANSION AND INNOVATION
1889–1899

Planning the Extensions and Alterations

Within weeks of their appointment as architects for the enlargement of the Workhouse, Messrs Charles Smith and Son had started to prepare draft plans. Their first consideration was the Tramp Wards in Thorn Street which the Building and Repairs Committee had recommended should be moved to the Oxford Road site. At this point (September 1889) Mr Wright, the Chairman, pointed out that it was unlikely that the alterations could be carried out before the following spring (1890). Furthermore the question of additional representation on the Board of Guardians was still unresolved. If the number of Guardians were increased from 15 to 21, the Board Room at Thorn Street, already inadequate, would be far too small. It was agreed to defer any final decision on the Tramp Wards and the Thorn Street premises for the time being.

Attention was then turned to the other parts of the Workhouse. The architects made accurate drawings of the existing buildings and, with Mr Wright, visited four other Poor Law Unions to see the accommodation they provided. The new Workhouse and vagrant wards of the Wandsworth and Clapham Union were inspected and also South Lambeth Workhouse, hospital, vagrant wards and outdoor relief offices. They then went to the Burton-on-Trent Union Workhouse, vagrant wards, board room and offices and finally to the Birmingham Union infirmary and vagrant wards. It was noted that some 'were arranged on the most approved and modern plans' and the visits had afforded 'valuable information'.

On the strength of this the architects submitted three different schemes for the consideration of the Board of Guardians and the Local Government Board. Scheme 1 was on the lines of the Guardians' instructions to carry out alterations and extensions to the existing buildings, provide new accommodation for imbeciles and children, extend the present receiving wards and build new vagrant wards.

Scheme 2 was more ambitious and incorporated various suggestions made by the Local Government Board's architect. The entrance and Porter's Lodge would be moved further west to the site of the labour yard and re-erected to form a new entrance. The Battle Place cottages would be demolished and, with the area freed by moving the Porter's Lodge, a site would be available for new Tramp Wards to be built with a frontage on Oxford Road. This site would have the additional advantage of being nearest to the town. Various additions would be made to the main building to provide administrative accommodation, a new dining hall, kitchen and imbecile wards. Most important of all would be the building of a new hospital quite separate from the main building.

Scheme 3 was similar to Scheme 2 in many respects but retained the present entrance, Porter's Lodge and Battle Place cottages. The new Tramp Wards would be built further back on the site of the labour sheds.

The Guardians voted to accept Scheme 2 which later was estimated would cost between £16,000 and £18,000. This was far in excess of what had been anticipated and the Guardians urgently looked for ways in which the price could be reduced. They first approached the adjoining Wokingham, Henley and Bradfield Unions to see if they could receive any inmates from the Reading Union 'upon terms sanctioned by the Local Government Board'. Bradfield could not help and the Wokingham and Henley Unions could only take a very limited number. This was not sufficient to meet the needs of the Guardians. They then consulted the architects to see if they could modify Scheme 3. If no new Tramp Wards, dining hall and Master's quarters were built perhaps a significant reduction could be made to the cost.

It was at this point the Local Government Board issued an Order informing the Guardians that their number would be increased from 15 to 21. The premises at Thorn Street would now have to be altered. An enlarged Board Room would have to be built as well as additional office accommodation. The Dispensary would not be affected. The Tramp Wards, condemned by the Local Government Board, would have to be demolished and new Tramp Wards built on the Oxford Road site. It was decided to proceed with Scheme 2 and it was agreed that the cost would be met by a loan repayable out of the rates.

In January 1890 plans were prepared for a new Board Room and offices at Thorn Street. Temporary accommodation for the Board was obtained in the school room attached to the Primitive Methodist's Chapel which adjoined the Union's Thorn Street premises. In March the plans were approved and the following month 12 tenders were received to carry out the work. The cheapest, that of Messrs Higgs and Hill, was accepted: £1,588 for the building work, £168 for the heating and a credit of £20 for the old bricks. It was estimated the work would take 26 weeks to complete.

The enlarged Board of Guardians was elected in April 1890. The Local Government Board had agreed to the suggestion made by St Giles' Vestry that the election should be held by wards rather than by parishes. For the first time the candidates included ladies and two were elected Guardians. Mr Wright was made Chairman and the following seven committees were appointed: Workhouse Visiting, Assessment, Dispensary,

Finance, Building and Repairs, Farm and Labour and a new Casual Wards Visiting Committee. The enlargement and administration of the Workhouse was now in their hands.

The building of new Tramp Wards was now a priority and until these were ready for occupation temporary accommodation for the casual paupers was rented at 19 and 21 Derby Street. It was also necessary to start work on the new hospital as soon as possible, as no work could be started on the main building until the new hospital was finished. The new entrance and receiving block, Tramp Wards and hospital would be built simultaneously. Tenders, to be submitted by the end of August, were requested from builders resident in the area of the Union. That of Mr G S Lewis for £3,373 was accepted for the entrance, receiving wards, vagrant wards and workshops, and that of Messrs Higgs for £7,100 was accepted for the new hospital.

The new Church of England Chaplain, the Revd A N Halpin, who had been appointed in May, suggested that this was the time to consider building a chapel at the Workhouse. The dining hall was not really suitable for worship and those who wished to kneel were not able to do so. He believed there were many residents in Reading who were willing to contribute to a chapel building fund.

Once again the debate that ensued centred on the role of the Nonconformist ministers and whether they could use a Workhouse chapel. The Reading vicars had said they were prepared to find the money to build a chapel but only on the condition that it should be used exclusively for Church of England services. The Guardians were divided in their views. Although a majority of the inmates were Church of England and only a few asked to attend services outside the Workhouse, many Guardians felt it would not be right to build a chapel to be used exclusively by one denomination. Enthusiasm for building a chapel declined when it was found it would cost £1,000 and the best site was the Master's garden. A compromise was reached and it was agreed that the architects should see if it would be possible to erect or equip a suitable 'room' in the main building. When it was pointed out that the new dining hall was larger and more convenient than the present one, the Guardians voted not to erect a chapel or equip a 'room' in the main building. The new dining hall would be perfectly adequate for services of all denominations. An awkward situation had been averted.

The new Board Room and offices at Thorn Street were opened in October 1890 and by February 1891 work was under way on the new entrance and Tramp Wards at the Workhouse. The Reading Town Council suggested this was now a convenient time to widen Oxford Road. It was arranged that the Town Council would pay the Guardians 10s (50p) for strips of their land on either side of the new entrance and the Guardians would obtain a strip of land belonging to the Council in front of the former Workhouse entrance. The road could now be made a more suitable width.

Union Offices, Thorn Street, from 1960s photograph

Once building the new entrance, Tramp Wards and hospital was under way, attention was turned to obtaining detailed plans for the alterations and additions to the main building. A new central administrative block was to be built with adjoining Master's quarters, a larger dining hall, offices and laundry. The present dining hall would be altered to provide a new kitchen, scullery and bakehouse. The present kitchen area would be used for stores. The new dining hall, Master's quarters and additional stores would be built west of the kitchen, and the laundry, boiler house and coal house to the east. At the same time the imbecile block would be enlarged and the drainage system, which had been a problem for many years, would be altered and connected to the main sewer in Oxford Road.

The New Entrance
The new entrance and Tramp Wards were the first buildings to be completed. The entrance, now between Battle Terrace and the New Inn, was conveniently placed to lead to the main building to the east and the new hospital to the west. The rebuilt Porter's Lodge was on the left of the gateway, with the women's receiving ward, bathroom and lavatory beyond. On the right of the gateway were an office and waiting room, behind which were the men's receiving ward, bathroom and lavatory. Stores for the male and female inmates' clothes were behind Battle Terrace gardens.

New entrance to Workhouse

The New Tramp Wards

By November 1891 the new Tramp Wards were nearing completion and new staffing arrangements had to be made. Mr Herrington, the Relieving Officer and Superintendent of the present Tramp Wards, would remain at Thorn Street as the Relieving Officer and would also act as the School Enquiry Officer. His salary would be unaltered at £180 a year. His wife, who was the Matron of the Tramp Wards, would be employed instead as Caretaker and Cleaner of the Board Room with a salary of £20 a year.

The other officers at the Thorn Street Tramp Wards were asked to resign and in their place a married couple would be appointed for the new Tramp Wards. The man would be the Porter and Assistant Relieving Officer for the vagrants with a salary of £25 per year and also Labour Master and Gardener with a salary of £20 per year. The combined salary of £45 would include accommodation, rations and washing. His wife would be employed as Portress at the new Tramp Wards and paid £10 per year.

The new Tramp Wards, opened on February 29th 1892, were a great improvement on those at Thorn Street. The red brick building, similar in style to the Porter's Lodge and main Workhouse building, fronted Oxford Road and occupied the site of the former entrance and Battle Place cottages. A wall with iron railings separated the building from the road. Accommodation was available for 45 tramps. A sleeping ward and day ward for 29 men were on the ground floor and also a room for the Porter. A kitchen and store room were in a small wing to the north as well as six sleeping and labour 'cells' for tramps who had to be segregated and given harsher labour tasks to perform. On the floor above there were sleeping

Mr Herrington, Relieving Officer 1891   Mrs Herrington, Caretaker 1891

and day wards for 10 women, a second room for the Porter and a store. There were bathrooms and lavatories on both floors. A disinfecting chamber and drying room were provided in the basement. The Labour Master's office, labour sheds and stone-breaking sheds were behind the building. Once the new Tramp Wards were in operation the Casual Wards Visiting Committee was disbanded and its work handed over to the Workhouse Visiting Committee.

The labour sheds were soon found to be inadequate for the work of wood chopping and additional sheds were erected. Alterations were then carried out to the labour yards. Later the grills on the labour 'cells', where tramps had to break stones to a certain size, were altered from square shaped to round and the holes reduced to $1\frac{1}{2}$ inches in diameter.

By the end of 1892 the Guardians noted a marked increase in the weekly number of tramps. This was believed to be partly due to the Reading Evening Mission who provided free meals to the tramps after they left the wards on Sundays. When approached on the subject by the Guardians, the Mission agreed to discontinue the practice when the cold weather was over, but only for the time being.

The tasks of work for tramps were then revised. Males who remained for one night would have to break 4cwt of stones and their hours of work would be from 7am to 10am between Lady Day and Michaelmas , and 8am to 11am between Michaelmas and Lady Day. Women would have to pick $\frac{1}{2}$lb of unbeaten oakum or 1lb of beaten oakum, or do three hours work washing, scrubbing and cleaning. It was found necessary to erect an additional 12 stone-breaking cells.

By October 1893 the number of tramps was proving alarming. On October 7th a total of 81 tramps were admitted between 6.30pm and

New Tramp Wards, from 1960s photograph

8.30pm. A labour shed had to be used for additional accommodation and extra assistance had to be obtained for the Porter. The Guardians agreed that in future the Tramp Wards would be connected by telephone to the Master's and Porter's quarters and police constables should be available to help, if required. To try and check the numbers wanting admission on Saturday nights, posters were put up telling tramps that in future they would be detained for the whole of Sunday and given tasks of work on the Monday morning before they could leave.

The Reading Evening Mission then asked the Guardians if they could hold services in the Tramp Wards on Sunday mornings and evenings. Each service would last 45 minutes and a band of 12 workers would sing sacred hymns and speak 'of the highest and purest things, pleading with them (the tramps) to repent and turn from the error of their ways'. The Guardians agreed to one service only on Sunday evenings but later allowed an afternoon service to be held for those tramps who had been admitted on the Saturday evening.

Within weeks the number of tramps wanting accommodation declined spectacularly and on November 11th 1893 only 21 were admitted and by the end of the month the number had only risen to 31. As a further precaution it was arranged that no Christmas dinner would be provided for the tramps that year. The previous year 97 had been fed and the Guardians did not want this to be repeated.

By December 1893 the position of Tramp Ward Porter was made separate from that of the Labour Master and Gardener. The work had become too much for one man. Mr Charles Fisher, who had undertaken both jobs, now became Tramp Ward Porter and Assistant Relieving Officer only with a salary of £35 a year and his wife continued to be Portress with a salary of £10 a year.

An incident in October 1895 drew unwelcome attention to the Workhouse and its officials and provoked much public criticism in the local newspapers. On Friday October 4th a tramp with his wife, young child and baby, were seen in Oxford Road at 8pm making their way to the Tramp Wards. The child was exhausted, wet through and filthy with his clothes in rags. The parents appeared to be the worse for drink. When a passer-by suggested the boy should be carried, the man refused so the passer-by carried him to the Tramp Wards where the family were admitted.

Once in the Tramp Wards the boy, aged five years and called James, was bathed and given bread and milk. The following day the Matron and Head Nurse visited him and said he was able to leave with his parents that morning. As soon as the family had left, the Tramp Ward Porter, Charles Fisher, on his own initiative, informed Inspector Bennett of the local NSPCC. He found the family in Queen's Road at 2.30pm and took them to his office and informed the police. James was exhausted and in a very dirty and verminous state. He weighed only 26lb, was an imbecile and dumb. It transpired that the father, David Phillips aged 74, was old and helpless. His wife, Mary Ann, was 40 and the baby four months old. The family had left Notting Hill on the Tuesday to travel to Newbury to visit a daughter. They spent that night in the Edgeware Union Workhouse. The next day they walked to Uxbridge and spent the night at that Union. The following day they walked to Windsor and on to Maidenhead where they spent the night at the Union. On the Friday they walked from Maidenhead to Reading. The child had walked the whole distance from London. The Reading Union Matron suggested they should return to London and they were doing so when apprehended by Inspector Bennett.

The family were taken into police custody and James was then sent to the Workhouse. They all appeared in Court the following Monday. After hearing the evidence, the Magistrates sentenced the parents to one month's hard labour in prison for child cruelty and neglect. James was returned to the Workhouse until his parents were released from prison. The Magistrates expressed their horror at the condition of the child and the 'over-walking' it had endured.

The case unleashed great fury with newspaper headlines of 'Shocking Cruelty to a Child in Reading' and 'Severe Magisterial Strictures on the Workhouse Authorities'. The Guardians were incensed by the criticism levelled at them and the Workhouse officials who had allowed the child to be discharged in a wretched and dirty condition. They rounded on Charles Fisher who had given evidence in court. Neither the Medical Officer, who had seen the child later, nor the Nurse, who had seen the child on the Saturday, had been called to give evidence. The Guardians were highly critical of Charles Fisher for not informing the Master for three days that he had been the person who had contacted the NSPCC. They believed he had no right to have done this without consulting his superior officer. A special committee was formed to investigate the matter and also the conduct of Charles Fisher.

The local branch of the NSPCC believed there had been ample evidence to prosecute the parents. The absence of medical evidence had been because the Medical Officer had refused to appear unless served with a subpoena and this had been impossible to obtain in the time available. The central office of the NSPCC informed the Guardians they believed an enquiry was needed into the whole affair. The Guardians then informed the Local Government Board of the facts and forwarded all correspondence. The Revd B Waugh, Director of the NSPCC, also wrote and sent copies of all the local newspaper reports.

The Guardians wanted two questions answered. Was the child sent out of the Tramp Wards in such a condition as to constitute an act of cruelty? If so which officer or officers were responsible and what course of action should be taken against them?

The Local Government Board held an official enquiry on December 20th before their Inspector, Mr Murray Browne. He reported that he believed Charles Fisher had 'acted by the dictates of humanity'. The child should not have left the Workhouse until he had been examined by the Medical Officer and he should not have been allowed to leave in a verminous state. He could not have been 'cleaned' on admission as required by the Casual Paupers Regulation Order of December 1882. Charles Fisher was exonerated. The Matron and Tramp Ward Portress were held responsible. The report was shown to all concerned and those implicated were reprimanded.

The problem of increased vagrancy recurred from time to time, especially in the winter months. By January 1896 the Local Government Board were urging the Guardians to exercise their powers to check the numbers admitted to the Tramp Wards. The Guardians believed their powers were inadequate and legislation was needed to introduce a uniform system of action throughout the country to deal with the situation.

In 1897 the Vagrancy Committee was re-appointed and asked to look into the best methods of checking the number of tramps admitted to the Tramp Wards. The Committee's recommendations were agreed. Casual paupers would be detained until the morning of the second day after admission and discharged after they had completed their tasks of work. However, at the Master's discretion, men over the age of 60 and women over the age of 50 could be discharged after one day. Women with children and the men accompanying them and 'such others' as the Master considered 'deserving', could also be discharged early. The Vagrancy Committee also introduced certain rules covering the hours of duty of the Porter and Portress of the Tramp wards.

The rules applying to the children of tramps had already been improved by the Local Government Board. An Order issued in May 1897 allowed children aged seven years and under to receive special diets according to their age and stated that they were to be fed every eight hours. All aged between seven months and two years were to be given milk, sugar and bread, and those aged between two and seven years would also be given cheese.

Later that year, probably bearing the James Phillips case in mind, the Local Government Board Inspector, Mr Murray Browne, issued a circular stating that the Master of the Workhouse should communicate with the NSPCC 'when parents with children leave the casual ward, so that in case a child should be ill-used or over-walked the officer could take appropriate action'. At last a little humanity was being shown towards the children of tramps and the Guardians were having to show some tolerance towards a section of society for which they had little sympathy.

Bodies for Dissection

In November 1892, in the middle of all the building work, the Guardians received a formal request from Professor Thomson of Oxford University, asking if the unclaimed bodies of paupers dying in the Workhouse and within the Union could be made available for dissection at the Schools of Anatomy. This was the second time the request had been made. In 1886 Dr J B Saunderson had approached the Guardians on the same subject and, after much discussion, the request had been turned down.

Professor Thomson attended a meeting of the Board of Guardians and pointed out how important it was for the medical profession, and ultimately the whole community, that these unclaimed bodies should be made available for dissection. He reminded the Guardians that, under the Anatomy Act, they had the authority to agree to his request.

Once again the matter received careful attention and, when put to the vote, Professor Thomson's request was carried by ten votes to four. The minutes recorded the name of every Guardian who voted. It was arranged that the Master would notify the University when a body was available. It would then be sent by rail to Oxford at the expense of the University. After dissection the bodies would be interred in Holywell churchyard 'in a decent and orderly manner'. No records have survived to show how many bodies were sent to Oxford or for how long the practice continued. The request, which in 1886 had been debated by the Guardians on a number of occasions, had been decided immediately in 1892.

The New Hospital

The new hospital was not completed until 1893. It was insured for £7,000 to cover the building, furniture and fittings. Two storeys in height and built of red brick, the hospital was designed on the pavilion system. The men's wards were in the southern pavilion and the women's in the northern pavilion. These two buildings were linked by a central, covered corridor in the middle of which was a two-storey administrative building.

Top: The New Hospital, Men's Wing; *Bottom:* Centre Block and Women's Wing

The two pavilions were similar in design with both the ground and upper floors divided into two wards. On each floor, between the two wards, there was a three-bed observation ward with bathroom and lavatory, and also a store room and a nurse's room. Each of the four male wards contained 18 beds and on the women's side two wards had 18 beds and two had 16 beds. Bathrooms and lavatories were situated in small turrets at the end of each ward. Heating was provided by a central stove in each ward and steam pipes round the skirting. At the end of the ground floor wards there were doors opening on to the grounds and on the floors above there were verandahs.

The central administrative building, linked to the pavilions by a covered way, contained a kitchen, nurses' quarters, stores, surgery and dispensary on the ground floor. Glass screens provided a waiting area for inmates from the other parts of the Workhouse who needed to see the Medical Officer. On the floor above were the maternity rooms. These consisted of a nurse's room, a labour ward with two beds, and two lying-in wards, one with two beds and the second with four beds.

The Workhouse now had an up-to-date hospital 'built to the modern requirements of the Local Government Board'. As the architects had noted, the most efficient treatment of the sick poor was of the first importance and in the end would be the most economical.

Nursing and Medical Arrangements
The nursing staff, which consisted of a Head Nurse and an Assistant Nurse with the additional help of a night nurse, would be inadequate for the new hospital. There were already problems with overworked staff. The male nurse, Joseph Beaton, resigned in September 1892 as he was having to work two Sundays out of three and had only two short periods free in the evenings each week. The following week a special committee was formed to consider the staffing of the new hospital.

It was agreed that the Head Nurse, Miss Pinnington, would remain in charge of the nursing department. Assistant Nurse Brown would also remain but no night nurse would be employed. Advertisements would be placed for two Assistant Nurses who would be appointed as day and night nurses. They should be single women or widows 'without encumbrances', not over 35 years of age and each should have at least one year's training in a hospital or infirmary. The salary of £20 per year, rising by annual increments of £1 to £25, would include accommodation, rations and washing. A suggestion that a uniform should be provided for the nurses was not agreed.

When no suitable candidates answered the advertisement, the Workhouse Infirmary Nursing Association was contacted and asked to provide two Assistant Nurses. Nurse Goodair and Nurse Goldsmith took up their duties at the end of 1892. Within weeks the Association was asked to send another nurse and Nurse Gladwell was appointed in March 1893. The nursing staff now consisted of the Head Nurse and four Assistant Nurses.

The question of providing a uniform for the nurses had been raised on several occasions but with no success. When, however, the Workhouse Infirmary Nursing Association told the Guardians the nurses supplied by them could not be asked to remain at the Reading Union without a uniform allowance, the Guardians immediately had a change of heart. In October 1893 indoor uniform, chosen by the Matron and lady Guardians, was supplied to the nursing staff.

When Nurse Gladwell resigned through ill health the Workhouse Infirmary Nursing Association suggested a salary of £25 per year would make it much easier to obtain nurses. This was agreed and when Nurse Clara Leakey was appointed in January 1894 the salaries of all the Assistant Nurses were raised to £25 and that of the Head Nurse from £30 to £35. Only nurses with training and experience were now being employed. Clara Leakey had been trained at the Royal Southern Hospital for one year between 1890–91 and had then worked in the Paddington and St George-in-the East Infirmaries.

One of the patients admitted to the new hospital provoked great consternation among the Guardians. It was only rarely that details of a case were ever recorded but those of Kate Englefield were exceptional. On the night of February 17th 1894 a local doctor, Dr Nixon, sent his servant girl, Kate Englefield, to the Workhouse between 10pm and 11pm. She had been prematurely delivered of a still-born child. Dr Nixon had sent the girl by cab as the ambulance was not allowed to attend at that hour of the night. When the girl reached the lying-in ward a brown paper parcel sent with her was found to contain the dead body of the baby. The Guardians, noting that no previous intimation had been given of the contents of the parcel and, bearing in mind the critical condition of the girl, 'unanimously desired' that a 'grave remonstrance' should be sent to Dr Nixon.

The letter sent to Dr Nixon stated: 'Your conduct was most reprehensible in turning the girl out of your house at that time of night in the bitter cold, you being fully aware of her condition and knowing, as a medical man, the serious consequences which might have ensued.' Dr Nixon attended a Board meeting to protest at the tone of the Guardians' letter. He believed it to be more severe than the circumstances of the case warranted. The Guardians replied that they believed they had 'erred on the side of leniency' as his statement to the Board showed he had acted in a most extraordinary manner. The highest standards of behaviour were expected of members of the medical profession whatever the circumstances.

In April 1894 the Medical Officer, Dr William Richardson, resigned. The position was advertised with a salary of £120 per year. Candidates, qualified both in medicine and surgery, were required to send their details and three recent testimonials to the Guardians by May 1st. There were ten applicants including, rather surprisingly, Dr Nixon. A short list of four, Dr Gilford, Dr Tench, Dr Withers and Dr Guilding, were asked to attend an interview. Dr L M Guilding MRCS, LRCP was appointed. Besides being in private practice Dr Guilding was also an Assistant Surgeon at the Royal Berkshire Hospital, a position he had held since 1889.

With his experience of working at the Royal Berkshire Hospital, Dr Guilding quickly drew attention to inadequacies at the Workhouse hospital. He requested alterations to the system of dispensing and suggested the small dispensary should be fitted with shelves and a proper supply of drugs. Furthermore, the Dispenser, who also attended daily at the Union Dispensary at Thorn Street, should attend at the Workhouse

Dr Guilding, Workhouse Medical Officer 1894–1926

Miss Pinnington, Head Nurse 1880–1906

two hours each day. Dr Guilding also commented that there were practically no instruments or medical appliances and suggested that a suitable supply of instruments, costing about £50 to £60, should be obtained.

Dr Guilding was asked to provide a detailed list of the instruments required. These were obtained for £49 from Messrs Down Bros, Surgical Instrument Makers of St Thomas' Street, London, and also a special airtight case in which to keep them. The Dispenser eventually worked full time for the Union and his salary was increased from £85 to £105 per year.

It was soon discovered that the nursing staff was insufficient for the 156 bed hospital and its six-bed maternity unit. Two probationer nurses were engaged to 'make the nursing staff in a state of greater efficiency'. Head Nurse Pinnington's salary was increased to £40 a year and a small Nursing Committee was appointed to deal with matters arising between Board meetings. Laura Eva Weaver and Helen Hodgkinson were appointed the first Probationer Nurses, each with a salary of £10 for the first year and £15 for the second year and the usual allowances.

The Royal Berkshire Hospital at this time had about the same number of beds as the Workhouse hospital but a much larger nursing staff. For some years they had been training their own nurses who attended lectures given by the nursing and medical staff. Through the influence of Dr Guilding, the Board of Guardians arranged that the Workhouse probationers, in addition to being instructed by the Head Nurse in nursing and midwifery, should attend the lectures given to probationers at the

Royal Berkshire Hospital. The standard of nursing at the Workhouse would now be comparable to that at the Hospital.

Unlike the Royal Berkshire Hospital, there was no operating theatre at the Workhouse hospital and patients requiring serious operations were sent there, as had been advised by the Local Government Board. In November 1894 the Guardians were notified that the Local Government Board would now sanction the payment of 'a reasonable sum' if an anaesthetic was required for operations which were not performed in a hospital. When minor operations had been performed no doubt anaesthetics had been used, but no additional money had been made available for administering an anaesthetic. With a Medical Officer who was also a surgeon, a trained nursing staff and improved facilities, the way was now open to extend the surgical work of the new hospital.

It was at this point that Miss C T Wood wrote asking for permission to inspect the Workhouse 'in order to make a report which will subsequently be published in *The British Medical Journal*'. This was to be one of 47 reports the *Journal* was to publish on 'The Nursing and Administration of Provincial Workhouses and Infirmaries' throughout the country. Miss Wood had previously visited the Reading Workhouse on behalf of the Workhouse Infirmary Nursing Association.

The Report, published on December 4th 1894, was highly favourable. Miss Wood was particularly glad to see that pauper nurses were no longer employed and inmates were only used to clean and service the wards and help the night nurses with bed-making. Another change which met with approval was that no male nurse was now employed. Night nursing was taken in turn with two nurses on duty for one month, followed by three months on day duty. It was noted 'with satisfaction' the improvement that had been made by employing trained nurses.

The Report criticised certain things on the wards. The 2ft 9in beds were considered to be 'rather too narrow' and advice was given on the way the mattresses had been divided into three sections. There were still some flock beds in use with feather beds on top. The furniture consisted of tables, benches and armchairs. Some of the lockers between the beds were open style and appeared untidy. There were no day rooms for the patients.

There was no separation of patients into medical or surgical wards, nor were there special wards for children. Most patients were suffering from problems associated with old age and paralysis. Incontinent cases were distributed throughout the wards and not isolated as often occurred in workhouses. There were cases of phthisis, heart diseases, rheumatism and paraplegia. On the male side there was a case of aneurism and another of pneumonia. On the female side there was a severe case of ulceration of the leg which was being treated with idoform in an observation ward. Although there were few surgical cases, Dr Guilding said he could undertake any operation and carry out any treatment with the facilities available. It was noted that the hospital was connected by telephone to the Master's office which in turn was connected to the Medical Officer's house.

The lying-in, or maternity, wards consisted of a two-bed labour ward with an adjoining two-bed ward for the women after giving birth. There was also a four-bed ward for convalescents as the mothers remained in the hospital for at least a month or longer if necessary. Miss Pinnington, the Head Nurse, was the midwife and also trained the other nurses in midwifery. The Royal Berkshire Hospital had no maternity beds at this time and only accepted difficult cases of childbirth. Most expectant mothers were attended by local midwives within the community.

A later Report pointed out that it was only in 'well-appointed' workhouse hospitals, like that at Reading where there was an adequate nursing staff, that it was found that the Guardians had 'broken through the old traditions' and were working their infirmaries or hospitals on the lines of a general hospital. The status of the nurse, however, was still subordinate to the workhouse matron, although the latter was untrained in hospital work. Much remained to be done to improve the position of workhouse nurses.

The Main Workhouse Building

As soon as the hospital was completed and the patients moved from the old infirmary, work began on altering the main building. It had originally housed both male and female paupers, with the men on the west and the women on the east. Now, with the old infirmary vacated, the women and children would be housed there and the men would occupy the main

Master's house and Administrative Block

New entrance to Men's Block

building where rooms were also provided for married couples. The division between the sexes was now to be north and south.

New accommodation was built for the Master on the western side of the main building with offices and stores. Adjoining this central administrative block were the new, larger dining hall, kitchen, sculleries, bakehouse and laundry. The main entrance was now to be in the centre of the west side of this block.

Alterations were carried out to improve the bathrooms and lavatories throughout the male and female buildings. A new drainage and sewage system was installed and linked to the town sewer. New water mains were laid with hydrants attached in case of fire. A new gas system was installed. Most important of all was an entirely new central coal-fired hot water and heating system for the enlarged Workhouse and the new hospital. Two large Lancashire boilers, each 19ft long and 6ft in diameter, would supply all the hot water and heating as well as steam for cooking and hot water for the new laundry. In August 1893 a stoker was appointed with a salary of £25 per year and all allowances.

At the end of 1893 advertisements were placed in the papers for a Workhouse Engineer. The Guardians carefully approved the wording. 'Practical working engineer, competent to take charge of steam boiler and heating apparatus at the Workhouse. Able to carry out fitting and repairs in and about the premises. Full time job. To reside near the Workhouse. Salary £2 2s per week. Must be a married man. Testimonials from present and past employers.' There were 113 applicants and, from a short list of six, Mr C Dummer from London was appointed.

The New Laundry

The new laundry did the washing for the whole Workhouse, with the exception of the Infectious Hut which was done on the premises. The building, situated on the north-east of the new central administrative block, was large and well lit. It consisted of a series of rooms, each equipped for the different stages of laundry work. Soiled washing was put in a large tank with Jeyes Fluid before being washed. Items to be disinfected were dealt with separately and put in a special disinfecting oven in the disinfecting room. In the large wash house there were coppers with water heated from the central boilers situated below the ironing room. Once washed the laundry was dried in the drying room and then transferred to the ironing room. The only fire was one needed to heat the irons in the ironing room. All the machinery was hand-operated. The officers' laundry was washed in a separate wash house.

The Matron had originally supervised the laundry work but, with a much enlarged establishment, a special laundress was appointed to take charge and direct the work of the pauper inmates who provided the labour. Miss Maud Jackson, appointed in November 1893, was dismissed within weeks for her 'habits of intemperance'. Miss Susan Holman was appointed in her place with a salary of £25 per year and the usual allowances. This essential part of the Workhouse was now fully equipped and able to undertake the washing for over 500 people.

The Imbecile Wards

By 1892 the accommodation provided for the imbecile patients in the old fever hospital had become inadequate. When the Superintendent of Moulsford Asylum asked if some cases of mild insanity could be sent back to the Workhouse, the Guardians had to refuse through lack of space. The Reading Justices noted that they were having to send cases to the Asylum which would be better sent to the Workhouse. They hoped the Guardians would provide the necessary accommodation. The Superintendent drew the Guardians' attention to a different problem. Patients sent to the Asylum from the Workhouse were arriving in 'a very unclean condition' with 'their heads positively swarming with vermin'.

It was first planned that the old fever hospital should be extended to accommodate 60 patients, both male and female. When it was estimated the cost would be £1,600 it was decided that instead of extending the building it would be used for female patients only. There would be a day room, dormitories and an attendant's room. The bathroom and lavatory facilities would be improved and a padded cell added. The male patients would be placed in the south-east part of the men's building where similar accommodation would be provided, including a padded cell. Two Imbecile Attendants were appointed: Miss Wells from the Bethnal Green Infirmary for the female patients with a salary of £20 per year (rising by annual £1 increments to £25), and Mr Hatto with a salary of £25 per year for the male patients, both with accommodation and the usual allowances. While the alterations were carried out the female patients were temporarily accommodated in one of the female wards of the new hospital.

The separation of the male and female imbeciles in different parts of the Workhouse was criticised by the Local Government Board. The *BMJ* Report was also critical saying that by having two separate units the services were duplicated. The floors of the padded cells were considered to be sub-standard and Dr Guilding also drew attention to the fact that they were uneven and screwed down in sections and could not be properly cleaned.

The Commissioner in Lunacy who visited the wards in August 1895 gave a favourable report. There were 26 males and 24 females looked after by the two paid attendants who were assisted by pauper helpers. The accommodation was cheerful and clean. The patients were well looked after with clean clothes and bedding, good food and ample indoor amusement. Many were usefully employed. There were no records of restraint. It was noted that a male epileptic was kept apart in a sick room with a pauper attendant and that a deaf, dumb and blind mental patient should have been classified as insane.

By 1898 Moulsford Asylum, with 600 beds, was having difficulty in accommodating all the patients needing admission. A further 200 beds were required. Dr Guilding noted he only sent patients there who could not be managed at the Workhouse, but here also the accommodation was almost full. When the Workhouse opened there were beds for 10 imbecile patients. Now provision had been made for 60 and this was becoming inadequate.

Infectious Cases

In 1893 there were two buildings at the Workhouse where patients could be isolated: the Cottage, where 'foul and dirty' cases were accommodated and the Infectious Hut Hospital, built in 1881 for infectious cases. When alterations were being planned for the main building it was discovered that 'dirty cases' had been removed from the Cottage to the new hospital. This was strictly against Local Government Board regulations as these cases had to be isolated and not in the same building as ordinary cases.

The Medical Officer noted the difficulty which might arise if different types of infectious cases occurred at the same time and had to be isolated in separate buildings. The present small observation wards in the new hospital were inadequate if this should happen. He described how a recent case in these wards had turned out to be typhus fever and the patient was removed to the Infectious Hut. If a case of smallpox had arisen at the same time it could not have been put in the same building. He advised it was a matter of 'urgent necessity' that an isolation ward for both sexes should be provided.

After much deliberation the Guardians decided not to erect another building. The Cottage would be adapted to provide 12 beds in two wards with an adjoining bathroom, supplied with hot water, available to both. The wards were heated by open fires and hot pipes. The *BMJ* Report in

December 1894 noted the Cottage was being used for cases of venereal disease and offensive ulcerated legs.

As no additional accommodation had been provided for infectious cases, the Guardians consulted the Urban Sanitary Authority. In 1896 they asked if any case of smallpox should arise in the Workhouse or Tramp Wards, could it be taken to the Smallpox Hospital in Bridge Street? The Guardians were advised to enforce the vaccination laws to prevent such an occurrence. Nevertheless the Sanitary Authority was prepared to take such cases but the Guardians would have to pay all expenses and £2 2s per week for medical attendance.

The question of the type of smallpox vaccination was then raised. The Guardians asked the Local Government Board if children could be vaccinated with calf lymph rather than the 'arm-to-arm' process then being employed. The Guardians were prepared to pay the cost. The Local Government Board could not agree. The Guardians were not allowed to provide calf lymph or provide a calf lymph establishment for vaccination within the Union. The arm-to-arm method would continue.

The Guardians were extremely anxious that preparations were made in case there should be an epidemic and believed it was 'absolutely necessary' that an infectious hospital should be built for the whole town. In November 1897 when they wrote to the Town Clerk they modified their demands and asked if the Sanitary Committee were satisfied that adequate provision had been made in case of an outbreak of infectious disease in the town. Did they propose to make further provision for isolating such cases and if so would they include cases arising among the poor and destitute outside the Workhouse? The letter added that if provision were to be made and the cost to come out of the rates, it would be better if the Sanitary Authority undertook the whole scheme rather than leave the Guardians to deal with their own cases.

Two months later the Guardians noted that, in view of the experience of other large towns, unless provision for infectious cases were made on a large scale, they were of no use in an epidemic. The Sanitary Authority and the Guardians would each discharge their own obligations and responsibilities. Each would take such steps as were necessary to prevent and check the spread of infectious diseases. The question of a special infectious hospital for the town was not considered.

The matter rested there but later a deputation went to the Sanitary Authority to 'make the best terms' for their acceptance in the town's infectious hospital of outdoor paupers suffering from infectious diseases other than smallpox. The outcome of the meeting was not recorded. The Local Government Board was then consulted as to whether the isolation hospital at the Workhouse was to be used solely for cases arising within the Workhouse. Would the Master be justified in refusing admission of such cases arising outside the Workhouse? Could the Guardians legally order the Relieving Officer to make suitable arrangements for isolating outdoor paupers suffering from such diseases?

The Local Government Board's reply was reassuring. The Infectious Hut at the Workhouse was intended for cases arising within the Workhouse and it would be 'very undesirable' for outside cases to be admitted. The Sanitary Authority should provide the necessary accommodation for treatment of dangerous infectious diseases and should accept pauper cases through arrangements with the Guardians about payment. The Board of Guardians should instruct the Master not to admit cases of dangerous infectious disease from outside. The Relieving Officer in such instances should apply first to the Sanitary Authority for accommodation and, failing that, he should make such arrangements as he could outside the Workhouse for isolating the cases.

Infection of a different nature, in the form of lice, was all too common among both tramps and paupers who were admitted to the Workhouse. Special disinfecting equipment had been provided in the basement of the Tramp Wards and in the Workhouse laundry to deal with such cases. In 1897 the Local Government Board notified the Guardians that, under the Cleansing of Persons Act, anyone who applied to the local authority now had the right to use, free of charge, 'the apparatus which the authority possesses for cleansing persons and clothing from vermin'.

As the Board of Guardians was the 'local authority' in this matter, it was emphasised that anyone applying to be cleansed would not be regarded as a pauper in receipt of parochial or charitable relief. It was important that people suffering from lice should be disinfected and not left to spread the infestation. A facility provided at the Workhouse had now been made more widely available without the stigma of pauperism attached to those who used it.

Public Interest

Great interest had been taken in the alterations made to the Workhouse. In November 1894 Dr Hurry and 90 members of the Reading Literary and Scientific Society were taken round the buildings with the architect, Mr Charles Smith. The alterations met with much approval and Mr Smith described what had been done to enlarge the establishment. It had been brought up to the standard required by the Local Government Board and some 500 paupers could now be accommodated, including 156 in the new hospital.

The following month the Reading Pleasant Sunday Afternoon Society asked if their members could be shown round the Workhouse. There were about 600 working men on their books and it was believed that 'great good would accrue to all concerned from their inspection of local arrangements for the care of the poor'. How many at a time were allowed to spend their Sunday afternoons at the Workhouse is not known. However, two years later when a request was made by the Reading Industrial Co-operative Society for a party of between 50 and 100 members to visit the Workhouse, the number was limited to 25 and the Society withdrew their request.

The Workhouse Fire Brigade

A special Workhouse fire brigade was formed in 1894. Until that time the fire precautions consisted only of the provision of hoses. Fire hydrants, installed with the new water main, now made it possible to provide a more effective system. The new brigade, manned by Workhouse employees, asked to be supplied with a suitable uniform, additional appliances and a 'small remuneration' for their services. The Guardians, ever cautious, agreed to provide a bucket and hand pump but would 'defer the other matters' until they had attended a fire practice.

Once reassured of the brigade's competence, the Guardians provided each member with a helmet (brass for the Captain), tunic, leggings and also a life-line, belt and axe. Charles Dummer, the Engineer, was made Captain and the Porter his Deputy. The Guardians agreed that, with practice, the brigade would reach 'a state of efficiency'. The question of remuneration would be considered in six months.

Six months later, after the Guardians had been sent a framed photograph of the Brigade, an annual remuneration of £10 10s was agreed to be divided between the eight members. This, however, did not meet with the approval of the Local Government Board and the Guardians were instructed to pay each member 30s after twelve months' service, or a proportion according to the length of time each member had served that year. The fire brigade was now firmly established and provided an important service in protecting the inmates and the greatly enlarged Workhouse establishment.

The Local Government Act 1894

Since the establishment of the Poor Law unions in 1834 a property qualification had been necessary for all those who wished to serve as guardians. The choice of candidates was therefore limited, even with the slight modification of the rules in the 1880s. The Local Government Act of 1894 abolished the property qualification. Anyone wishing to stand for election as a guardian now had to be either an elector of a parish within the union, or a resident within the union for 12 months, or eligible to be elected a councillor for the borough within which the union was situated. Each nomination paper had to be signed by two electors.

The Act also replaced the Urban and District Sanitary Authorities by Urban and District Councils. Guardians as such would only be elected in parishes in urban areas. In rural areas persons elected as Rural District Councillors would be eligible to serve as guardians.

The Reading Guardians were notified in March 1894 that they would remain in office until the end of the year and new elections would be held on December 7th. One third of the Guardians would go out of office on April 15th each year. On April 15th 1895 the Board would be reconstituted for the year ending April 1896.

The election held on December 7th caused greater interest than those of previous years. The newspapers noted that for the first time the

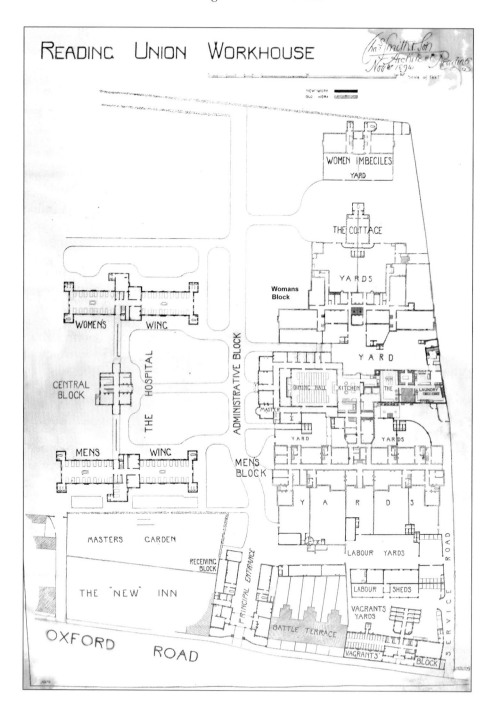

Plan of Workhouse 1894

elections would be held 'on purely democratic lines'. Each elector had two votes. No premises used for the sale of intoxicating liquors could be used as a polling station. Two members of the Board of Guardians did not stand for re-election and in two of the ten wards there was no contest.

The turn out for the poll was disappointing with only about 50% of those eligible bothering to vote. It was reported that there were only two or three sandwich boards and practically no 'mural literature'. Unfortunately the election had 'not been free from political, religious and personal influences'. Several candidates stood as 'Socialists', others had 'strong temperance views' and personal abuse was also recorded.

The election produced a great change in the Board of Guardians. Eight new members were elected. Of the 17 male members four held liquor licences and a fifth had recently held one. Two of the four Socialist candidates were elected. It was applauded that the number of women on the Board had increased from two to four, as those who had served before had been most effective. As the *Reading Observer* noted, a new element had been introduced on the Board.

At the first meeting of the new Board, held on January 5th 1895, Mr Apsley-Smith was re-elected Chairman and Mr D Cook Vice-Chairman. The various committees were appointed to hold office until April. It was emphasised that reporters from the local papers could attend the Board meetings but the public could not. When Mr Apsley-Smith had to resign through ill health in September, Mr D Cook took his place and remained Chairman until 1899.

The Nursing Department
Although great care had been taken in planning the new hospital, it had not been appreciated that within a short time the nursing staff would be increased from three to seven. All too soon the nurses' accommodation was found to be inadequate.

Miss Warner, one of the Guardians, drew attention to the difficulties faced by the night nurses as there was nowhere for them to sleep undisturbed. When the Infectious Hut was unoccupied they could go there, otherwise they had to share the same accommodation as the day nurses. When the matter was raised in 1895 the Workhouse was still undergoing alterations and enlargement and it was decided to postpone any decision until later.

In 1896 Miss Warner, supported by two other lady Guardians, raised the subject again. The nurses worked extremely hard. Apart from their annual two weeks holiday, they were always in the infirmary and had no privacy. The Guardians agreed that better accommodation for the nurses must now be provided.

Two alternative plans were suggested. The first was to board out all or some of the nurses. This would mean all the nurses would have to be fully trained and the hospital could no longer train their probationers. The second proposal was to build new quarters for the nurses. This would enable the hospital to continue to train probationers and the present nurses' rooms could be used as wards. The financial implications of both proposals were investigated. It was agreed that a nurses' home would be built behind the hospital, on the west of the Workhouse land.

In order to select an architect the Guardians submitted the names of all the local architects to a ballot. Four, J Greenaway, W E A Hambling, J S Stallwood and Charles Smith and Son, were then put on a short list. From this J Greenaway of Duke Street obtained the most votes and was asked to prepare draft plans for the new building. Within two weeks outline plans had been produced, but when they were sent to the Local Government Board for approval, 'further consideration' was required on several points. The amended plans were not accepted either. The Local Government Board architect pointed out that, in view of the size of Reading, sufficient provision had not been made for future requirements. The building should be enlarged to provide three additional bedrooms, a nurses' private retiring room and a cellar.

The plans were eventually agreed and in January 1897 twelve tenders were obtained for the building work. The lowest, that of Mr David Taylor of South Street for £1,300, was accepted. The Guardians obtained a loan of £1,500, to be repaid over 30 years, to meet the costs.

The Nurses' Home was a two-storey, red brick building. On the ground floor there were three nurses' bedrooms, a sitting room, a retiring room, bathroom, kitchen and pantry. On the floor above were a further seven nurses' bedrooms and a servant's bedroom. Stores and a larder were in the basement. The building was completed and ready to be furnished in February 1898.

By the time the building work was under way changes had already been made in the nursing department. New probationers now had to produce medical certificates to show that they were strong enough to undertake the training. The work was hard and illness and exhaustion took its toll among the staff.

The Workhouse probationers were able to attend lectures at the Royal Berkshire Hospital during their two years' training. Lectures were given by the Matron on bandaging, nursing and economy. The medical staff lectured on anatomy, surgical nursing, physiology and medical nursing. Dr Guilding gave lectures on surgical nursing. In 1895 the Royal Berkshire Hospital increased their own probationers' training from two to three years. Two certificates were then issued, one after the training was completed and a second after an examination had been passed.

It was not until 1897 that the Guardians extended their probationers' period of training to three years and gave a certificate when the training was completed. By this time the Workhouse Nursing Committee and the Medical Officer were deciding all questions concerning the nursing department.

Difficulty was frequently found in obtaining assistant nurses. The Workhouse Infirmary Nursing Association was no longer asked to supply trained nurses and if vacancies could not be filled by probationers when their training was completed, advertisements were placed in *The Hospital, The Local Government Chronicle* and *The British Medical Journal*. Assistant nurses should be between 25 and 30 years old and should have had at least 18 months' hospital or infirmary training. The salary of £20 a year with indoor uniform, accommodation and usual allowances was estimated to be worth £35 per year. When no suitable nurses could be found through advertising, two Assistant Nurses were promoted to be Charge Nurses with a salary of £23 rising to £30 per year.

Although pauper inmates were no longer undertaking nursing duties in the hospital, some were still being used to help in the imbecile wards. Dr Guilding found such help to be inadequate and inefficient. His suggestion that a paid, resident wardswoman should be appointed to assist Mrs Wells in the female imbecile ward with a salary of between £12 and £15 per year, was not approved. The Guardians were, however, prepared to allow the Master to obtain temporary help from outside in an emergency if no adequate help could be found within the House.

In August 1897 the Local Government Board issued an Order on 'Nursing the Sick in Workhouses'. The Order embraced many different aspects of workhouse nursing. It emphasised the important role of the nurses and their assistants and that they should be trained and paid. Pauper inmates should not be used for nursing the sick or maternity cases. If any workhouse employed three or more nursing staff it would now be necessary for a Superintendent Nurse to be appointed. She must have undergone at least three years' medical and surgical training in the wards of a hospital or infirmary which was a training school for nurses and which also retained a resident physician or house surgeon. Her duties would be to control and supervise the other nursing staff under the direction of the Medical Officer. For matters not concerning the sick she would be responsible to the Master and Matron. If boards of guardians appointed one of their existing nurses to be the superintendent nurse, these qualifications would still apply.

This Order advanced the status of the nurses but posed a great problem for the Reading Union Workhouse as they had no resident physician or house surgeon. There was no difficulty in the Head Nurse, Miss Pinnington, becoming the Superintendent Nurse but there would be problems with the training of the probationers. Those who completed their three years' training and passed their examinations would not be qualified to become superintendent nurses.

The Local Government Board were notified of the difficulty. The Workhouse nurses were undergoing exactly the same training as the Royal Berkshire Hospital nurses but, unlike them, the examinations did not qualify them to become superintendent nurses. When the Guardians asked if this regulation could be reconsidered in respect of the Reading Workhouse, the Local Government Board insisted that a resident medical officer was essential.

In March 1898, probably through the efforts of Dr Guilding, the Royal Berkshire Hospital agreed that the Workhouse nurses who attended lectures at the Hospital would be examined at the end of three years training and, if they passed, they would be given certificates in the same way as the Hospital nurses. This was later amended so that the Workhouse nurses' certificates would be 'distinct' from those of the Hospital nurses. Dr Guilding then met the Local Government Board medical officers and asked if these certificates would be accepted as evidence of the qualification for the office of Superintendent Nurse.

Eight months later, in December, when nothing further had been heard on the matter, it was decided to formally submit two certificates gained by the Workhouse nurses to the Local Government Board for approval. The Guardians' Minutes for December 15th 1898 recorded that E Pendry and E C Pennicott had attended lectures and passed satisfactorily the examinations for nurses at the Royal Berkshire Hospital. Certificates to this effect had been signed by the Workhouse Medical Officer and Superintendent Nurse and by lecturers and examiners at the Royal Berkshire Hospital. The certificates were approved by the Board of Guardians, signed by the Chairman and Clerk and the common seal affixed.

The certificates were then sent to the Local Government Board asking for them to be sanctioned as 'sufficient to qualify the holders for the appointment of a superintendent nurse'. After a further delay of three months the Guardians were notified that the certificates had been accepted and endorsed by the Local Government Board. The qualifications of the Workhouse nurses were now acknowledged to be of equal value to those given to the nurses at the Royal Berkshire Hospital.

By the end of the century the nursing staff had increased to nine and consisted of the Superintendent Nurse (Miss Pinnington), two Charge Nurses, two Assistant Nurses and four probationers, as well as the female imbecile attendant and the male imbecile attendant.

Additional Land

Every winter Reading, like other towns, was faced with the problem of seasonal unemployment. In January 1893 the Chairman of the Guardians received 87 applications from unemployed men who needed work. It was decided that men who had resided in Reading for the last six months would be employed from 8am to 5pm and given a wage of 2s per day. What this work was or where is not known, but the Guardians believed if work on widening the Wokingham Road were 'pushed forward' unskilled labour could be employed.

Later that year a deputation asked the Guardians if land could be obtained on which the unemployed could work. The Local Government Board also raised the subject and asked the Guardians for their 'observations' as, although the unemployment and distress were no greater than usual, some 820 good workmen were 'going about in an actual state of starvation'.

The Guardians were sympathetic but they felt they were not able to help. Nevertheless in February 1894 a committee was appointed to consider buying land at the back of the Workhouse for 'the purpose of providing profitable labour in the shape of spade husbandry'. No land was available to purchase but a five-year lease was obtained for 5 acres 3 roods (five and three quarters of an acre) of land belonging to Mr Fidler with a rent of £34 16s per year. This land would be supervised by the Farm and Labour Committee with the day-to-day management added to the duties of the Labour Master and Gardener.

The following winter the Guardians were faced with the problem once again. In January 1895 they employed 12 men at 4d per hour from 8am to 5pm, with half an hour off for dinner, to remove the surplus earth left as a result of the building work at the Workhouse. The following month a deputation asked the Guardians what was being done to relieve the distress. Unfortunately nothing more could be done but the Town Council was asked to take steps to help the unemployed and, if necessary to open a stone yard as had been done before in emergencies. They should also see if men could be employed on the roads.

In 1896 the Guardians tried to buy the low-lying land on the west of the Workhouse property. The land belonged to Mr W S H May and was formerly a GWR gravel pit which had provided ballast for the construction of the railway line. Although most of the land, apart from that abutting Oxford Road, was below flood level , it would be of value to the Guardians. It would enable the Workhouse grounds to be enclosed within a ring fence, it could be used for gardening at practically no cost and it would provide additional exercising ground for the inmates. Unfortunately the idea had to be dropped as publicity had meant that the land could no longer be obtained at the right price.

The lease on Mr Fidler's land was extended but an offer to sell $8\frac{1}{2}$ acres of rod beds was turned down as being of no use to the Guardians. In 1898 Mr May's land on the west became available and also a small plot on the south-east corner of the Workhouse belonging to Mr Vandersten. The price of the latter was too high but in 1899 some 10 acres of Mr May's land were bought for £240 per acre, and also a 30ft frontage to Oxford Road at £4 per foot. The Guardians could now have service roads at both ends of their property and an access road to the newly purchased land. The Local Government Board approved a loan of £3,000 to cover the costs and a further £250 to be spent on raising the land. By the end of the century the Workhouse land, including the rented land, had almost trebled in size from the original $8\frac{1}{2}$ acres to nearly 24 acres.

The Resignation of the Master and Matron

Mr and Mrs Pope had been the Master and Matron of the Workhouse since 1878. In April 1897 they resigned as Mr Pope was now nearly 68 years old, his health was not good and the time had come for him to retire. In the $18\frac{1}{2}$ years they had been at the Workhouse they had overseen many changes.

They had proved to be excellent officers of the Union and the Guardians thanked them for their loyal service.

The posts were advertised in the papers. Candidates should be married couples, not under the age of 30 years, with experience in a joint capacity as master and matron of a workhouse. The advertised salaries, with superannuation, were rather lower than those received by Mr and Mrs Pope. The new Master would be paid £90 a year with furnished apartments, rations and washing valued at £75 per year. The new Matron would be paid £50 a year with emoluments valued at £65 per year. Mr Pope's salary had been £105 a year and Mrs Pope's salary had been £55 per year with the same allowances.

It was stressed that the posts would be full-time and would include the Master keeping the books and accounts, maintaining discipline and overseeing the employment of the inmates. The Matron would superintend all the domestic arrangements. A bond of £200 would be required.

The positions of Master and Matron of the Reading Union Workhouse were much sought after. The Workhouse, recently modernised and extended, with its own purpose-built hospital, was regarded as one of the best in the country. It was therefore not surprising that there were 73 applications for the posts. Mr and Mrs George Hayes, Master and Matron of the Thame Union Workhouse, were elected. They would take up their duties on July 24th 1897.

Mr Hayes, Workhouse Master 1897–1906   Mrs Hayes, Workhouse Matron 1897–1906

General Improvements

During the ten years it had taken to plan and carry out all the Workhouse alterations and building work, the day-to-day conditions of the inmates were gradually being improved.

Smoking had not been allowed except on special occasions such as Christmas, but in 1892 a General Order from the Local Government Board announced that inmates who were not classified as able-bodied, who 'were employed upon work of a specially disagreeable character', would be eligible for an allowance of tobacco or snuff. The Order would apply to about 100 inmates, some 60 of whom said they would like tobacco and 40 said they would prefer snuff. It was estimated that it would cost £70 a year to provide 1oz of tobacco or $\frac{1}{2}$ oz of snuff each week for these inmates.

While the subject was under consideration the Guardians received a letter signed by 90 ratepayers stating their objections to the proposed allowance and hoping it would not be agreed. One Guardian suggested that, instead of this allowance, some 'light employment' should be found for the aged men and women to relieve the 'great monotony' of their lives. In return they could be given some special 'luxury'. As these inmates were already undertaking objectionable duties, presumably associated with the sanitary arrangements, employment was not the question. The Guardians agreed to issue a tobacco and snuff allowance and they would also decide in which rooms smoking could take place.

While life in the Workhouse was monotonous for many inmates, the tedious, restricted diet was monotonous for all. The Local Government Board regulations required each category of inmates to receive a certain diet which was strictly measured out at every meal. Provision contracts were always put out to tender with the result that quality was sacrificed to cost. Able-bodied men were given 7oz bread and $1\frac{1}{2}$ pints of gruel for breakfast. The women had 6oz of bread, $\frac{1}{2}$ oz butter and 1 pint of tea. For dinner both had soup and hash on some days, meat and vegetables on others and on two days bread and cheese. For supper the men had 7oz bread and $1\frac{1}{2}$ oz cheese and the women 6oz bread and $1\frac{1}{2}$ oz cheese.

The aged and infirm and the imbeciles were given meat on Mondays, Wednesdays and Fridays (5oz for men and 4oz for women) and on other days hash, suet pudding or meat pie. Children had smaller helpings and the younger ones were given milk for breakfast and supper. Infants and the sick had diets as directed by the Medical Officer.

Modest alterations were made to the diets from time to time but always within the bounds of the Local Government Board regulations. The inmates for their part scrutinised the size of their portions and were quick to complain if their helpings were too small or did not contain the regulation amount of meat or vegetables. When Dr Guilding suggested a better quality of meat should be provided, thick chuck ribs of beef without the bone, at 6d per pound, was allowed on Fridays.

Bread had always formed a large part of the diets and often much was wasted and fed to the pigs. In 1897 a special Dietary Committee was formed to review the diets. It was believed that up to 35% of the bread issued was wasted. Other unions were consulted and it was discovered a considerable reduction had often been made by putting half the bread allowance out at a meal and letting the inmates have a second portion if requested. The Charlton Union had made great savings by making bread puddings out of the left-over bread and, in addition, 12cwt of bread was saved each month.

The Guardians agreed that, for a trial period of one month, the method of dividing the bread allowance into two would be adopted at dinner for those classified as aged and infirm. At the end of the month out of the allowance of 582lb 9oz of bread only 455lb 3oz had been issued and a saving of 22% had been made. The system was not popular and, following a visit to the Poplar and Islington Unions, the Guardians decided bread should be served 'ad lib' at each meal to all inmates except the able-bodied, up to the total allowed on the diets.

Small alterations were made to the tea allowance, its strength, quantity and at which meals it could be served. In 1899 the Local Government Board were asked if the aged and infirm could have a choice of milk puddings (rice, sago and tapioca) instead of soup, suet pudding and barley broth on Tuesdays and Thursdays. They then asked if food could be given to the inmates according to their individual requirements, as had been adopted at some unions.

The Local Government Board's reply was typical. After quoting paragraph after paragraph of the regulations, the suggestion of milk puddings would be 'considered favourably' if they could be 'informed in detail of the quantities of each food supplied as an alternative to the dinner at present prescribed' and would bread be supplied with the alternative meals? The question of individual requirements would be referred to their medical officers. This illustrated the great difficulty the Guardians encountered at every step if they wished to adapt or alter even the smallest regulations.

All the indoor officers were given a weekly allowance of provisions with each item carefully weighed in pounds and ounces. In 1891 the officers asked if they could be given money in lieu of their rations as this would enable them to obtain a greater variety of food. The Guardians agreed that the Master and Matron should each be allowed 12s per week plus vegetables from the Workhouse garden and the other officers should be allowed 10s each per week with vegetables. When the proposition was put to the Local Government Board objections were raised. The local Inspector pointed out that none of the 52 unions in his District gave money in lieu of rations. The Local Government Board were adamant that money must not be given as it would lead to abuse. The Guardians rescinded their decision and drew up an amended list with a wider variety of provisions.

Once again it had proved impossible to change the system but by the end of the century the allowances had been improved and covered 28 different items compared with the 14 on the list in 1891. The Master and Matron were each given slightly larger allowances for some items such as meat (8lb per week compared with 7lb for other officers), eggs and sugar. By any standards the rations had become generous compared with those of the pauper inmates.

The paupers' uniform added to the stigma attached to the Workhouse inmates. In 1895 the newly elected Board of Guardians considered a suggestion that the uniform should be abolished. Complete abolition was not allowed but a compromise was reached and a 'less-distinctive' uniform was agreed for inmates over 60 years when they went out on Sundays and when on leave of absence. The men's suits were to be dark blue or black serge with unlined trousers and coats cut 'sack-shape' costing 12s. In winter they would be supplied with 'non-distinctive' overcoats. The women were to wear dark blue or black serge dresses with a shawl costing 17s. Aged paupers acting as messengers who were employed on outdoor work would be allowed to wear 'non-distinctive' clothing at the discretion of the Master. All these items were probably made 'in house' by the inmates in the tailors' shop. A progressive idea had been limited to the elderly and only when they were off the Workhouse premises.

The inmates were still given treats and occasional outings from time to time as well as a special dinner of roast beef and plum pudding at Christmas. Two Royal occasions provided additional reasons for a celebration. The first was the wedding of the Duke of York in July 1893 when those who were able to leave the Workhouse were entertained at Elm Park and given a meat tea. The other inmates were given a meat tea and an entertainment in the Workhouse.

The second Royal occasion was Queen Victoria's Diamond Jubilee which was celebrated on June 22nd 1897. Inmates who wished were allowed to leave the Workhouse and see the sports and festivities in the town. Within the Workhouse a special meal and entertainment, as at Christmas, were provided to celebrate the Sixty Glorious Years. The suggestion that additional beer should be allowed was not agreed. The officers were given an extra two days holiday to be taken with their annual leave.

The End of the Century

Much had been achieved in the last decade of the century and the Workhouse in 1899 bore little resemblance to that of 1867. When the new Workhouse was opened the population of Reading was under 26,000 and the building could accommodate 250 paupers, including 43 in the infirmary. By the end of the century, with the boundary changes, the population had risen to 71,000 and the Workhouse had been enlarged to accommodate 500 paupers, including 156 in the purpose-built hospital.

Although the number of indoor paupers had increased substantially, the cost per head for their maintenance (including clothes) had fallen from 5s 10d to 3s 10d per week and the poor rate, which funded the Union, had been halved from between 2s and 2s 2d per £1 to between 1s and 1s 2d per £1 in 1899. During the same period the number of Guardians had increased from 15 to 21 and the Union officers from 18 to 41.

Since 1867 there had been several Guardians whose service of many years had provided continuity and stability to the work of the Board.

Among these was Mr D Cook who retired in 1899. Regarded as the 'Father of the Board', he had been elected a Guardian in 1869, served as Vice-Chairman from 1882 – 1895 and Chairman from 1895 – 1899. On his retirement he was presented with an album containing an illuminated address and photographs of the Board of Guardians and the Union officers.

The administration of the Union had improved and become more enlightened since 1867. The volume of work undertaken by the Guardians had increased substantially and embraced matters of health, welfare, social security and education. Resources were limited to what could be raised by the local poor rate or afforded by way of a loan, and all decisions were strictly controlled, or curtailed, by the Local Government Board. Nevertheless, in the 33 years since the new Workhouse had opened, slow but significant strides had been made in looking after the poor and needy of the community.

The work of the Guardians was arduous and in many ways depressing, with a seemingly endless stream of unfortunate people needing help. Occasionally there were lighter moments, as in 1891 when the Guardians were informed that they had been left a sum of money by a pauper called Cooper who had two wooden legs and had been in the Workhouse for 11 years. It transpired that Cooper had a son in the army who had died suddenly in India and he had been notified by the War Office that £17 was due to him.

Cooper wrote to the Guardians and said he wished them to have this money as he had been well looked after in the Workhouse and he was grateful. Before the matter had been settled Cooper had died but had left a note, witnessed by the Chaplain, that he wished the Guardians to have this money. However worthy the thought might first appear, there were problems as it was discovered that Cooper had a wife still living and also a daughter. Although they had looked after him at home for many years, there was no love lost between them as his disability and difficult behaviour had forced them to put him in the Workhouse, a fact which he had been loath to forget.

Probably the most significant improvements for the Workhouse inmates had been the provision of better facilities for the sick. The new hospital, with its enlarged staff of trained nurses and very competent Medical Officer, offered the sick paupers much better conditions. It was also possible for those who could not be treated in the Workhouse hospital to be sent elsewhere. In 1867 the Guardians had refused to subscribe to the Royal Berkshire Hospital. By 1899 they were subscribing not only to that Hospital, but also to the Royal London Ophthalmic Hospital, the Royal Orthopaedic Hospital, Henshaws Blind Asylum, Margate Sea Bathing Infirmary and the Bath Mineral Water Hospital. The Reading Blind Aid Society and the Lending Library for the Blind were also supported.

In spite of the expansion of the Workhouse, by 1899 there were signs of problems ahead. The Wargrave District School was almost full and often

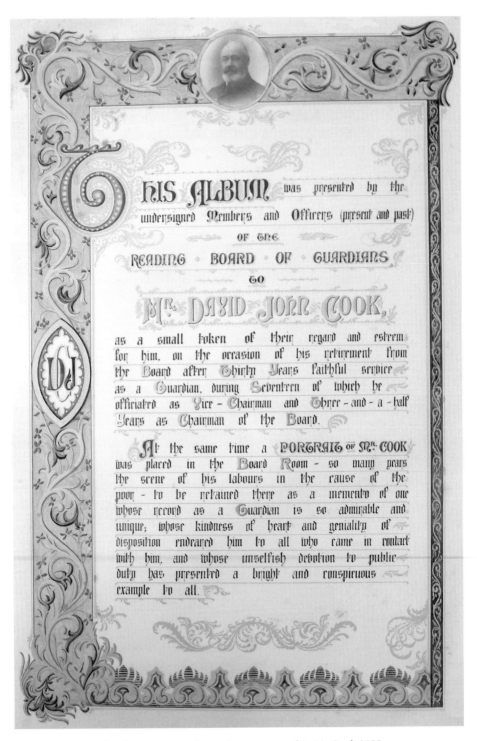

This Album was presented by the undersigned Members and Officers (present and past) of the

READING · BOARD · OF · GUARDIANS

to

Mr. DAVID JOHN COOK,

as a small token of their regard and esteem for him, on the occasion of his retirement from the Board after Thirty Years faithful service as a Guardian, during Seventeen of which he officiated as Vice-Chairman and Three-and-a-half Years as Chairman of the Board.

At the same time a PORTRAIT OF Mr. COOK was placed in the Board Room - so many years the scene of his labours in the cause of the poor - to be retained there as a memento of one whose record as a Guardian is so admirable and unique; whose kindness of heart and geniality of disposition endeared him to all who came in contact with him, and whose unselfish devotion to public duty has presented a bright and conspicuous example to all.

Illuminated address from album presented to Mr Cook 1899

children were having to remain in the Workhouse and attend the local Battle Board School (in non-distinctive clothing) until there was a place for them. Occasionally parties of children were sent to Canada and the system of Scattered Homes was investigated to see if this would ease the problem. Accommodation difficulties were occurring throughout the Workhouse. Dr Guilding reported that the imbecile wards were almost full. The Local Government Board Inspector reported that the number of male inmates exceeded the accommodation available and beds were being placed in corridors. The male and female wards in the hospital were also almost full. His suggestion that the Board should consider the provision of additional accommodation must have filled the Guardians with dismay.

5

THE NEW CENTURY
1900–1914

There were many changes in the early years of the 20th century. In January 1901 the nation mourned the death of Queen Victoria. She had come to the throne in 1837, two years after the Reading Union had been formed, and her long reign had witnessed the implementation and development of the New Poor Law system. The Guardians sent a telegram of condolence to Her Majesty's Private Secretary.

All the celebrations planned to mark the coronation of King Edward V11 in June 1902 had to be postponed when the King developed appendicitis. On August 9th Reading, like other towns, celebrated the coronation in style. The Guardians took part in the procession, the Mayor gave the Workhouse inmates dinner and an entertainment, after which they were allowed leave of absence between 3pm and 7pm to enjoy the town's celebrations. King Edward's reign was short and on his death in 1910 his son, King George V, came to the throne.

These early years were also a time of many social changes and a more enlightened attitude was gradually developing towards those in receipt of poor relief. Any hope the Guardians might have had that this would be a period of consolidation after all the building work undertaken in the 1890s proved to be short-lived. All too soon they were faced once again with problems of overcrowding.

GENERAL IMPROVEMENTS

Workhouse Children
The most immediate problem facing the Guardians concerned the children in their care. In January 1900 there were a number of children among the 386 inmates of the Workhouse in addition to over 200 others who were also the responsibility of the Guardians. Of these 152 were in the District School at Wargrave, a further 47 were boarded out or in institutions, and six were under supervision in four homes under the Infant Life Protection Act. Occasionally a Workhouse child was adopted and from time to time groups were sent to Canada on emigration schemes.

The custom of sending children to the District School had been perfectly satisfactory until the number had increased substantially with the growth of Reading and the extension of the Borough boundaries. The cost to the Union was 3s 6d per child per week. As recently as July 1899 a group of Guardians had visited Bath and inspected a system which had been adopted by that Union. The Bath Guardians had arranged for small groups of children to be cared for in homes set apart from the Workhouse. This system of 'Scattered Homes' had not yet been approved by the Local Government Board but the Guardians believed it would be advisable to have such an arrangement when the Wargrave School became full.

In August 1900 the Local Government Board issued a Circular concerning workhouse children. Guardians were urged to do their utmost to remove children from workhouses and workhouse surroundings. By this time the system of Scattered Homes had been approved and guardians were advised to use a combination of these, boarding out and emigration for the children in their care.

The Reading Guardians were already looking for houses for their children and had found two which would be suitable. In September, with accommodation at the District School almost exhausted, the Guardians asked the Local Government Board if they would sanction an experiment using the Scattered Homes system for children unable to be admitted to the District School. At that time these children remained in the Workhouse and attended the local Board school.

With Local Government Board approval two houses in King's Road, adjacent to the Wycliffe Chapel, were rented for £65 per year. 'Camarra', 17 King's Road, was the first to be opened in September 1900 and 'Rosemont', 19 King's Road, opened a few weeks later. Both houses could accommodate 15 children, with those under ten years of age of both sexes at Camarra and boys only at Rosemont. Each house had a foster mother in charge. Dr Guilding extended his duties and visited the houses once a week to provide medical attention for the children and their foster mothers. Medicines were supplied by the Union Dispensary. The children's clothing was obtained from the Workhouse and all the laundry was taken to the Workhouse laundry.

The Guardians believed it would be better for the children to be in smaller houses with more home-like conditions and to attend local Board schools. It would also be cheaper for the Union. The children slept in four-bed dormitories and, it was particularly noted, all the beds had spring mattresses. They were given a 'good liberal diet' and in their free time were expected to do light housework. Outside each house there was a large playground with swings.

The experiment was a success and in May the following year a further three houses were opened: 'Alexandra House' in Queen Street and 'Wilson House' and 'Clifford House' in Southampton Street. Other houses were opened in 1901 and it was decided to end the connection with the

Scattered Homes

Wargrave School at the end of the year. All the children could now be housed in Scattered Homes. An important step had been taken to provide better surroundings and conditions for pauper children and all but the very young had now been removed from the Workhouse.

Following the passing of the Education Act in 1902 School Boards were abolished and elementary education was placed under the control of town and county councils. In 1903 the Reading and Wokingham School District was dissolved and the schools which the children in the Scattered Homes attended came under the control of the local Education Committee.

Aged and Deserving Poor
The Circular sent to the Guardians in August 1900 also concerned the treatment of the aged poor. In January 1900 over one third of the 386 inmates of the Reading Union Workhouse were over 65 years of age. Out of the total of 169, one had celebrated his 100th birthday, 126 were over 70 and 42 were between 65 and 70. The Local Government Board stated that the elderly who had led decent lives and needed help in their old age should be differentiated from those 'whose previous habits and character had failed to exercise thrift in the bringing up of their families' and in other ways. The 'deserving poor' should not be encouraged to enter the workhouse unless their infirmities made it necessary. Instead guardians should give them adequate help to remain in their homes and, if they were admitted to the workhouse, they should receive certain privileges.

Guardians were asked to consider seven recommendations, most of which, it was pointed out, they already had the authority to implement.

1. Inmates over 65 years of age should form a special class if guardians believed their character and behaviour made them sufficiently deserving to be members of that class.
2. For these inmates extra day rooms should be provided where they could be separated from more disruptive characters and where they could be served their meals.
3. Sleeping accommodation in separate cubicles should be provided for this class.
4. Privileges should be allowed regarding hours for going to bed and rising.
5. Greater liberty should include more frequent visits by friends.
6. Each of these inmates should have a locker with a key, though the contents should be opened for inspection.
7. For these inmates orders relating to tobacco, dry tea and sugar should be made compulsory.

The Guardians noted that they already gave outdoor relief to the deserving poor. This would be continued and extended. In the Workhouse a special class of aged deserving poor would be formed with privileges as recommended. Lack of space, however, made the provision of extra day rooms impossible. One day a week would be allowed for 'free liberty' but the present system of visiting hours was considered ample. In future the 'deserving' aged poor would have a more comfortable life but the 'undeserving' would find that their character and past behaviour would be held against them.

Diets

The question of diets was raised once again. The Guardians felt the present diets were 'thoroughly adequate' and could not recommend any alternative. The Local Government Board, however, believed new dietary tables should be adopted and issued an Order to come into force on Lady Day 1901. Dr Guilding noted that the tables sent to him for consideration were 'most generous and liberal'.

The Stores Committee raised certain points concerning the new dietary and in particular the division of inmates into classes and sub-classes for dietary purposes. There were 12 different classes and, including sub-classes, 20 separate diet tables were described. Each table showed what type of food and amount should be provided for each meal each day of the week. This must have appeared to be a culinary nightmare for those cooking and serving the food.

Class 1. Plain diet for men not employed in work.
Class 1a. Plain diet for men employed in work with an additional meal on week days only.
Class 2. Infirm diet for men not employed in work.
Class 2a. Infirm diet for men employed in work with an additional meal on week days only.

DIETARY FOR CLASSES 1 and 1a.—Plain Diet.

Class 1.—Men not employed in work.
Class 1A.—Men employed in work. (Same diet as for Class 1, with an additional meal on week days only, to be given as lunch or at such times as the Guardians may direct.)

MEN	Breakfast Bread (oz)	Butter (oz)	Coffee (pt)	Gruel (pt)	Lunch Bread (oz)	Lunch Cheese (oz)	Dinner Bread (oz)	Meat Stew (pt)	Beef (oz)	Potatoes or other Vegetables (oz)	Pea or Lentil Soup (Winter) (pt)	Barley Soup (Summer) (pt)	Cheese (oz)	Broth (pt)	Boiled Bacon (oz)	Suet Pudding (oz)	Treacle (oz)	Alt. Bread (oz)	Alt. Cheese (oz)	Alt. Coffee (pt)	Supper Bread (oz)	Butter (oz)	Tea (pt)	Broth (pt)	Cheese (oz)
Sunday	8	½	1				6	1										8	3	1	8	½	1		
Monday	6		1½		4	1½	4		4½	12								8	3	1	8			1	2
Tuesday	6		1½		4	1½	6				1½	1½						8	3	1	8			1	2
Wednesday	6		1½		4	1½	8								3	1		8	3	1	8			1	2
Thursday	6		1½		4	1½	4			12						3		8	3	1	8			1	2
Friday	6		1½		4	1½	4		4½	12								8	3	1	8			1	2
Saturday	6		1½		4	1½										16	2	8	3	1	8			1	2

Diet Sheets. Plain Diets for Men

DIETARY FOR CLASSES 3 and 3a. (Plain Diet).

Class 3.—Women not employed in work.
Class 3A.—Women employed in work. (Same diet as for Class 3, with an additional meal on week days only, to be given as lunch or at such times as the Guardians may direct.)

WOMEN	Breakfast Bread (oz)	Butter (oz)	Coffee (pt)	Tea (pt)	Lunch Bread (oz)	Lunch Cheese (oz)	Dinner Bread (oz)	Meat Stew (pt)	Beef (oz)	Potatoes or other Vegetables (oz)	Pea or Lentil Soup (Winter) (pt)	Barley Soup (Summer) (pt)	Cheese (oz)	Broth (pt)	Boiled Bacon (oz)	Suet Pudding (oz)	Treacle (oz)	Alt. Bread (oz)	Alt. Cheese (oz)	Alt. Coffee (pt)	Supper Bread (oz)	Butter (oz)	Tea (pt)	Cocoa (pt)
Sunday	6	½	1				4	1										6	2	1	6	½	1	
Monday	6	½		1	4	1½	4		4	8								6	2	1	6	½		1
Tuesday	6	½		1	4	1½	4				1	1						6	2	1	6	½		1
Wednesday	6	½		1	4	1½	6								2	1		6	2	1	6	½		1
Thursday	6	½		1	4	1½	4			8						3		6	2	1	6	½		1
Friday	6	½		1	4	1½	4		4	8								6	2	1	6	½		1
Saturday	6	½		1	4	1½										16	2	6	2	1	6	½		1

Diet Sheets. Plain Diets for Women

Class 2b. Special infirm diet for feeble men with an additional meal daily.

Class 3 and 3a, 4, 4a and 4b were similar categories for women.

Class 5. For children between three and eight years with an additional meal on week days to be given as lunch (mid-morning) or at such time as the Guardians might direct.

Class 6. For children over eight and under 16 years with an additional meal on weekdays.

Class 7a. For children between two and three years.
Class 7b. For children between one and two years.
Class 7c. For children from birth to 12 months.
Class 8. A full or varied diet for sick inmates.
Class 9. A middle diet for sick inmates.
Class 10. A low diet for sick inmates.
Class 11. For infirmary patients diet 10 with an additional pint of milk and one egg per day.
Class 12. For phthisical patients.

DIETARY SCALE, No. 12.—For Phthisical Patients.

Day	Breakfast	Lunch	Dinner	Tea	Supper	Night Meal
SUNDAY ..	Boiled Egg Bread, 5 oz. Butter, ½ oz. Cocoa, ½ pt.	Biscuit, 2 Cheese, 1 oz Milk, ½ pt.	Meat Stew, ¾ pt. Beef Tea, ½ pt.	Bread, 5 oz. Butter, ½ oz. Fish Paste Tea, ½ pt.	Milk, ½ pt. Bread, 3 oz. Cheese, 1 oz.	Milk ½ pt.
MONDAY ..	Fried B'cn, 2 oz. Bread, 5 oz. Cocoa, ½ pt.	Do.	Boiled or Roast Mutton, 2½ oz. Potato & other Vegetable, 8 oz. Milk Pudd., ½lb. Fruit, Apples, Rhubarb and Bananas	Bread, 5 oz. Butter, ½ oz. Treacle, 2 oz. Tea, ½ pt.	Milk, ½ pt. Bread, 3 oz. Butter, ½ oz.	Do.
TUESDAY ..	Porridge, ½ pt. Fried B'cn, 2 oz. Bread, 5 oz. Cocoa, ½ pt.	Do.	Fish, 8 oz. Potatoes, 8 oz. Milk Pudd., ½lb.	Bread, 5 oz. Butter, ½ oz. Boiled Egg Tea, ½ pt.	Milk, ½ pt. Bread, 3 oz. Butter, ½ oz.	Do.

DIETARY SCALE, No. 12.—*continued.*

Day	Breakfast	Lunch	Dinner	Tea	Supper	Night Meal
WEDNES. ..	Pot'd Meat, 1 oz. Bread, 5 oz. Butter, ½ oz. Cocoa, ½ pt.	Biscuit, 2 Cheese, 1 oz. Milk, ½ pt.	¼ Fowl or ⅙ Rabbit Potatoes, 8 oz. Bread Pud., ½lb.	Bread, 5 oz. Butter, ½ oz. Jam, 2 oz. Tea, ½ pt.	Milk, ½ pt. Bread, 3 oz. Cheese, 1 oz.	Milk ½ pt.
THURSDAY	Porridge, ½ pt. Boiled Egg Bread, 5 oz. Butter, ½ oz. Cocoa, ½ pt.	Do.	As above (cold) or Boiled Bacon, 3 oz. Potato & other Vegetable, 8 oz. Milk Pudd., ½lb.	Bread, 5 oz. Butter, ½ oz. Fish Paste Tea, ½ pt.	Milk, ½ pt. Bread, 3 oz. Cheese, 1 oz.	Do.
FRIDAY ..	Porridge, ½ pt. Bread, 5 oz. Butter, ½ oz. BoiledB'cn, 2 oz. Cocoa, ½ pt.	Do.	Roast Beef, 3 oz. Potatoes, 8 oz. Milk Pudd., ½lb. Fruit (as Monday)	Bread, 5 oz. Butter, ½ oz. Marmalade, 2 oz. Tea, ½ pt.	Milk, ½ pt. Bread, 3 ozs. Cheese, 1 oz.	Do.
SATURDAY	Bacon, 1 oz. Sausage, 2 oz. Bread, 5 oz. Cocoa, ½ pt.	Do.	Fried Chop Potatoes, 8 oz. Suet Pud., 6 oz. Treacle, 1 oz.	Bread, 5 oz. Butter, ½ oz. Boiled Egg Tea, ½ pt.	Milk, ½ pt. Bread, 3 oz. Butter, ½ oz	Do.

Diets for Phthisical Patients

The diets contained a large proportion of bread and cheese and, by today's standards, little meat. Even the men who were employed only received meat four times a week with 1 pint of meat stew on one day, $4\frac{1}{2}$ oz beef twice a week and 3oz boiled ham once a week. Phthisical patients (those suffering from respiratory diseases including pulmonary tuberculosis) were given a much better diet with reasonable quantities of meat, poultry, fruit and vegetables.

Mothers were expected to breast feed their babies for nine months, at first every two hours and then at gradually longer intervals. After nine months and until one year the babies were given an additional two meals daily of bread and milk sop. Mothers who were unable to breast feed gave their babies bottles of milk diluted with water according to age. Children between one and two years had milk, biscuits, bread, beef tea, potatoes, vegetables, bread pudding and suet pudding added to their diet and this remained unchanged, except for quantities, between the age of two and three years. Older children had similar food to the adults but in smaller quantities and also milk and cocoa.

Additional instructions were given that 'a sufficient supply of water, with a separate mug for each inmate, shall be provided at dinner for all classes'. Salt was also to be provided at all meals for all classes, but pepper, vinegar and mustard would only be provided as directed by the Guardians. Only a proportion of the bread ration would be put out at each meal but inmates would receive the remainder if requested.

The Local Government Board sent the Guardians a copy of 'Manual of Workhouse Cookery' prepared by the National School of Cookery with the hope that 'it would be of service'. The following month, August 1901, the Guardians approved the new dietary tables but for various reasons they were not brought into use until the end of the year.

The Laundry
By January 1901 the laundry, rebuilt and equipped only eight years previously, was proving inadequate for the work now expected of it. It was reported that some 8,000 articles were laundered each week including 389 sheets. The hospital, with an exceptional number of incontinent cases, sent a large quantity of washing to the laundry as well as aprons, collars, cuffs, dresses and linen for the 11 nurses.

There were problems with drying the washing and often clothes could not be dried outside for weeks on end. The inside drying apparatus needed to be improved and an ironing machine, washing machine and extra equipment were also required.

It was not until the following autumn, some eight months later, that the Local Government Board authorised the improvements requested. These would be in place before the winter months. In March 1903, by which time the washing from all the Scattered Homes was now being done at the laundry, an Assistant Laundress was appointed with a salary of £20 per year, rising to £25 after 12 months. This essential part of the

Workhouse was now able to undertake the considerable demands made upon its services.

Administrative Changes

Until 1901 outdoor relief for the Reading Union was administered by one Relieving Officer based at the Union premises at Thorn Street. That year it was decided to divide the Union into two Relief Districts. District 1 would be the parish of St Giles, Whitley, and those parts of Earley, Shinfield and Burghfield added to the Borough when the boundary was extended. District 2 would be the parishes of St Lawrence and St Mary with Southcot and the part of Tilehurst now included within the Borough of Reading.

A Relieving Officer would be appointed for each District with a salary of £100 per year and £10 for a pay station. Both would be provided with houses which would also act as pay stations. They would also act as Collectors for the Guardians for which they would each be paid an additional £20 per year.

Mr F H Herrington, the Relieving Officer based at Thorn Street, was appointed Relieving Officer for District 1 with a house at 21 Queen's Road, and Mr H C Lavers was appointed for District 2 with a house at 71 Friar Street. As Mr Herrington's wife had been the caretaker at the Thorn Street premises, her job was advertised and Mr and Mrs Salter were appointed with a joint salary of £1 per week with accommodation and the usual allowances. Mr Salter would also act as the Clerk's messenger.

The Guardians then suggested that the three parishes of St Lawrence, St Mary and St Giles should be amalgamated for administrative purposes. The Borough Council was consulted and asked to issue an Order under the Local Government Acts whereby the three parishes could be joined to form one civil parish of Reading. It was not until 1903 that the Borough Council finally agreed to support the Guardians' request and the Local Government Board arranged to hold a public enquiry before one of their Inspectors on July 6th 1903.

The Borough Council wanted the rate collection of the three parishes to be consolidated and to have the power of appointing overseers and assistant overseers transferred from the parish vestries to them. They also wanted members of the Council to be included on the Union Assessment Committee. This Committee had the task twice a year of assessing the Union's expenditure for the ensuing six months and of fixing the poor rate accordingly. The Guardians also wanted the power of appointing overseers and assistant overseers transferred to them.

Following the enquiry the Local Government Board issued an Order to come into effect on March 31st 1905. The three parishes would be amalgamated to form one civil parish of Reading. The Borough Council would have the power of appointing overseers and assistant overseers and the Union Assessment Committee would in future include members of the Council.

In April 1905 the reorganisation was finalised. The Union Assessment Committee would consist of 12 members as before but eight would be appointed by the Board of Guardians and four by the Reading Borough Council. It was emphasised that the Guardians could not appoint any of their members who were also members of the Council. For the first time a Union committee included members who were not Guardians.

It was also arranged to divide the town into two Districts on a line north to south for all purposes. These Districts, corresponding with the previously formed Relief Districts, would now cover medical relief as well as outdoor relief, registration and vaccination. St Lawrence's Medical District would be combined with St Giles, part of Earley, Shinfield and Burghfield to form No 1 Medical Relief District. No 2 Medical Relief District would consist of St Giles, St Mary's, Southcot and that part of Tilehurst included in the Borough of Reading. Mr E L Cropp was appointed Medical Officer for No 1 District with a salary of £120 per year and Dr Stansfield was appointed for No 2 District, also with a salary of £120 per year.

In 1903 the Association of Poor Law Unions had written to the Guardians expressing their alarm that a speech made by the President of the Local Government Board intimated a desire to transfer the powers of boards of guardians to local councils. Later it had been suggested that Union Assessment Committees should be abolished and their duties undertaken by local councils. The first move in this direction had now taken place with the inclusion of members of the Borough Council on the Union Assessment Committee.

Unemployment

Co-operation between the Borough Council and the Guardians already existed in times of unemployment when men were given work on the Workhouse land. In 1900 work started on building up the recently purchased land which was liable to flooding. Top soil and other suitable material costing 9d a load was used. Tramps were given the task of removing rubbish deposited on the land. In 1902 it was arranged that the Labour Master, Mr J Cooper, would live off the premises and his salary was adjusted accordingly from £30 to £80 per year. He was also required to assist in relief work when needed.

Two years later, when unemployment again became a problem in winter, the Guardians consulted the Borough Council regarding the employment of men on relief work. The local MP was approached as it was believed such problems should have national rather than local solutions. The matter of distress, however, was not considered to be a subject which could command a special session of Parliament.

By the end of the year (1904) the Guardians were paying $4\frac{1}{2}$d per hour to unemployed men to infill land at the Workhouse. This was the same wage as paid by the local Council and a maximum weekly wage of 12s was agreed. The Local Government Board raised no objections provided the work could not be done by inmates. A foreman was employed at 28s per week to supervise the men. Those who queried whether men thus employed could be regarded as paupers and be disenfranchised were reassured that this would not happen. Throughout the winter of 1904 men were employed daily on the Workhouse land from 8am to 5pm.

Following the passing of the Unemployed Workmen Act in 1905 the Borough Council formed a Distress Committee. Eight of its members were Guardians. A letter from the Reading Trade and Labour Council expressed their 'indignation' that a Labour member was not included on the Committee as such a member, they believed, would have helped considerably in 'getting at the real cause of distress'.

Later in 1905 the Government set up a Royal Commission to investigate the Poor Laws and the relief of distress. The Guardians were asked to provide information for the Commissioners and a list of subjects was given on which the Guardians could give their opinions. The Commissioners noted that they believed the fundamental principles of the Poor Law system should be maintained but the rules for administration should be sufficiently elastic in detail to enable the Guardians to encourage habits of industry, thrift, good conduct and independence.

It was to be four years before the Report of the Royal Commission was published. In the meantime the Guardians continued to pay unemployed men to raise the low-lying land at the Workhouse. In 1909 a further 13 acres adjacent to the Workhouse were bought for about £3,000 from the Saunders Estate. The Workhouse land now extended to some 36 acres.

The Tramp Wards
The number of vagrants admitted to the Tramp Wards had gradually decreased. Altogether 79 were admitted in the first week of January 1900 compared with 149 in the corresponding week the previous year. Mr and Mrs Fisher, who had been Porter and Portress at the Tramp Wards since they were built, resigned in September. Mr and Mrs Henry Lowman were appointed in their place with salaries of £30 and £15 per year respectively, accommodation and allowances.

In 1904 concern was expressed at the way tramps congregated in Oxford Road waiting to be admitted to the wards later in the evening. The Vagrancy Committee suggested a suitable building should be provided where the tramps could wait out of the cold and rain. Messrs Greenaway and Slade were asked to prepare plans to erect a building on ground now occupied by the stone-breaking bunks. It was estimated the building would cost about £122 10s.

This problem of congestion in Oxford Road was discussed at a meeting of the Reading and District Trades and Labour Council. The Guardians were then informed by letter of a decision which had been passed unanimously: 'This Council strongly urge the Board of Guardians to take immediate steps to provide adequate shelter for casuals awaiting entrance to the Casual (Tramp) Wards and we consider it a public scandal to keep these people waiting in the public highway exposed to the inclement weather while waiting for admission.' By this time it was October and the winter weather was approaching.

On receipt of this letter the Guardians decided, by 11 votes to one, that the proposed alterations would be postponed and the 'present system of dealing with tramps' would be continued. It is a matter of conjecture whether the Guardians would have gone ahead and erected the building if the Trades and Labour Council had not involved themselves in the subject.

It was not until 1906 that the problem was raised again and it was suggested that if tramps were admitted at the time they applied for admission, the congestion could be stopped and the alterations would be unnecessary. By this time the Borough Council was providing municipal lodging houses and tramps unable to be accommodated at the Tramp Wards were sent there. Some 1,800 fewer tramps were admitted to the Tramp Wards in the six months up to Lady Day 1907 compared to the 9,658 that had been admitted in the corresponding period the previous year.

The tramps' diets were considered from time to time. The Local Government Board remained adamant that there must be 'uniformity in the treatment of the casual poor'. The request that tea or cocoa should be available instead of gruel for supper in winter was turned down. The Guardians challenged the decision and asked on what grounds this refusal had been taken. They asked Mr Rufus Isaacs KC, MP to take up the matter, but still the answer was 'no'.

Tramps continued to be given tasks of stone-breaking and oakum-picking in return for their accommodation. Corn-grinding was suggested as an alternative but when it was discovered that only one union had found it to be profitable, the matter was dropped. In the matter of hygiene, however, action was taken when it was discovered that up to four tramps were having baths without the water being changed. This 'objectionable' practice was quickly stopped. Even in the Tramp Wards there was a limit to what was acceptable.

Imbeciles, Epileptics and the Feeble-minded.
The inclusion of imbeciles, epileptics and the feeble-minded in one category caused many problems. Often paupers were admitted whose condition was found to be beyond the capabilities of Workhouse care and they eventually had to be removed to the asylum at Moulsford. There was no form of treatment for any of these patients in the Workhouse and the primary duty of the Guardians was to keep them safe from harm. All were admitted to the wards known collectively as the 'imbecile' wards with the female patients in the old fever wards and the males in the southern part of the main building. There were on average about 50 patients in these 'imbecile' wards, almost equally divided between males and females.

The Visiting Commissioner in Lunacy continued to make regular inspections and report to the Local Government Board and the Guardians. In 1900 Mr Frere noted everything to be in good order. The patients were treated with consideration and were on good terms with the Master and Matron. He advised that one patient was not suitable for the Workhouse and should be sent to the asylum. This patient had been in Broadmoor and various other asylums as well as three different prisons.

In view of a recent suicide Mr Frere recommended that an additional padded room should be provided for the male and female wards and that there should always be a night attendant on duty on each side. The suicide in question had occurred in May when Robert Bryan, aged 31, had threatened suicide and had been diagnosed as a lunatic. He was put in a padded cell but later removed to a ward when the cell was needed for a patient suffering from delirium tremens. In the ward Bryan had somehow obtained a knife and had cut his throat.

The Guardians agreed to obtain a male attendant for night duty 'when necessary'. He would be paid 4s or 5s per night. They did not believe additional padded rooms were needed but later changed their minds and in 1903 one was added to the male side. The Local Government Board for their part issued a General Order that when a suicide occurred among the inmates it must be reported to the Coroner accompanied by a statement from the Medical Officer. They also issued various regulations regarding the detention of lunatics in workhouses.

When he made his inspection in 1903, the Visiting Commissioner reported again that the patients were well looked after and generally content. The bedrooms were bright, cheerful and comfortable. Many patients were able to undertake useful tasks. Since 1900 there had only been two occasions when mechanical restraint had been needed. The new padded room met with approval and also the fact that the male imbecile wards were now connected by telephone to the Master's quarters. One criticism was that many men were bathed in water used for three baths. They should have clean water each time as was customary on the women's side. He also suggested that some patients should be able to have walks beyond the Workhouse boundaries and cheap, simple books should be supplied for those who were able to read.

It was at this time (1903) that the Guardians established an Asylum Visiting Committee to visit the County Asylum at Moulsford every three months and report back to the Board. The Committee was impressed by Moulsford and the way in which the inmates were made happy. They noted there were no complaints from 'those capable of being communicated with' and the Superintendent had said the inmates appreciated such visits as they had few friends. Over the next few years the number of Reading patients at Moulsford gradually increased. In 1900 there had been 139, by 1906 this had risen to 148 and in 1909 to 170, by which time the cost to the Guardians for each patient had risen to over 9s per week.

The Royal Commission by now was considering removing epileptics and imbeciles from workhouses to suitable institutions. The question of feeble-minded inmates and the guardians' power to detain them in the workhouse was also on the agenda. The Commissioners' Report was eagerly awaited.

Infectious Diseases

In January 1902 a case of smallpox was diagnosed in the Workhouse. The patient was immediately removed to the Sanitary Authority's Isolation Hospital in Bridge Street. A second case, two days later, was also quickly admitted. Every precaution now had to be taken to prevent the spread of the disease. The Relieving Officers were instructed that the Workhouse could take no further admissions for the time being and outdoor relief must be given instead.

Vaccination and revaccination was imperative and Dr Guilding reported two weeks later that 202 inmates, including 19 children, had now been vaccinated or revaccinated. One woman complained that she had been vaccinated without her husband's consent. When the Guardians asked how many inmates had not been vaccinated, the information appears to have been unobtainable. Over the years many people had refused to be vaccinated although the service was free. In 1853 vaccination had been made compulsory for children and in 1899 smallpox had become a notifiable disease.

The outbreak was not confined to the Workhouse and cases occurred in Reading and throughout the country. A conference was held at the Reading Town Hall at which the Local Government Inspector, members of the Sanitary Authority, the Guardians and others discussed measures to be taken to check the spread of the disease.

Among the duties of the Guardians was the appointment of the Public Vaccinator. For many years this post had been filled by Mr Lousley. Following his death in 1900 Dr F W Stansfield of Oxford Road had been appointed in his place. Vaccination was also carried out by the Poor Law Medical Officers, of whom Dr Stansfield was one. Although in theory everyone was able to obtain free vaccination, in practice many people had not bothered or were loath to take it up.

The Local Government Board wrote a very critical letter to the Guardians complaining they were not discharging their duties properly. For a 'prolonged period' the administration of the Vaccination Act had been neglected and in consequence the population had been left unprotected. The Guardians were immediately on the defensive. They believed their facilities were adequate and Vaccinating Officers and the Public Vaccinator were performing their duties properly.

In May 1902 the Guardians published lists of people who had been revaccinated by the Union's Public Vaccinator. This provoked an immediate response from the Local Government Board who believed such lists would deter the better off from being vaccinated. Furthermore the

Guardians had no legal authority to spend money on 'such publications'. The public should know vaccination was not regarded as public relief and was free for all.

Following this outbreak of smallpox the Sanitary Authority obtained land at Whitley and built a smallpox hospital to replace the small building in Bridge Street. The Council now felt more prepared should a further outbreak occur.

The question of compulsory vaccination was still debated and in 1904 the Board of Guardians presented a petition to the House of Commons against vaccination. Those who signed it believed such compulsion was a breach of liberty and dangerous to health. Mr W A Mount MP, who presented the petition, emphasised that he did not agree with what it contained. The law was not changed, but those who did not agree with vaccination took advantage of a conscience clause which enabled parents to obtain exemption if they believed vaccination might affect a child's health. Difficulties arose when the Board of Guardians excused some who were later prosecuted as defaulters by the Vaccination Officers. The Local Government Board firmly pointed out to the Guardians that they had no authority to excuse anyone from being vaccinated. It was the duty of the Vaccination Officers to prosecute and it was then the decision of the Magistrates whether to accept or reject the reasons given.

The anti-compulsion attitude of some of the Guardians remained and in 1904 they discussed whether to discontinue their £5 5s a year subscription to the Bath Mineral Water Hospital. Patients were now required to have been revaccinated within seven years prior to admission. The Hospital drew attention to the fact that they received on average 12 patients a year from Reading. The cost to the Hospital was £50 per year and, although the Guardians were discussing withdrawing their subscription, they still continued to send patients. The Guardians reassured the Bath Hospital this attitude was not the official policy and they would continue to subscribe to the Hospital's funds.

Cases of diphtheria were not uncommon and in 1906 the Guardians were asked to consider supplying anti-toxin serum to the Medical Officers for use in urgent cases. The serum was expensive but had been found to reduce the death rate considerably. The Guardians refused to authorise its use but, when a case developed in the Workhouse the following year and Dr Guilding said the serum was 'absolutely necessary', the Guardians relented. The patient was removed to the Infectious Hut Hospital in the Workhouse grounds and a special nurse was employed from the Queen Victoria Nursing Institute in Reading to take charge of the case. This was the first time a Queen Victoria Nurse had been employed at the Workhouse.

The Queen Victoria Institute for Nursing the Sick Poor of Reading had been founded in 1897 to celebrate Her Majesty's Diamond Jubilee. Funded by donations and subscriptions, trained nurses based at the Institute's headquarters at Abbot's Walk attended poor patients who could not afford to employ nurses to look after them. Many of these patients were receiving outdoor medical relief through the District Medical Officers but there had been few means of obtaining nursing assistance until the Queen Victoria Institute had been founded. The Private Nurses, trained and based at the Royal Berkshire Hospital, were, in theory, available to treat the poor free of charge but in practice their services were usually required by the better off who were able to pay for private nursing.

In 1901 the Queen Victoria Nursing Institute had asked the Guardians if they would make an annual grant of £50 to cover half the cost of one nurse. By this time a number of cases in receipt of poor relief, who were later admitted to the Workhouse hospital, had been looked after by the Queen Victoria Nurses. The Guardians agreed to subscribe £20 a year on condition that they could appoint a representative on the Management Committee of the Institute. The next year they increased the subscription to £21 and in 1907, following the case of diphtheria, the annual subscription was raised to £50.

The Infectious Hut Hospital at the Workhouse was only opened when needed and in 1908 a case of scarlet fever in one of the Scattered Homes was admitted. Once again a special nurse was employed and was paid £1 per week to look after the child.

By this time the Borough Council had at last decided to build the special Infectious Hospital which had been badly needed for many years. In 1905 a ten-acre site at the north-west of Prospect Park had been obtained and the architect Charles Smith was asked to prepare plans. Park Hospital was opened on May 30th 1906. It consisted of three main blocks, one for scarlet fever, one for diphtheria and the third for 'uncertain' cases. Altogether 40 patients could be admitted to the public wards and four in single private rooms. Patients from within the Borough were admitted free but those from elsewhere were charged one guinea per week. It appears that for some time the Guardians did not use Park Hospital for infectious cases within the Workhouse and Scattered Homes but preferred to treat these in the small Infectious Hut Hospital in the Workhouse grounds. Poor Law cases outside the Workhouse, however, could now be admitted to Park Hospital at no expense to the Union's funds.

Tuberculosis

Tuberculosis was prevalent throughout the country in the early 1900s. Overcrowded houses with poor sanitation, inadequate heating combined with lack of food and clothing, made the poor particularly vulnerable to the disease. Most patients remained in their homes as there were few facilities to treat such cases and those who were admitted to the Workhouse usually came there to die.

For some years the Guardians had subscribed to the Margate Sea Bathing Infirmary and the Bath Mineral Water Hospital to enable some patients to be treated in these institutions. Within the Workhouse patients suffering from chronic respiratory disease or pulmonary tuberculosis were classified as 'phthisical' patients and were given a better diet than the other patients. Those who were able were encouraged to undertake gentle work in the Workhouse grounds.

At Peppard, a few miles from Reading, Dr Esther Colebrook (later to become Dr Carling after her marriage), the daughter of a former Mayor of Reading, had become interested in a method of treating pulmonary tuberculosis which was then being employed with success in sanatoriums on the continent. The 'open-air treatment', consisting of rest, a good diet and fresh air, had been found to be most beneficial. In 1899 she accepted her first patient at her home at Peppard and in 1902 she bought Kingswood Farmhouse where she could treat a few fee-paying patients. The results of this treatment were most encouraging and in 1905 the Guardians discussed the proposal that they should subsidise two beds at the Peppard Sanatorium. This would enable Workhouse patients with pulmonary tuberculosis to receive the new treatment. The proposal was defeated by 13 votes to 2.

By this time the Medical Officer of Health for Reading had written to the Guardians warning of the dangers of tuberculosis and the need to prevent the spread of the disease. Spitting was particularly dangerous and the Guardians were asked to provide spittoons in prominent places. The public must be educated in this matter and all patients with phthisis should be given a leaflet with instructions on the need to use spittoons. At the same time the Local Government Board ordered that they must be notified of all persons in receipt of poor relief who were suffering from tuberculosis. The extent and cost of the disease had to be known.

The Guardians had few means of treating tubercular patients in the Workhouse. In 1907 they sent a patient to Sandgate Sanatorium at a cost of £1 1s per week. When the patient was found to be incurable he was returned to the Workhouse and admitted to the hospital. The Royal Berkshire Hospital had built balconies on the south side of their wards to enable patients to obtain open-air treatment. At Dr Guilding's suggestion the Guardians inspected these balconies. Such an addition to the Workhouse hospital would, he believed, in no way disfigure the buildings architecturally, and would enable cases of pulmonary tuberculosis to be treated 'to much greater advantage'. The idea was not approved and no balconies were built as the treatment was regarded as 'experimental'.

The benefits of open-air treatment were now being acknowledged throughout the medical profession. In 1909 a special Tuberculosis Exhibition was held at Whitechapel at which Mr John Burns, the President of the Local Government Board, made an opening speech. Dr Guilding attended the exhibition and reported his visit to the Guardians. Following this a special committee was formed to consider the provision of accommodation at the Workhouse for pthisical and 'other ailments' likely to benefit from open-air treatment.

Later that year Dr Carling wrote to the Guardians on behalf of the Committee of the proposed Oxfordshire Association for the Prevention of Consumption. Various lectures were to be given on the subject in Oxford. It was arranged that Miss Williams would attend the lecture on 'How Children Become Consumptive'. She had been appointed Lady Relief Visitor and Infant Life Protection Visitor in 1909 with a salary of £80 a year. The following year (1910) Maitland House, an extension to Dr Carling's Peppard Sanatorium, was opened. This additional accommodation would enable both fee-paying and free patients to be treated. The Chairman and members of the Board of Guardians were invited to attend the opening ceremony.

THE NEED TO EXPAND

The Hospital and Nursing Staff
Dr Guilding, the Medical Officer, and Miss Pinnington, the Superintendent Nurse, were the mainstays of the 160-bed Workhouse hospital and its nursing staff of two Charge Nurses and eight probationers. In 1900 the Guardians, impressed by Miss Pinnington's 'efficient and tactful manner', her ability to 'effect economy' and her increased work with the probationers, raised her salary from £40 to £50 per year.

The Dispensary and Hospital Committee were in charge of the day-to-day arrangements in the hospital but all important matters could only be decided with the approval of the Board of Guardians, to whom the Medical Officer gave regular reports. All nursing appointments made by the Board and all nurses' salaries had to be sanctioned by the Local Government Board who also endorsed all nursing certificates awarded by the Guardians.

There was a steady turnover of nursing staff and many left as soon as they received their nursing certificates. Thanks to its links with the Royal Berkshire Hospital, the Workhouse hospital had been recognised as an official training school for nurses. In 1903 the Local Government Board proposed to establish two classes of training school, major and minor. The Reading Union would qualify as a major training school but for the fact that the hospital had no full-time resident medical officer. As a minor training school they would be at a great disadvantage and would find difficulty in attracting a sufficient supply of suitable probationers. This difficulty was resolved when the Local Government Board agreed the Workhouse hospital should retain its status.

In 1904, on the advice of the Local Government Board Inspector, a third Charge Nurse was appointed with a salary of £30 per year, the usual residential allowances and a uniform. The Hospital Committee recommended that the three Charge Nurses should have a slightly different uniform to distinguish them from the other nurses. They would be required, in turn, to be on day duty for two months followed by one month on night duty.

There were some other changes within the hospital. After a visit to the Royal Berkshire Hospital the Guardians authorised the installation of slop sinks but sun traps for consumptive patients were not agreed as, at that time, there was only one such patient in the Workhouse. Better facilities were provided at the hospital dispensary and the Dispenser, Mr Jones, was appointed separately to the Workhouse as an assistant to the Medical Officer and under the supervision of the Workhouse Visiting Committee. One quarter of the Dispenser's salary of £104 would relate to his work at the Workhouse and three quarters to his work at the Union Dispensary in Thorn Street.

In 1906 Dr Guilding recommended that the nursing department should be reorganised. Problems had arisen with the resignation of a nurse and two of the three Charge Nurses. The system of Charge Nurses changing from day to night duty was not satisfactory. Dr Guilding proposed there should be only two Charge Nurses, one in charge of each block. They would be permanently on day duty and receive salaries of £30 a year. There should be three trained nurses with salaries of £25 a year who would act as night nurses in turn. When on day duty one would be on each block and act as an assistant to the Charge Nurse. Following advertisements over the next few weeks the new staff were appointed and the nursing department was brought up to strength.

Miss Pinnington, Superintendent Nurse for 26 years, resigned at the end of 1906. Her eyesight had begun to fail and she felt unable to discharge her duties as she would wish. In her letter of resignation, which enclosed letters from a London eye specialist and another from Dr Guilding, she said she had spent the best years of her life working at the hospital. The Guardians expressed their appreciation of her efficient service and decided to add four years to her length of service to enable her to have additional superannuation. The post of Superintendent Nurse and Midwife was advertised in the papers.

There were 37 applications and, from the six candidates chosen for interview, Miss Martha Louisa Mancer aged 33 from the Wallingford Union was appointed. She was asked to make sure any lectures she gave to the probationers did not clash with those attended at the Royal Berkshire Hospital.

Probationers also attended lectures given by both Dr Guilding and the Superintendent Nurse on midwifery. Following the Midwives Act of 1903 the Guardians had agreed to pay the registration fee of 10s for each of the three Workhouse nurses who were practising midwives and in 1907 the Workhouse hospital was recognised as a training school for midwives.

There was great reluctance on the part of mothers to register the births of their babies as having taken place in the Workhouse and it had been customary to leave the place of birth blank on the birth certificate. When this was disallowed in 1904, to avoid any feeling of stigma, it was arranged that the Workhouse should be described as 344, Oxford Road.

Midwifery cases outside the Workhouse were attended by midwives on application to the Relieving Officers. There were two midwives, one for each Medical District. They were paid 10s 6d per case by the Union and if the District Medical Officer was required he was paid £1 per case. If an anaesthetic was needed a further charge of £1 was made, provided the patient's relatives were unable to pay.

In 1908 a meeting was held between representatives of the Queen Victoria Institute, the Reading Dispensary, the Chairman of the Board of Guardians and their representative on the Committee of the Institute, to consider the training and provision of midwives in the Borough. No decisions were made and no action recommended on extending or consolidating the midwifery service, although the Local Government Board emphasised its importance. Co-operation between the various branches was not yet possible.

Miss Mancer resigned as Superintendent Nurse within a year of her appointment, giving ill health as the reason. There had been 'much unrest' among the nursing staff and this was believed to have been due to a lack of proper discipline on the part of the Superintendent Nurse. Nurse Hall, one of the Charge Nurses, was promoted to be Superintendent Nurse on a six months' trial.

These changes came at a time when there had frequently been reports of overcrowding both in the main building of the Workhouse and also in the hospital. By November 1909 the large number of patients who required constant nursing made it necessary to advertise for two additional Staff Nurses and one probationer. This would enable an improved roster to be arranged which would benefit the nurses and the patients. No suitably qualified applicants replied to the first advertisement. As candidates for the positions of Staff Nurses had to be fully trained and certified, the posts were re-advertised with an increased salary of £30 per year plus uniform and residential allowances.

When the positions were filled the day duty staff consisted of the Superintendent Nurse, two Charge Nurses, two Staff Nurses and seven probationers. This would enable the male and female blocks to each have one Charge Nurse, one Staff Nurse and three probationers on duty with a spare nurse for the central block or for duty wherever required. The night duty staff consisted of a senior Staff Nurse in charge of the whole hospital with one Staff Nurse and one probationer for each of the male and female blocks. One probationer would be in charge of the female imbecile block at night time only as there was an attendant employed for day duty and the male imbecile wards had attendants for both day and night duty.

By the time these arrangements were in place overcrowding in the Workhouse and hospital had reached crisis point.

The Need for More Accommodation

For several years the Master and Dr Guilding had drawn the attention of the Guardians to the problem of overcrowding, especially in the winter months. Various methods had been tried to remedy the situation but none had proved to be sufficient.

Attempts had been made to reduce the number of paupers needing to be admitted by extending outdoor relief, particularly to the elderly. In 1901 the Reading Workers Electoral League had commended the Guardians on their 'humane administration of outdoor relief'. The Guardians also urged people under the age of 40 to become provident members of the Reading Dispensary or a Friendly Society rather than to rely on poor relief in times of sickness. These measures made little difference to the number of admissions.

In the hospital patients included not only Workhouse inmates and paupers admitted by the District Medical Officers, but also children from the Scattered Homes. The system of Scattered Homes which had been introduced in 1900 had removed many children from the Workhouse but those to be admitted to the Homes were still taken to the Workhouse first. Here they were cleaned and assessed and, if necessary, were admitted to the hospital for treatment. In 1904 a house away from the Workhouse, 13 Milman Road, was obtained to act as the Headquarters for the Scattered Homes. However, the Workhouse still acted as a receiving centre for these children and those in the Homes who became ill were admitted to the hospital.

Dr Guilding believed the problem of overcrowding in the hospital was due, not to the number of sick patients, but to the number of children and infirm cases who needed attention but not medical treatment and skilled nursing. There were many babies and even toddlers in the hospital who were perfectly healthy and should be removed to the main building. In November 1906 there were ten children under the age of two in the hospital who were perfectly healthy, besides others who were suffering from ringworm, rickets, epilepsy, scarletina and TB spine who needed treatment. The Guardians agreed that a two-storey nursery should be built and asked Mr Hambling, the architect, to draw up plans. Messrs R Webber's tender of £436 9s was accepted and the nursery, able to take 14 children, was completed in the autumn of 1907. A Nursery Attendant was appointed to be in charge with a salary of £18 a year (rising by £1 a year to £25) with uniform and residential allowances. It was also arranged that babies up one month old and their mothers could remain in the lying-in ward, after which they would be moved to the rooms formerly used as a nursery in the main building. These measures, it was hoped, would relieve the pressure on the hospital.

Within months the nursery was found to be inadequate and by the end of 1908 it held 18 children with others remaining in the hospital who should have been in the nursery. To reduce the numbers it was arranged that children aged four years should be sent to the Scattered Homes and not remain in the Workhouse until they were five years old as had been the rule.

Bed-blocking by the infirm was also a problem as these 'patients' did not need to be in the hospital and should be looked after elsewhere. There was now 'no margin of accommodation' and Dr Guilding was having to treat cases in the Tramp Wards and the receiving wards which should have been admitted to the hospital. The Guardians arranged to transfer as many infirm cases as possible to the main building.

Efforts to relieve the pressure on beds in the hospital by moving infirm cases to the main building only added to the overcrowding there. In January 1908 there were 291 males compared with 256 at the same time the previous year. In 1903 there had only been 197 male inmates Some additional beds had been added but these did little to remedy the situation. Neighbouring workhouses were asked if they would accept inmates transferred from Reading.

The Local Government Board Inspector had urged the Guardians to 'take immediate steps' to provide additional accommodation and in April 1908 emphasised that this was necessary to avoid serious overcrowding the following winter. The Guardians were reluctant to accept the Inspector's advice. They wished to await the Report of the Royal Commission before undertaking the extensive rebuilding the Inspector thought to be necessary. More modest alterations, they believed, would be more appropriate at this time.

Additional Problems

As the problem of overcrowding gradually became worse, the Guardians were facing problems of a completely different nature. In October 1906 they had to dismiss Mr Herbert Lavers, the Relieving Officer, Collector and Vaccination Officer for District 2, for the embezzlement of £50 he had received as Collector. Mr Dredge took over temporarily and the Lavers family were allowed to remain at the Friar Street house for the time being. Mr Lavers was later convicted of the charges preferred by the Guardians.

Within a few months, in February 1907, the Guardians dismissed the Workhouse Master, Mr Simmons. He and his wife had been appointed Master and Matron in 1906 following the resignation of Mr and Mrs Hayes due to ill health. In February 1907 there had been a gas leak in the Tramp Wards and, after an enquiry at which it was believed he had not told the truth and had shown 'grave incompetence', Mr Simmons was dismissed. Mr Hayes returned temporarily until a new Master and Matron were appointed.

There were 57 applicants for the post of Master and Matron, including the dismissed Mr and Mrs Simmons. A petition was received from a number of ratepayers asking the Guardians to consider the Simmons' application favourably. However, after reconsidering the evidence concerning the gas leak, they were not among the three candidates chosen to be interviewed.

Although the Guardians wanted to appoint Mr and Mrs Jones from Nantwich, the Local Government Board would not sanction the appointment. They believed none of the candidates was good enough and higher salaries than the £85 and £55 advertised should be offered to secure 'a good class of officer'. Eventually Mr and Mrs Fryer from Loughborough were appointed with the increased salaries of £115 and £85. Their residential allowances were valued at £60 and £50. They took up their appointments in July 1907.

Nine months later, in April 1908, a Special Committee was formed to enquire into the conduct of the inmates of the Workhouse. At the Extraordinary Meeting that followed the enquiry the Guardians were told of the Master's difficulty in maintaining order among the able-bodied women and that the task was made more difficult by the conduct of one of the Guardians. Such a problem had never occurred before and whether this was due to the inability of the Master to maintain discipline or whether there were particularly difficult inmates at that time, is not known.

After hearing the evidence the Guardians stated that they had found the conduct of certain able-bodied women inmates to be 'of a most degrading character'. A 'most disgraceful' assault had been made by two women on another, 'the substance of which is too repulsive for embodiment in this report'. It transpired that one Guardian, Mr Jones, had been holding private meetings with certain women who threatened to report officers to him.

It was decided that Ellen White and Annie Squench should be prosecuted for the assault on Alice Snow on April 12th and the children of the two women should be adopted. All the able-bodied women in the Workhouse were then cautioned by the whole Board regarding their future behaviour. The two women were sent for trial, found guilty of the assault and sent to prison for one month with hard labour. At the same court another inmate, William Montague, was sent to prison for three months for an assault upon the Master. Relations between the Master and the inmates left much to be desired.

Matters did not rest there and another incident that month was reported by the Reading and District Trades and Labour Council in a letter to the President of the Local Government Board, the Rt Hon. John Burns MP. One of their representatives, the Guardian Mr Jones, had notified the Council of a letter he had received from Mrs Harris, a Workhouse inmate. Mrs Harris had reported the ill-treatment of a three-year old child whose body was covered in sores as a result of being whipped by the Master. The Guardians immediately looked into the matter. The Master said the child had been wilfully disobedient. He had not said the child's parents were suffering from syphilis but he had told Mr Jones that the Medical Officer had said practically all the Workhouse children were syphilitic. Tactfully the Guardians recorded that Mr Jones's statement to the Council had been 'misleading'. Poultices applied to the child's body had been put on $5\frac{1}{2}$ months after the alleged ill-treatment. There had been no report of ill-treatment after the whipping and the two incidents were unconnected. Mr Jones then withdrew his allegations.

Increased Accommodation

The Guardians had been reluctant to take the Local Government Board Inspector's advice that additional accommodation was urgently needed, saying they wished to wait until the Report of the Royal Commission was published.

In July 1909 two Reports were published, a Majority Report and a Minority Report. The evidence taken by the Commissioners filled 37 volumes and the two Reports took up a further three. Both Reports recommended that boards of guardians should be abolished. The Majority Report suggested that the section of the Local Government Board which dealt with poor relief should be called the Public Assistance Division. General workhouses should be abolished and replaced by separate institutions which were appropriate to the various categories of inmates in the present workhouses. Poor Law guardians would be replaced by Public Assistance Authorities. These, it was believed, would help to remove the stigma of pauperism. More use would be made of voluntary and charitable organisations.

Mrs Sydney Webb was among those who signed the Minority Report. Its suggestions were regarded at the time as being quite revolutionary. All Acts relating exclusively to the Poor Law should be repealed. All boards of guardians should be abolished and their powers transferred to county or county borough councils. These would have various committees to deal with different aspects such as education, health, pensions and asylums.

The Guardians believed the proposals would lead to an increase in pauperism and felt that many of the reforms advocated regarding medical aid had already been adopted by the Reading Union. Mr Rufus Isaacs KC, MP for the Borough, was reported to favour the Minority Report. The Guardians invited him and also Mr W A Mount, MP for South Berkshire, and Mr Gardner, MP for East Berkshire, to meet them so they could put their views on the Reports to them and also 'give them some practical proof of the work that was being carried on'. The Government took no action on either Report but legislation that was passed some years later embraced many of the suggestions embodied in both Reports.

The Old Age Pensions Act came into force in 1909. This allowed people over the age of 70, who had an income of less than £31 10s a year, to be given a pension of 5s (25p) a week. It was anticipated that this would make a difference to the number of people needing to be admitted to the Workhouse. However in 1910, when there were 129 inmates over the age of 70, only 18 had made a claim to receive the pension.

For the Guardians the most important event in 1909 was the proposal to extend the Borough boundaries. A Local Government Board enquiry held at the Reading Town Hall decided that parts of Theale and Tilehurst and the whole of Caversham should be included in the Borough of Reading. This would greatly increase the area of the Reading Union. There was now no question about enlarging the Union Workhouse.

Action was quickly taken and in December 1909 the Guardians asked Mr Howell, the architect, to prepare plans for a new building to accommodate 150 aged and infirm inmates. The Nurses' Home should be enlarged to provide rooms for 26 nurses with new bathrooms and additional storage in the basement A new mortuary would be built behind the Infectious Hut Hospital and a committee room built near the entrance in Oxford Road. Alterations would be made to the Master's office and the Matron's stores. Minor alterations were also to be made to the main building and the offices in Thorn Street.

At the same time as the plans were being prepared, the Superintendent Nurse, Miss Hall, resigned to take another job. When the post was advertised with a salary of £50 a year, there were 32 applicants. Miss Emily Booth Slack, from the Bagthorpe Infirmary, Nottingham was appointed to take up the position in June 1910.

A new Committee called the Workhouse, Infirmary and Casual Ward Visiting Committee was now formed. Its title was significant as over the years the Guardians had always referred to the Workhouse infirmary as a hospital and the Casual Wards had been called Tramp Wards or Vagrant Wards. The Local Government Board, however, always referred to such institutions as infirmaries and casual wards. For the purposes of clarity and continuity the terminology 'hospital' and 'tramp wards' will continue to be used here in reference to the Reading Union.

The new Committee consisted of 12 Guardians who would meet monthly. They had a wide range of duties including the management and control of the Workhouse, the hospital (now called the infirmary) the Tramp Wards and the inmates. This Committee could appoint and dismiss all officers with the exception of the Master, Matron, Medical Officer, Superintendent Nurse and Chaplain. This was one of nine Committees, two of which, the Building and Farm Committee, and the Stores and Furnishing Committee, were to be especially busy in the months ahead.

To relieve the overcrowding several inmates were sent to Wallingford Workhouse at a cost of 7s each per week. It was suggested that boys in the hospital who were suffering from ringworm should be sent to Broome House in Leatherhead for treatment. The subscription to the Margate Sea Bathing Hospital was increased to enable six patients to be sent there. Labour Exchanges had recently been set up to register vacant jobs and several inmates had been allowed leave to register their names. Such measures made only a marginal difference to the overcrowded state of the Workhouse.

More surgical work was now being undertaken and in May 1910 considerable alterations to the central block of the hospital were approved. An operating theatre with 'up-to-date fittings' would be built at the south-west corner of the central block behind the covered way. There would be an adjacent anaesthetics room and also a sterilising room with steam sterilising equipment.

Nurses' Home

Tenders for the building work were accepted with that of McCarthy E Fitt of Oxford Road for £8,700 for the aged and infirm block, the mortuary and the new committee room, H W Godwin of Church Street for £1,909 for the Nurses' Home and Mr Francis Newberry of Kings Road for £1,155 for the theatre and central block and the Porter's Lodge additions. The Local Government Board sanctioned a loan of £13,738 for the whole of the building work.

Work began on the Nurses' Home first and was completed in December 1910. By now the work of the Superintendent Nurse had greatly increased and it was agreed to appoint an Assistant Matron to help her. Miss Clarissa Maud Parsons was chosen from among 69 applicants. Her starting salary of £30 would rise by £5 a year to £40, with uniform and residential allowances.

The hours of duty and the holidays of the Workhouse staff were now officially recorded. Most officers worked 12 hours a day and seven days a week, though the clerical staff worked a five and a half day week. It was recommended that all staff should have half a day off each week, one Sunday per month and an annual holiday of 14 days.

The hours of duty of the hospital staff were noted in detail. The Superintendent Nurse was on duty 24 hours a day. Her average hours were described as being 'as necessary', her weekly leave was 'by arrangement' and her annual holiday was for 14 days.

Charge and Staff Nurses were on duty seven days a week, working on average a total of 72 hours a week, which would be reduced to 60 hours when more staff were employed. Nurses on day duty worked from 8am to 9pm and night nurses 9pm to 8am. They were allowed two hours off duty per day, one day off per month and an annual holiday of 14 days.

Probationers worked similar hours to the Charge and Staff Nurses with two hours off duty each day. They were allowed three hours off each evening and study time as required for the lectures they had to attend. They had one day off each month and 14 days' annual holiday.

The male imbecile attendant worked from 6am to 10pm with two hours off daily, half a day off each week from 1pm and alternate evenings from 6pm to 10pm. He had Sundays off from 12 noon once a month and 14 days' annual holiday. The night attendant worked from 8pm to 8am with one night off each month and an annual holiday of 14 days.

The female imbecile attendant worked from 5.45am to 10pm in summer and 6.45 to 10pm in winter, with two hours off each day, four hours off every alternate evening, one day off a month and 14 days' annual holiday.

THE ENLARGED WORKHOUSE

The new buildings were officially opened on August 5th 1911 by the Rt Hon. John Burns MP, the President of the Local Government Board. A special programme was prepared for the ceremony which was attended by the Rt Hon. Sir Rufus Isaacs KC, MP, now the Attorney General, the other MPs for the area, Mr J H Benyon the Lord Lieutenant of Berkshire,

Committee Room exterior

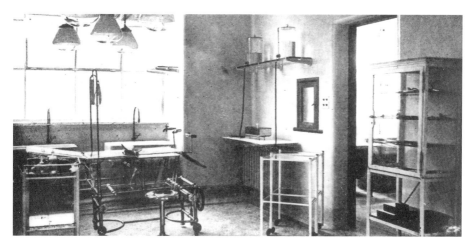

Theatre

Mr J W Martin the Mayor of Reading, the Councillors, Aldermen and Magistrates of the Borough, the Local Government Board Inspector, the Guardians and Union officials, the Architect and the builders.

There had been no ceremony to open the Workhouse in 1867 or in subsequent years when considerable additions had been built. This time it was different. The Workhouse had been enlarged to accommodate 650 inmates and its hospital, now considered to be one of the best workhouse infirmaries in the country, was recognised as a Training School for nurses and midwives. The nursing staff had been increased to 18, with two Charge Nurses, six Staff Nurses and ten probationers besides the Superintendent Nurse. The enlarged Nurses' Home allowed for additional nursing staff in the future.

For many years the Board of Guardians had remained relatively unchanged with Mr W Frame JP the Chairman and Mr J Tutty JP the Vice-Chairman. It had been under their guidance that the recent extensions had been built. The new aged and infirm block could accommodate 150 inmates under the care of two attendants, a married couple with salaries of £25 and £20 a year. The high gabled section in the centre housed the Administrative Department with living rooms for the officers on the first and second floors, kitchen, larder, stores and linen rooms on the ground floor and boilers in the basement. The male and female dormitories, day rooms and bathrooms were on either side of the central section. On the top floor there was accommodation for patients with phthisis. From here there was access to the open roof where these patients could benefit from fresh air and be protected from the wind by glass screens.

As before, the elderly and infirm were divided into classes, each with its own responsibilities and privileges. The Guardians provided details of this classification of the aged and infirm:

CLASS A.   To consist of persons of 65 years of age and upwards, who have entered the Workhouse through no fault of their own, and are through age or infirmity incapable of doing ordinary work either in the House or on the land.

Persons in this Class will be required to do sweeping, dusting, window cleaning or bed making, and to keep their own apartments tidy according to their ability.

Privileges. To be at liberty to go out each weekday except in inclement weather. One ounce of tobacco weekly. Afternoon tea and sugar.

Aged and Infirm Block

Dormitory for Class A

CLASS B. To consist of persons of 65 years and upwards of indifferent character before admission, but who have conducted themselves properly while in the House for a period not less than three months. To be required to work as in Class A or at any other work the Master or Matron may deem suitable.

Privileges. To be at liberty to leave the House on Tuesdays and Thursdays except in inclement weather. One ounce of tobacco weekly.

CLASS C. To consist of the ordinary inmates over 60 years of age who shall (as at present) be allowed out for one day in each month.

Clothing. All persons in Classes A and B to be provided with two suits of clothes: tweed suit for going out on leave, and the other suit for wear in the House only.

EXCEPTIONAL CASES. Any person may be voted to either of the foregoing classes irrespective of age, upon the special recommendation of the Workhouse Visiting Committee.

The new theatre and adjacent anaesthetics and sterilising rooms were particularly praised. Every internal angle had been rounded and other precautions taken to make the rooms antiseptic. The floors were laid with marble terrazzo and the walls and ceilings were finished with paint and enamel. All the fittings were 'up-to-date without being extravagant'.

Workhouse nurses with Matron Slack 1911

Nurses' sitting room

More operations were now being performed. Dr Guilding, as before, obtained the help of colleagues at the Royal Berkshire Hospital to assist in giving anaesthetics for which they were paid £1 1s each time. The Local Government Board suggested that on those occasions when two or more minor operations were performed on the same day, the Guardians should consider paying the anaesthetist a reduced fee in respect of the second and subsequent operations. Dr Guilding pointed out that in Reading the minimum fee for giving an anaesthetic, either chloroform or ether or both, had been fixed by the Medical Society at £1 1s, and the risk and responsibility of the anaesthetist were the same whether the operations were major or minor.

A few months before the new buildings were opened the Guardians received invitations to attend the ceremony of laying the foundation stone for the new wing at the Royal Berkshire Hospital. Both the Workhouse and the Royal Berkshire Hospital had grown considerably over the years but each had developed in different directions. In 1912, when the new buildings were opened, the Royal Berkshire Hospital had 188 beds. It also provided special departments including X-ray, ophthalmic and aural departments. A pathologist, Dr R Donaldson, had been appointed the Hospital's first pathologist and a new laboratory had been provided for him.

The Workhouse hospital could offer none of these facilities and the patients were mainly suffering from chronic illnesses. Causes of death included bronchitis, senile decay, acute pneumonia, cardiac disease, meningitis, cancer, tetanus, alcoholism and syphilis. There were no facilities for carrying out pathological examinations on the premises. In 1909 the Royal Institute of Public Health had notified the Guardians that investigations could be arranged in their laboratories. The Guardians decided not to follow this up. At the same time Dr Guilding suggested the Guardians should subscribe to the Royal Clinical Association to enable him to have certain cases examined. Once again the Guardians did not respond.

Phthisis

The wards in the new building for cases of phthisis were not ready for occupation until the end of July 1912. There were two wards, one with four beds for women and the other with eight beds for men, with day rooms and bathrooms. There was also a bedroom and sitting room for the Attendant, Miss Edith Hewitt, who had been appointed from St George's Infirmary with a salary of £30 a year, rising by £2 10s a year to £35 a year. As well as nursing the patients she was expected to cook any special diets that might be required.

Regulations, based on the Sanatorium system, were issued which included the patients' treatment, length of stay, expectoration, exercise, rest, clothing, visitors, recreation and discipline. These were so detailed and so rigorous that it was not surprising that Dr Guilding found he had difficulty in getting the patients to remain in the Workhouse for the full course of treatment. The provision of newspapers such as the *Daily Mail*, the *Daily Chronicle*, the *Daily Sketch* and the *Daily Mirror* probably helped to relieve the strict regime.

By this time tuberculum serum and an animal extract called Dr Carl Spengler's Immunkosper Losung had been used by the District Medical Officers on some patients. It had been found to relieve the symptoms but not to cure the disease. Dr Guilding had not used either on his Workhouse patients, preferring to rely on fresh air, moderate work or exercise and a good diet. This was very similar to the treatment given by Dr Carling at the Peppard Sanatorium.

In 1912 special Public Health regulations were issued regarding the notification of cases of tuberculosis by medical officers and relieving officers, to come into force early in 1913.

Further Changes, Acts and Orders

The new buildings greatly helped to relieve the overcrowding. The new mortuary, with its adjoining post mortem room, was made available to the Town Council on a temporary basis while the Council's new mortuary was being built. It was agreed that the Coroner could hold inquests in the new Committee room for a fee of 5s for each inquest or adjourned inquest. The further payment of 1s for a fire was disputed and eventually an inclusive charge of 5s for both room and fire was accepted.

The National Insurance Act, passed by Parliament in 1911, came into

REGULATIONS FOR PHTHISICAL PATIENTS

Treatment
The Sanatorium System consists of a graduated scale of rest, exercise and work, ordered for each individual according to his or her condition, with the constant accompaniment of pure, bracing air and good food and careful supervision. The system of graduated work has proved to give such good results that it is considered as essential a part of the treatment as fresh air or good food.

Patients should realise when they come that unless they are prepared to co-operate heartily with the medical and phthisical staff in every detail of the daily routine, the Sanatorium will be of no use to them. They can help materially in the management of the Sanatorium by cheerfully acquiescing in every direction given to them.

For men patients the classes of work are as follows:

CLASS A. Light domestic work such as cleaning brass, lamps, basins etc., tarring wood work, painting etc.
CLASS B. Light gardening, window cleaning, small repairs, wood chopping (outdoors)
Class C. Spadework (light and heavy spades), wheeling barrows, path making, trenching, farm work, carpentry etc.

The women patients to do needlework, housework, gardening etc., in various degrees.

Length of Stay
The average length of stay is three months and it is assumed that every patient will be able to stay as long as the Medical Officer may deem advisable.

EXPECTORATION Noted that consumption is spread to others by infection contained in expectoration and the swallowing of sputem is dangerous to patients themselves. Sputem cups or flasks must always be used. Patients must not cough into handkerchiefs nor spit on the ground and should cover the mouth when coughing. These rules are of the greatest importance and must be strictly adhered to.

EXERCISE Each patient will be directed as to the daily amount of exercise. Walking is regarded as an exercise for the lungs and must be practised slowly. Rest should be taken frequently during a walk if coughing or shortness of breath occurs. Patients should practise slow, deep breathing to induce the greater expansion of the lungs.

REST All patients must rest for one hour before dinner and before supper.

CLOTHING Clothing will be determined by the Guardians. In the case of female patients washing dresses will be provided.

VISITORS Visiting times: Wednesday and Sunday afternoons between 1.30pm and 2.30pm.

RECREATION Games may not be played in the morning except in inclement weather when outdoor work and exercise is impracticable.

SMOKING Smoking is allowed out of doors in moderation but not during working hours.

DISCIPLINE Strict obedience is required. Communication between men and women patients is strictly forbidden. The Medical Officer can discharge any patient who is either physically unsuitable or who fails to observe regulations.

LEAVE OF ABSENCE At the discretion of the Medical Officer.

operation in July 1913. This enabled workers whose income did not exceed £160 a year (later raised to £250 and then £420 a year) to obtain insurance in case of sickness and unemployment by means of contributions from the State, the employer and the employee. For a weekly contribution workers could enrol on a doctor's panel and obtain medical attention free of charge.

The Guardians would now have to contribute towards the scheme in respect of their employees. To what extent the Act would affect the administration of medical relief remained unknown. Only workers themselves would be insured. Their families would still have to turn to the Union for medical attention and possibly admission to the Workhouse hospital. By this time the Local Government Board had notified the Guardians that the term 'pauper' must now be avoided when referring to the 'chargeable poor'. However politically correct this might be, this change in nomenclature would not alter the fact that those in need would have to turn to the Union for help and the stigma of pauperism would remain for generations to come.

There had always been problems distinguishing between tramps who were beggars and those who genuinely wanted to find work. Following a conference held in Reading in 1908 a Joint Vagrancy Committee had been formed of various unions in Berkshire, Buckinghamshire and Oxford-shire. It was agreed to establish a system whereby Way Tickets were issued and Bread Stations established in the tramp wards of those unions partaking in the scheme. This would enable those genuinely seeking work to obtain a meal of bread and cheese. The system would be funded by contributions from the various unions.

The Guardians agreed to co-operate in the scheme but the Way Ticket system was not started in the Reading Union until early in 1911. In 1913 the Vagrancy Committee advised that bread and cheese should be given to all tramps and not just the Way Ticket holders. At that time non-ticket holders received 8oz of bread only. It was believed that, by giving cheese as well as bread, the excuse for begging for food would be removed. The Way Ticket holders would still have an advantage as they could leave the Tramp Wards early on the morning after admission. The number of tramps in Reading steadily declined from 17,056 in 1910 to 10,424 in 1913. The following year it was estimated the Guardians' contribution to the Way Ticket system would be £82 15s 11d in 1915.

Overcrowding difficulties remained in the part of the main Workhouse building which acted as a receiving home for children to be admitted to the Scattered Homes. As more children were to be expected with the extension of the Borough boundaries, a new, larger Headquarters building was needed. It should be able to take 24 children, provide administrative offices and act as a receiving home for the children. The Workhouse could then be bypassed and the children sent directly to Headquarters. A site in Russell Street was first considered in 1913 but in February 1914 The Beeches in London Road, for sale at £2,500, was preferred. However a petition from neighbours, protesting that the building would become a public nuisance, held the purchase up until May and it was not until the end of June that the Headquarters were moved there from Milman Road.

When the children left the Scattered Homes the Guardians helped to find them employment. A chart was made in 1912 to show the number of Poor Law boys who had found employment between 1909 and 1911 and in what capacity. Some had emigrated, others had entered the army, navy or merchant navy. Many had entered service and, for those entering private service, situations were found which offered the possibility of promotion. Apprenticeships were found for boys wanting to learn a trade. The careers of all the boys were noted until they were at least 18 years old.

The Children's Act of 1908 had made a limit of six months in which a man could be prosecuted for making an under-age girl pregnant. In 1912 the Guardians were anxious that this limit should be extended to 12 months. It had been found that frequently girls did not enter the Workhouse until after six months, by which time it was too late for the Guardians to prosecute the father and any hope of redress for the mother and the Union was impossible. The problem of illegitimacy was great at this time and the Union was usually left to provide for the mother and child.

The accommodation of imbeciles, epileptics and the feeble-minded in the Workhouse had always been unsatisfactory. In 1911 a conference was held in the Thorn Street offices with representatives from boards of guardians of unions in Berkshire and Oxfordshire. A joint committee was formed to consider the matter further. Unions were asked to provide details of the number of these patients in their workhouses. The Reading Union Workhouse at that time had a total of 58 inmates in this category: 30 imbeciles (16 men, 13 women and one child), 20 epileptics (11 men and 9 women) and eight feeble-minded (three men and five women).

The Mental Deficiency Act, passed by Parliament in 1913, would come into operation on April 1st 1914. In January that year the Joint Committee reported to the unions on how they would be affected by the Act. The Berkshire County Council and the Reading Borough Council would become two separate Local Authorities, each of which would appoint a committee containing councillors, guardians and others with special knowledge of the subject. It would be this committee's duty to find out which persons in their area were mentally defective and see that they were sent to institutions or looked after in accordance with the Act. These institutions had to be certified by the Secretary of State. The premises could be provided by boards of guardians or a combination of boards and, once certified, agreements could be made with the Local Authority for the reception and maintenance of the mentally defective.

It was noted that most of the mentally defective cases in Berkshire, believed to number some 300, were either inmates of workhouses or receiving outdoor relief. A large proportion of those in workhouses were elderly or middle-aged and were of great assistance helping within the

146

workhouses. If the guardians wished to retain these inmates the workhouse must be certified through the Local Authority with the consent of the Local Government Board. The Reading Board of Guardians decided to ask representatives of the Berkshire County Council and the Borough Council to meet them to discuss the subject with the view to co-ordinating the several duties to be undertaken by the Local Authority under the Act.

In the meantime the boundaries of the Borough were being extended. This took place in two phases. Parts of Tilehurst and Theale were transferred in 1911 and Caversham on March 31st 1914. The former added a further 3,000 people to the civil parish of Reading, bringing the population of the Borough to 78,214. From the Union's point of view it added some 39 paupers, 15 of whom (five men, seven women and three children) would be removed to the Workhouse and 10 children to the Scattered Homes. This new part of the Union was added to District 2 for relief, vaccination and medical purposes. Dr B B Hosford, who lived in Tilehurst, was appointed an additional Medical Officer for District 2 with a salary of £50 a year.

The parish of Caversham had been part of the Henley Union for Poor Law purposes. Its transfer to the Reading Union in 1914 resulted in the formation of District 3. Dr G H Cheyney was appointed the Medical Officer for the new District with a salary of £85, to be increased to £100 a year. The Reading Guardians would pay the Henley Union £500 per year for eight years in respect of the loss of the Poor Law income they had received from Caversham. They would also waive all claims in respect of the Henley Union property. Guardians would be elected to represent the additional area of Tilehurst, Theale and Caversham making a total of 28 Guardians for the Reading Union.

Two Poor Law Institutions Orders were issued in 1913. One, the Poor Law Institutions (Nursing) Order 1913, would come into force on March 31st 1914. This rescinded the Orders of 1847 and 1897 and, among other things, described the duties of the Matron and Superintendent Nurse and the qualifications necessary for all nurses and midwives.

Precedence in the sick wards should be:

1. The Medical Officer
2. The Master or, in his absence, the Matron
3. The Superintendent Nurse who was responsible under the Medical Officer for the welfare and nursing of the sick and under the Master for the government and conduct of the nurses and control of the servants while in the sick wards. She was also responsible for the cleanliness and good order of the interior of the sick wards, the furniture and fittings and also the stores for use in the sick wards.
4. The Matron was responsible under the Master for cooking the nurses' and patients' food, for making, washing and mending the

clothes and linen of the sick except when there was a laundry or kitchen for the use of the sick wards.

The second Poor Law Institutions Order, to come into force on April 1st 1914, covered many aspects of the organisation and administration of workhouses. Among other things it stipulated that all children over three years of age, except the sick, should be removed from workhouses. The work of medical officers would be increased as records were now required to be kept of patients in sick wards.

It was suggested that Dr Guilding's salary should be increased by £25 a year for two years as his already substantial work load would now be increased. Dr Guilding was disappointed that the increase could not be given all at once. His present salary of £140 a year, with an additional £45 for attending the Scattered Homes, was less than those for similar appointments such as medical officer for a school board or an infectious hospital. He pointed out he had been Workhouse Medical Officer for 18 years without a rise in salary. During this period it had been through his influence that the Guardians had been able to train their probationers, thereby saving about £1,600 in salaries. The Board reconsidered and agreed his salary should be increased by £50 at once. They valued his work for the Union and no doubt they had learned that he had now been elected an Honorary Surgeon at the Royal Berkshire Hospital.

There had been significant improvements to the Workhouse and the life of its inmates since the turn of the century. The hospital was now regarded as one of the best workhouse infirmaries in the country and, under the guidance of Dr Guilding, was recognised as a training school for nurses and midwives. The enlarged nursing staff were housed in a greatly improved nurses' home with room for additional staff in the future. The aged and infirm had their own building and phthisical patients had their own quarters with facilities for open-air treatment. Children also had more space and those who could not be treated in the hospital were sent to special institutions such as the Kindercot section of the Peppard Sanatorium, Great Ormond Street Hospital and Margate Sea Bathing Hospital.

The daily routine of the inmates had also improved with better diets and more privileges. The regime was still strict but some relaxation of the rules had been allowed. The Guardians, however, did not hesitate to prosecute any inmate when necessary, as in the case of William James Harrison in 1911 who was sent for trial at the Assizes and found guilty of publishing a defamatory libel against the Master and a Guardian.

The role of the local Councils was gradually being extended and facilities were now being provided which benefited those in receipt of poor relief. Park Hospital for infectious diseases and Whitley Smallpox Hospital were administered by the Borough Council, Moulsford Asylum was administered by the Berkshire County Council, and in 1914 the Berkshire and Buckinghamshire County Councils purchased Peppard Sanatorium from Dr Carling. Co-operation between the Guardians and the local authorities existed in several areas such as the Union's Assistance Committee and the Council's Distress Committee and would be further extended under the provisions of the Mental Deficiency Act.

There was also co-operation between the Guardians and those providing voluntary or charitable health care. The services of the Royal Berkshire Hospital were greatly appreciated and in 1914 the Guardians increased their annual subscription from £15 15s to £21. In 1909 they had requested representation on the Hospital's Board of Management but this had not been agreed. Links with the Queen Victoria Nursing Institute had also been forged and a Guardian served on their Management Board. The Report of the Royal Commission had drawn attention to the fact that radical changes would have be made to the whole system of providing health care. Many believed it was only a matter of time before the Poor Law system was abolished.

At their Board Meeting on July 16th 1914 the Guardians noted there were 518 inmates in the Workhouse. Since their last meeting in June there had been 78 admissions, 78 discharges and no births. The eight deaths were all of elderly inmates except one, a five-year old child who had died of tubercular meningitis. The next meeting of the Board of Guardians would be held in August. By that time war had been declared on Germany and a new chapter in the life of the Workhouse was about to begin.

6

THE FIRST WORLD WAR
1914–1918

The First Five Months, August to December 1914
Within days of the declaration of war on August 4th 1914, a Special
Meeting was convened of the Reading Union Board of Guardians 'to
consider what arrangements would be necessary in view of the serious
situation'. The Chairman, Mr Farrer, had been in daily contact with the
Master, the Clerk and the chairmen of the various committees. The
Guardians should prepare 'for any contingency which might arise'.

Steps had been taken to ensure the maintenance of supplies to the
Workhouse and the Scattered Homes. As the coal contractors had already
had their horses requisitioned by the military authorities, the Master was
instructed that, if necessary, he should hire a horse and dray to maintain
supplies. No farm produce would now be sold and any surplus eggs
should be preserved. At this time no one knew how the situation would
alter from day to day. An Emergency Committee, consisting of the
Chairman, Vice-Chairman and nine Guardians, was formed to deal with
matters concerning the Workhouse, the Scattered Homes and outdoor
relief.

A letter from the Local Government Board instructed the Guardians
to take steps to give employment to men who had been put out of work 'in
consequence of the probable dislocation of trade'. The Reading Distress
Committee had also contacted the Guardians and the Town Council to see
if employment could be given to such people under the provisions of the
Unemployed Workmen Act of 1905. Following this the Mayor set up a
Relief Committee to administer the National Relief Fund of HRH the
Prince of Wales in the town. The Committee included several Guardians,
the Union Clerk and the Superintendent Relieving Officer. District
Committees were to be formed which would include other Guardians.

The Royal Berkshire Hospital was also facing problems, but of a very
different nature. Eight nurses were reserved for Queen Alexandra's
Imperial Military Nursing Service, 15 others were Territorial Army nurses
and practically all the honorary medical staff were members of the
Territorial Army RAMC. All were now liable to be mobilised. Among them
was Dr Guilding who was also the Medical Officer at the Reading Union
Workhouse.

Preparations for the reception and distribution of the sick and wounded from overseas had been made by the War Office and on August 25th instructions were issued to military commands and voluntary organisations throughout the country. All sick and wounded would disembark at Southampton and would be taken to military and Territorial Army hospitals. (Later many more ports were to be used for disembarkation.) Beds would also be made available at civilian, private and auxiliary hospitals. By this time the headquarters of the 3rd Southern General Hospital had been established at the Examination Schools in Oxford. The Territorial RAMC medical staff at the Royal Berkshire Hospital were now liable to be mobilised to serve at this Oxford Base Hospital.

Col Rankin, the officer in charge at the 3rd Southern General Hospital, was asked if half the medical staff could be on duty at Oxford at one time with the periods of duty possibly fixed at one month. This would enable the medical staff to continue to work part time at the Royal Berkshire Hospital and also to maintain their private practices in the town. A meeting of all the medical practitioners of Reading was held at the Hospital on August 26th to discuss 'the question of conducting the private practices of medical men absent on military service'.

With many offers of help from local doctors and retired practitioners, arrangements were made to cover the work of the Hospital when the medical staff were mobilised. The Board of Management of the Royal Berkshire Hospital now offered to make 50 beds available to the War Office for serious cases of sick and wounded. In an emergency this number could probably be increased.

Life at the Workhouse continued much as usual at this time. The Guardians had managed to purchase all the Scattered Homes. It was arranged for three children to emigrate to Canada. All the buildings were in good repair and any necessary painting was put in hand. The Fire Brigade Rules and Regulations were printed and conveniently placed so all the Workhouse inmates could see what to do in an emergency. Additional fire escapes were agreed but the work was delayed 'owing to the remarkable decrease in the number of men in the institution of the artisan class who were to carry out the work'. The laundry was again needing additional drying facilities, but these had to wait as there were more urgent matters to be attended to.

Prices were constantly rising and several contractors said they could no longer keep to their original tenders. The drug contracts were particularly affected. On the farm nine pigs were ready to be sold and it was decided to sell eight and slaughter the ninth and have it cured for Workhouse consumption. In response to a request from the Reading Distress Committee men were now employed raising the land at the Workhouse and it was agreed the Guardians would contribute towards the cost. Difficulty was found in obtaining probationers until the starting salary was raised. The salaries of the Master and Matron and the Tramp Ward Porter and Portress were also increased.

Dr Guilding was consulted and agreed the Guardians should make 100 beds in the aged and infirm block available to the War Office for the wounded. The operating theatre could also be used if required. By this time Dr Guilding had been notified that he would shortly be called upon for military service in Oxford. He arranged that Dr Purnell would take over his duties at the Workhouse during his absence.

Preparations were also being made by the Berkshire Branch of the British Red Cross Society. Formed in 1910, the Branch now had 24 women's detachments and seven men's detachments with a total personnel of 767, of which 356 were nursing members. The Voluntary Aid Detachments (VADs) were now called upon to prepare and make available to the War Office as many auxiliary hospitals as possible. These would be equipped, staffed and administered by the individual detachments. All this work was voluntary. Although the nursing members held certificates in First Aid and Home Nursing they had no experience in hospital work. The Royal Berkshire Hospital arranged for small groups of these Red Cross nurses to attend short courses at the Hospital to fill this gap.

The Red Cross also contacted the Reading Guardians and asked if some of their VADs could work as probationers at the Workhouse hospital to gain experience. The Guardians turned down the request. They had no vacancies for probationers. A few months later when the Red Cross asked again, the Guardians still refused to help.

The St John Ambulance Brigade, formed in Reading in 1890, was also making preparations and its services, like those of the Red Cross, were to prove invaluable in the months ahead.

By October the Territorial RAMC medical staff at the Royal Berkshire Hospital were working at the Oxford Base Hospital and Dr Parnell had taken over Dr Guilding's duties at the Workhouse. Staff at both the Hospital and the Workhouse were now leaving for military service. There was no conscription at this time but many felt they must volunteer. It was arranged that if any Workhouse officers or servants wished to join the army their jobs would be kept open for them and their salaries would be paid, less the amount paid by the army authorities. Mr W Bibby, the attendant in charge of the aged and infirm block, asked for leave of absence as he wanted to volunteer for foreign service as a member of the St John Ambulance Brigade attached to the RAMC. Mrs Bibby would remain at the Workhouse during his absence.

Nothing was heard from the War Office following the Guardians' offer of 100 beds but by October the Royal Berkshire Hospital was notified that their offer of 50 beds had been accepted. The military wards of the Hospital would be classified as a Section of the 3rd Southern General Hospital at Oxford. A charge of 3s 4d per day for each military patient was agreed. Only serious cases would be admitted and the patients would be subject to military discipline. By drawing on the Private Nurses a sufficient number of nursing staff was obtained and only two additional male nurses and one ward maid needed to be engaged. The Hospital received its first

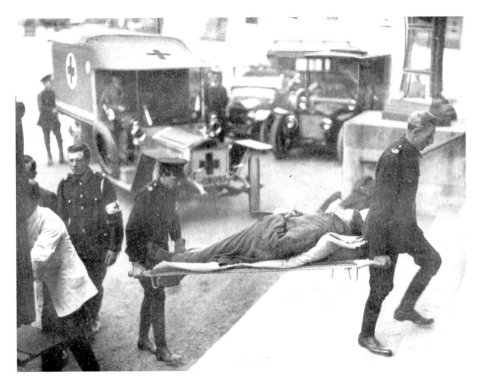

First convoy arriving at the Royal Berkshire Hospital

convoy of 50 wounded on November 4th. Among the army medical staff to meet them was Major Guilding.

The first Red Cross auxiliary hospitals had by now begun to be opened, several of which were in private houses. One of the earliest to be opened was at Englefield House, the home of Mr and Mrs J Benyon. Mr Benyon was Lord Lieutenant of Berkshire and both he and Mrs Benyon were Presidents of the Berkshire Branch of the British Red Cross Society. The gallery at Englefield House was converted into a 25-bed hospital and opened on October 29th. It was administered and staffed by Berks. 8 VAD with Mrs Benyon as the Commandant and Dr Joy, the local doctor, the Medical Officer.

Other Red Cross hospitals had opened in the Grand Stand at Ascot, the Drill Hall in Maidenhead, The Club House at Mortimer, Heatherside at Crowthorne and Kitemore at Faringdon. A convoy of 20 wounded had also been received at Newbury District Hospital on October 31st. Two auxiliary hospitals were opened in Reading in November. The first, Struan House in Maitland Road, was a large rented property, equipped, staffed and administered by Berks. 52 VAD with Lady Berkeley the Commandant, Miss Fanshaw the Assistant Quartermaster and Drs Rowland, Cane and Fosbery the Medical Officers. This hospital was particularly fortunate in having Miss Knowles, a former Matron at the Royal Berkshire Hospital, to

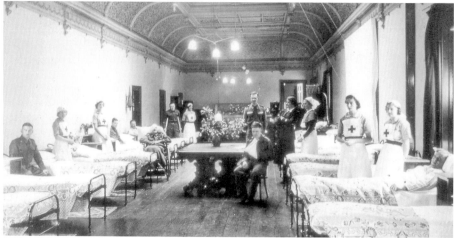

Top: Englefield House; *Bottom*: Gallery

help with its establishment and to be its first Matron. The hospital opened on November 25th with 77 beds and was the last auxiliary hospital in the county to close in 1919.

The second, St Luke's Church Hall, opened as an auxiliary hospital on November 27th with 30 beds. The Hall was lent by St Luke's parish and was equipped and run by Berks. 34 VAD. Mrs Abram, wife of one of the honorary physicians at the Royal Berkshire Hospital, was the Commandant, Mrs Poulton the Quartermaster, Mrs Hartnett (wife of a Reading doctor) the Lady Superintendent. Major Abram, RAMC TA, was the Medical Officer.

Christmas 1914 was celebrated at the Workhouse as usual with a special dinner and entertainment. At the Royal Berkshire Hospital and the

Struan House

auxiliary hospitals great efforts were made to give the wounded a very special day. Wards were decorated and numerous gifts were sent by the public in appreciation of the gallantry of the servicemen and the work of the staff who looked after them.

War Office Requirements

At one time it had been thought that the war would be over by Christmas 1914 but by then still more beds were needed for the constant stream of wounded and sick. On February 3rd 1915 representatives from the War Office visited the Workhouse and asked the Guardians to make all the buildings available as soon as possible 'for the reception and treatment of wounded soldiers'. Over 1,000 additional military beds were now required in Reading and these would be provided by taking over the Workhouse and several elementary schools in the town.

The Workhouse was one of many similar institutions throughout the country to be requisitioned as a military hospital. The Reading Workhouse was particularly suitable. It had recently been extended, the buildings were in good order, the hospital and theatre facilities were up-to-date and there was plenty of room for staff and patients alike. There were over 500 inmates at the Workhouse at this time. All would now have to be boarded out and arrangements made for the staff.

The Education Committee also faced similar problems. The War Office required Battle School, Wilson School, Redlands School, Katesgrove and Central Schools to provide more military beds. Accommodation would have to be found quickly for some 3,500 pupils in neighbouring schools as

St Luke's Church Hall

work would have to be started straight away to carry out the considerable alterations required to adapt the buildings for hospital purposes.

The Guardians had little time to spare. They notified the War Office that they would hand over the whole institution with the exception of the Tramp Wards and the farm 'on the understanding that they (the War Office) will deliver it over to the Guardians in as good a state of repair as they received it and reimburse to them any extra expenses which they may be put to in providing accommodation for the inmates and officers of the institution elsewhere'.

Neighbouring Unions were asked if they would be able to accommodate inmates from the Reading Union. Relatives were informed of the situation and were asked if they could look after their relations at home. Those who did so would receive outdoor relief to support them. Relatives of inmates sent elsewhere would have the expenses paid for one person per family to visit them twice each quarter. Further consideration would be given in cases of illness and emergency.

For the next few weeks the Emergency Committee worked tirelessly making arrangements for the evacuation of the Workhouse. In the meantime Union work had to continue as usual. Agreement was reached with the Reading Distress Committee for carrying out further land-raising work. Annual subscriptions to hospitals and institutions were confirmed. The Royal Berkshire Hospital would receive £21, the NSPCC £33, the Reading Blind Aid Society £5 5s, the Queen Victoria Institute £50, the Caversham Nursing Association £10. The usual subscriptions were sent to the Royal London Ophthalmic Hospital, the Royal Orthopaedic Hospital, the Margate Sea Bathing Hospital and the Royal Bath Mineral Water Hospital. Added to the list were the Girls' Training Home in Clapton, the Church Army Labour Home, the Waifs and Strays Society and the Reading Branch of the Oxford Diocesan Association for Rescue and Preventative Work.

The Guardians hoped to be able to hand over the Workhouse to the military authorities by the end of March. The Army Council had agreed to make good any additional expenditure falling upon the Poor Rate as a result of the transfer of the premises. They would not pay the loan charges upon them nor would they pay any rent for the use of the premises. The Local Government Board expressed their appreciation 'of the patriotic action of the Guardians' and assured them that the financial interests of the Union would be adequately safeguarded.

Finding accommodation for over 500 Workhouse inmates and staff was a daunting task. Neighbouring Unions had agreed to help. It was arranged that the Tramp Wards would be closed on March 13th and the building adapted into receiving wards with padded rooms for cases sent to the institution under the Lunacy Act. Work on the farm would continue to be carried out by the Guardians. The tenants of Battle Cottages were given notice to leave to enable accommodation to be provided for the men who would work on the farm.

The Education Committee agreed to hand over their school in Grovelands Road with its caretaker's house to the Guardians. It would be adapted as an infirmary for the most serious cases in the Workhouse who could not be transferred elsewhere. At the suggestion of the Local Government Inspector, the Parks Committee agreed to make the Mansion at Prospect Park available for phthisical patients and infirm men. The building was most suitable and would also save the Guardians the expense of moving the patients elsewhere. Collier and Catley undertook the alterations at Grovelands School, including providing kitchen and laundry facilities, G Lewis and Bros would carry out the work at the Mansion House, and H Margetts and Son the adaptations needed at the Tramp Wards.

By the last week in March all the necessary arrangements had been made. The work converting the various buildings had been completed and the inmates were moved from the Workhouse. Thirteen inmates were boarded with relatives. Neighbouring Unions accepted 231 with Newbury Union taking 122, Wallingford Union 64, Hungerford Union 24 and Basingstoke Union 21. Offers of help had been received from other Unions but these were not yet required.

A large number of inmates remained in Reading. Sixty seriously ill patients were transferred to Grovelands School, 47 phthisical patients and infirm men were sent to the Mansion at Prospect Park. Some 49 able-bodied men and women (to be employed at Grovelands School and on the farm) were accommodated at the former Tramp Wards. Two stone-breaking cells had been adapted as padded rooms for lunatics. One of the

Grovelands School

six Battle Cottages had been turned into an office, another into a general store. The remaining four cottages now housed six elderly women and a number of able-bodied inmates who worked on the farm or in the laundry. Other inmates who were responsible for mending and repairing the clothes of all the Workhouse inmates (including those temporarily moved to other unions), were also accommodated in the Battle Cottages. The Scattered Home at 40 Russell Street had been adapted to look after 12 sick children and the former Alexandra Home, at 12 Russell Street, had been converted to receive the very young children and nursing mothers.

All the Workhouse officers and staff were retained by the Union except the Engineer, the Stoker and the Painter who would now work for the military authorities. Private houses were rented for other members of the staff: 140 Tilehurst Road for the Master and Matron and stores, 197 Cranbury Road for the Tramp Ward Porter and Portress, 507 Oxford Road for the Baker and Laundress. Westlands, 167 Tilehurst Road would be used as the Nurses' Home and a Maternity Home.

All was now ready for the military authorities to take over the Workhouse.

The Reading War Hospital
Within one month the Workhouse buildings had been adapted into a 400-bed War Hospital. Lieut-Col E A Hanly, the Commanding Officer, assisted by his Quartermaster, Lieut E E Ward, and the Matron, Miss Willets, from Queen Alexandra's Imperial Military Nursing Service (QAIMNS), organised the buildings to accommodate the needs of a military hospital.

Reading War Hospital

The Receiving Wards at the entrance would be used for the reception and examination of patients before they were moved to appropriate wards. The Board Room opposite, now vacated by the Coroner, would become the Registrar's office.

The patients would be accommodated in seven blocks, each identified by a letter. The male wing of the Workhouse hospital became A block and the female wing B block. The former maternity rooms between the two blocks were converted to provide an additional operating theatre and an X-ray room. The theatre, Matron's room, surgery and dispensary on the lower floor would also be fully used. The aged and infirm building became C block. The former imbecile block became D block, for infectious cases. The Cottage became E block, for patients with skin diseases. The women's block was also used for patients and became F block. The Master's quarters and offices became H block to be used as a barracks for non-commissioned officers and men.

Rooms were provided for electrotherapy and massage treatment and others for pack stores, clothing stores, linen stores and other essentials. A separate pathology laboratory was provided in the hospital grounds behind D block, away from the main buildings.

The speed with which the hospital was converted was due in great measure to the efficiency of the Commanding Officer, Lieut-Col Hanly, and the Matron. Miss Willets, QAIMNS, was very experienced. She had served through the South African War and had spent several years in Hong Kong before coming to Reading. Her ability in organising and supervising the conversion of the Workhouse was greatly praised. As

Reading War Hospital. Oxford Road entrance

Reading War Hospital. Entrance from north

additional help was needed to augment the military personnel at this time, both the Red Cross and the St John Ambulance Brigade supplied a number of orderlies.

Once the hospital was ready for occupation a large medical and nursing staff was required. Nurses were needed to supplement the QAIMNS nurses and army nurses. On March 21st the Berkshire Branch of the Red Cross wrote to their VADs and asked for volunteers to work at the War Hospital. They must be aged between 23 and 38 years old and hold certificates in First Aid and Home Nursing. They would be subject to military discipline and would have to wear uniform. They would be paid £20 per year with expenses for travelling, board, lodging, laundry and £1 for the upkeep of uniform. Altogether 48 Red Cross nurses volunteered. They would be accommodated at the Nurses' Home or at Park House School, which Mr and Mrs Bartholomew had made available to the military authorities.

The honorary medical staff from the Royal Berkshire Hospital who were serving at the Oxford Base Hospital were now recalled to serve at the Reading War Hospital. The asterisks on the following list of the medical staff at that time show that over half were honorary medical staff from the Royal Berkshire Hospital and represented every department.

Reading War Hospital. Inside entrance

Reading War Hospital. H Block

Reading War Hospital. D Block

Reading War Hospital. F Block

Commanding Officer............................	Lieut-Col E A Hanly
Surgical Division	Lieut-Col Mayo-Robson CVO
Medical Division	*Lieut-Col W T Freeman
Surgeon...	*Lieut-Col W T Maurice
General Duties....................................	*Major G S Abram
	*Major L M Guilding
	Major J A P Price
	*Major R Ritson
Surgeons	*Captain G H R Holden
	Captain N Clowes
	*Captain W B Secretan
	*Captain G F Murrell
Registrar..	*Captain H M Clarke
X-ray Specialists	*Captain W J Foster
	Captain Fielding Clarke
Resident Surgeon................................	Lieut V C Pennell
Quartermaster	Lieut E E Ward
Assistant Quartermaster	Lieut C W Beaumont
Ophthalmic Surgeons..........................	*Dr R P Brooks
	*Dr Powell
	Lieut G A Bird
	Lieut G H Culverwell
Secretary	Mr D G Pugh

War Hospital Medical Staff 1915

Lieut-Col Mayo-Robson had recently returned from France where he had been sent by the War Office, at the request of the French Embassy, to open an emergency hospital near the front line. His experience would be invaluable to the War Hospital.

Outbreak of Cerebro-Spinal Meningitis
While preparations were being made to vacate the Workhouse and convert it into a War Hospital, an outbreak of cerebro-spinal meningitis (spotted fever) occurred in the town among the civilians and troops stationed there. All the civilian cases were sent to Park Hospital where special tents were erected; two for patients, two for nurses and others for kitchen and services. The old Bridge Street Hospital was reopened.

The Royal Berkshire Hospital was asked to take the military cases

Miss Willetts

Marquee at the Royal Berkshire Hospital

and, although it was against the Hospital rules, it was agreed they would be admitted and treated in the isolation block. The military authorities would supply marquees for additional beds and more nurses and orderlies if required. A higher rate of 7s 6d per day would be paid for each of these cases. All pathological work would be undertaken by Dr Donaldson, the Hospital's Pathologist. At the same time the Hospital was asked to provide a further 50 beds for the wounded, which would bring the total to 100 military beds.

Altogether 34 cases of cerebro-spinal meningitis were admitted to the Royal Berkshire Hospital and the death of six, in a disease usually considered fatal, was believed to be the lowest ever recorded. When the outbreak was over it was decided to make the infectious wards available should another outbreak occur in the future.

Preparations for the Reception of the Wounded

By the middle of April 1915 the Berkshire Branch of the British Red Cross had formed six additional women's detachments and one additional men's detachment. This brought the total to 30 women's and eight men's VADs with 1,224 personnel.

Sixteen auxiliary hospitals had now been opened and staffed by the VADs and it was arranged that 12 which were within a reasonable distance of Reading would become affiliated to the Reading War Hospital when it opened. Six had opened in 1914: The Club House at Mortimer, Englefield House, Struan House and St Luke's Hall in Reading, Benham Valence at Speen (25 beds) and Oaklea in Bracknell (12 beds). Six others had opened between January and April 1915: Church House in Wokingham (17 beds), Albion House in Newbury (60 beds), Ridgelands in Finchampstead (20

Berkshire Voluntary Aid Transport Service

beds), West Woodhay House (24 beds) and Park House in Newbury (56 beds). The military wards at Newbury District Hospital would also be affiliated to Reading. Other hospitals were added as they were opened in the months ahead.

The military authorities were unable to arrange for the reception and transport of the wounded when they arrived. A Joint Committee was formed of representatives of the Berkshire Automobile Club and the Berkshire Branch of the British Red Cross Society to organise the Berks. Voluntary Aid Transport Service. It would be funded by subscriptions and a grant from the Berkshire Branch of the Red Cross. Captain Cyril Tubbs, son of the former Chaplain at the Workhouse, was appointed Transport Officer at the War Hospital. All stretcher work would be carried out with the assistance of Berks. 13 VAD under Commandant Powell and Quartermaster Thake. The Berkshire Automobile Club undertook to provide suitable transport and many volunteers offered their services and lent or gave cars to be converted for use as ambulances.

A Red Cross appeal was launched by the Lord Lieutenant, Mr J Benyon, to raise funds for the provision and maintenance of ambulances. As he explained: 'The authorities are relying on us to provide the means of conveying our wounded soldiers from the railway station to the various hospitals which are being established and of moving them when necessary from one hospital to another.' The work would be considerable and funds of at least £2,000 would be required. Within a short time 11 motor ambulances able to take 38 stretchers or 56 seated cases, nine service cars able to take 59 men and various private touring cars had been made available and a central garage provided in Friar Street.

At the same time a committee to be known as the Reading Care and Comforts Committee was formed through the efforts of Mrs Benyon, who became its President. At a well-attended meeting called by the Mayor, Mr Leonard Sutton, the audience was told that the War Office would be unable to supply all items which the wounded would require and it was the purpose of the Committee to arrange for these to be obtained. Included, among other things, would be tobacco and cigarettes, fruit and flowers, cakes, special garments, books, newspapers and magazines. A depot for the assembly and distribution of these items had been lent, free of charge, at 62 Minster Street.

It was agreed that the Commanding Officer at the War Hospital should have a fund of money at his disposal which he could use to purchase special items for immediate use. This fund could also be used to pay the fares of relatives of the wounded who were in poor circumstances, so they would be able to visit them. The auxiliary hospitals and the hospitals to be opened in the Reading schools would also benefit from the work of the Care and Comforts Committee. The meeting ended with the audience prepared to do everything in its power to raise funds and see that all items required were provided for the wounded. Within days the first lists of subscribers and contributors had appeared in the newspapers.

The First Convoys

The first convoy with 120 wounded soldiers arrived at Reading station on Thursday April 22nd at 4.15pm. All had been wounded at Hill 60 in France the previous Sunday and had come from the front via Southampton. Half the wounded were stretcher cases and, apart from a few walking wounded, the rest were wheelchair cases. Their wounds had been attended to briefly in France but, as one observer noted at the time, their clothes 'still bore traces of the trenches and deep red stains' and 'their wan faces and shattered limbs told their own tale'.

A large crowd had gathered outside the station and barriers were put up by the police to keep the way clear for the long line of ambulances provided by the Berkshire Automobile Club. Inside the station a detachment of the Bucks. Infantry was on duty at platform 1 where the Mayor (Mr Leonard Sutton), the Deputy Mayor (Mr C G Field) and the Chief Constable (Captain J S Henderson) had assembled to meet the train.

All the work of removing the wounded from the train and taking them to the War Hospital was carried out by the Red Cross VADs under the direction of Captain Tubbs, the Transport Officer at the War Hospital. Cigarettes and refreshments were distributed by VADs while the orderlies with trolleys removed the stretchers and wheelchair cases from the train. Red Cross nurses were there to help the wounded as they were taken to the waiting ambulances, each of which had a Red Cross orderly and nurse in attendance. The efficiency of the VADs enabled the station to be cleared by 6.15pm. They had carried out a great service and were warmly congratulated on their work.

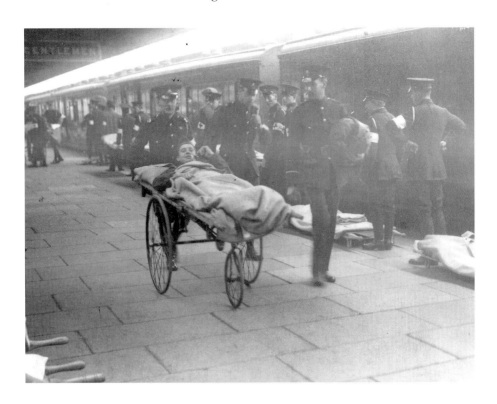

Top: Unloading hospital train at Reading station; *Bottom*: WVS Refreshments at station

Top: Ambulances at station; *Bottom*: Ambulance ready for patients

Crowds had also assembled outside the War Hospital and, like those at the station, found the arrival of the wounded a very emotional occasion. As one person noted: 'Very realistically was it brought home to us that war is war.'

Once at the Hospital the wounded were examined by the medical officers. Details were recorded of each patient's regiment, number, rank, religion and the names and addresses of the next of kin, the nature of the injury and its severity. An admission number was given and the patient was assigned to a ward in one of the blocks where he would begin what might prove to be a lengthy period of recovery.

Ambulances at War Hospital

This first convoy was followed by a second on May 8th when 100 casualties from Ypres and Hill 60 were admitted to the Hospital. One week later 150 wounded were transferred to Reading from the hospital at Tidworth, 46 of whom were admitted to the Royal Berkshire Hospital. A convoy of a further 102 wounded straight from the front were admitted the next day. The War Hospital was now almost full and some earlier arrivals were transferred to the auxiliary hospitals in the area.

The Section Hospitals
Work had started in February to convert the four Reading schools which had been taken over by the War Office. These would become Section Hospitals and, with the military hospital at the former Workhouse (now to be called No.1 Reading War Hospital) and the military wards at the Royal Berkshire Hospital, would provide beds for over 1,300 wounded men.

It had been comparatively straightforward to adapt the Workhouse but the four schools needed considerable alterations. Each was inspected by a medical officer and an officer from the Royal Engineers to establish what was required and how many patients and staff could be accommodated. The alterations were then to be carried out under the direction of the District Officer of the Royal Engineers.

The Section Hospitals in the former schools were all very similar and, besides the wards, each provided an operating theatre, dispensary, disinfecting chamber, a Matron's room, Medical Officers' room, numerous rooms for stores, kitchen quarters, bathroom facilities and a recreation room. Once the alterations were completed the buildings were cleaned by orderlies and the Quartermasters began to assemble the large quantity of equipment needed, as detailed in numerous lists which had been sent to the Ordnance Department. When all this had been completed the Medical

No. 1 Reading War Hospital

Officers, Matron and nursing staff could take over and prepare for the reception of the wounded.

The first school to be converted was Redlands School which opened on June 25th 1915. In May it had been agreed that the Board of Management of the Royal Berkshire Hospital should take over the administration of Redlands Hospital. This would be more convenient than running it from the main No.1 War Hospital which would administer the other Section Hospitals when they opened. As with the other Section Hospitals, all expenses for adapting and running Redlands Hospital would be paid by the War Office.

The Board of Management quickly got to work. A Matron, Mrs Beatrice Jamieson, was appointed 'for the duration of the war, if possible' with a salary of £100 per year and allowances. Mr Reginald Mount was appointed Secretary, also for the duration of the war, with a salary of £3 per week. A Porter cum Messenger was also appointed with wages of 22s 5d per week and a uniform. He would pay 6s per week rent for his cottage and be allowed one ton of coal every three months and light at the rate of $6\frac{1}{2}$d per week. Part of the Headmaster's House, adjoining the school, would be used as a nurses' home. The Royal Berkshire Hospital Dispenser would attend daily to provide the necessary drugs and medicines.

By June 25th all the arrangements were complete and the first 16 patients were admitted. Lieut-Col Freeman was in charge with Dr Lambert and Lieut Collier the other Medical Officers. Eventually Redlands Hospital was able to provide 140 beds.

No. 2 Reading War Hospital, Battle School

The next Section Hospital to be opened was Battle School with 200 beds on July 1st. This was followed by Wilson School with 300 beds on September 7th and a few months later Katesgrove and Central Schools opened with 200 beds. The former Workhouse became known as No.1 Reading War Hospital, Battle School No.2 War Hospital, Wilson School No.3 War Hospital, Redlands School No.4 War Hospital, Katesgrove and Central Schools No.5 Reading War Hospital. The military wards at the Royal Berkshire Hospital became No.6 Reading War Hospital. All would now be known collectively as the Reading War Hospital with No.1 the main Hospital for the whole group.

Public Support
From the outset of the war the public had generously supported the armed forces with both financial and practical help. All too soon the lists of volunteers were joined by other lists of those killed, wounded or missing. A wave of patriotism swept the town with the arrival of the wounded and help from individuals and groups was provided in many different ways. Four voluntary organisations became particularly noted for their work.

A branch of the National Egg Collection was organised in Reading in March 1915 and a depot was opened at the Corn Exchange. Three times a week fresh eggs, collected throughout the area, were delivered to the military and auxiliary hospitals in the town and neighbourhood. Even the smallest villages contributed and their combined efforts were impressive.

No. 3 Reading War Hospital, Wilson School

The work of the Care and Comforts Committee was a great success and by the time the No.1 War Hospital was opened its helpers were able to provide many items for the wounded. This voluntary organisation was quite separate from the administration of the War Hospital and it undertook its work with great efficiency and dedication. Funds were raised by donations and subscriptions and a wide variety of gifts were received. As the number of wounded increased the volume and range of the work expanded and the support of the public never wavered.

Every morning the matrons of the various hospitals were contacted to find out what was required and, if possible, everything was delivered later that day. Some dozen sub-committees were formed, each of which was in charge of one particular type of help. Flowers, fruit, vegetables, cakes, biscuits and other foodstuffs were obtained and distributed. The Tobacco and Cigarettes Committee supplied pipes and each patient was given a quarter of an ounce of tobacco or five cigarettes a day. The Games and Cards Committee equipped recreation rooms with chairs, billiard tables, pianos, gramophones and records as well as items such as jig-saws, paints, games and playing cards. The Library Committee provided newspapers, books and magazines and also writing paper. A large stock of books was kept at the depot and patients were able to change their books twice a week. The Handicraft Committee enabled patients to learn fretwork, basket-making, rug-making and a variety of other crafts. All the materials were provided as well as tuition.

Outdoor needs were also provided such as garden chairs, rugs and cushions and even wheelchairs and spinal carriages. The Entertainment

Top: No. 4 War Hospital, Redlands School; *Bottom*: No. 5 War Hospital, Katesgrove and Central Schools

Committee organised concerts and, for those able to leave the hospitals, visits to the theatre, river trips and entertainment in private houses. Unusual requests such as a particular type of crutch or walking aid, or even a mouth organ, were provided and nothing was considered to be beyond the scope of the Committee.

Later in 1915 a third voluntary organisation, the Reading War Hospitals Supplies Depot, was established in Reading under the auspices of the Reading Chamber of Commerce. Its purpose was to make and

Care and Comforts group

supply a wide variety of items essential to war hospitals both at home and abroad. These would supplement those supplied by the War Office. The Reading War Hospital and its auxiliary hospitals were to benefit very considerably from its work.

The first depot opened at 24 Cross Street, Reading but soon had to move to larger premises at 16 Duke Street, lent by Mr H B Blagrave. Eight departments were established: bandages and swabs, splint padding, papier-mache splints, slippers and shoes, carpentry, French polishing of crutches, crutch head filling and packing. Specialised articles such as pneumonia jackets were made and great ingenuity was shown in making steel splints and artificial limbs which were increasingly needed in the local hospitals.

As the war progressed the work of the Depot increased considerably and eventually some 60 working parties were established throughout the county and an additional branch opened in Maidenhead. These working parties involved some 1,500 people, all voluntary helpers, and the volume of their output was remarkable. Large sums of money were raised to purchase the materials and thousands of articles were made and dispatched each year. The Depot closed on March 12th 1919 having provided an invaluable service to the Reading War Hospital and to military hospitals both at home and abroad.

Later a fourth voluntary organisation was established when Mrs Cope opened a depot at her home, Finchampstead Place, for the Hants. and Berks. Moss Guild and offered to supply sphagnum moss dressings free of charge to hospitals in the area. These dressings, in a variety of sizes, could be used in place of absorbent wool for all kinds of aseptic dressings. Soon they were used extensively in the military hospitals. Mrs Cope and the

Reading War Hospitals Supply Depot

Guild continued their invaluable work throughout the war and enabled considerable savings to be made at a time when the cost of dressings was constantly rising.

The Auxiliary Hospitals
Between April and December 1915 a further four auxiliary hospitals were opened near Reading and affiliated to the Reading War Hospital. Cliff House in Caversham, lent by Mrs Cotton and staffed by Berks. 22 VAD, opened on May 10th with 22 beds. St Anne's Hall, Caversham, opened three days later with 23 beds. This was a private hall lent by Mrs Crawshay who also generously paid all its expenses. It was staffed by Berks. 60 VAD. Buckhurst in Wokingham, a private house lent by Mrs Murdoch, opened on November 2nd with 20 beds and was staffed by Berks. 10 VAD. Woodclyffe Hall in Wargrave and the adjoining Hostel, lent by the Trustees, was opened on December 10th with 50 beds and staffed by Berks. 58 VAD. Later an annexe, the Gladdy House, was lent by Sir William Cain. There were now 290 beds in 16 auxiliary hospitals affiliated to the Reading War Hospital.

The following year, 1916, two large auxiliary hospitals were opened in Reading. Inniscarra in the Bath Road, rented from Trustees, opened on March 11th with 50 beds. It was staffed by Berks. 68 VAD with Mrs Henderson the Commandant and Drs Cane, Hurry, Walters and March the Medical Officers. Sutherlands in Christ Church Road was a rented private house. It opened on November 2nd with 80 beds. An annexe and

Top: Polishing crutches; *Bottom*: Work on artificial limbs

ground adjoining were lent by Mr Leonard Sutton. It was staffed by Berks. 50 with Mrs Childs the Commandant and Drs Hastings Gilford and March the Medical Officers.

Popeswood in Binfield was also opened on November 2nd 1916. A rented private property with 30 beds, it was staffed by Berks. 10 VAD with Mrs Bullen Smith the Commandant and Dr Ward the Medical Officer.

Inniscarra

During 1916 the hospitals at Benham Valence, Ridgelands in Wokingham and Buckhouse in Bracknell were all closed. Cliff House in Caversham, now too small, was also closed and transferred to Devonshire Lodge in Reading with 50 beds. There had been an overall gain of 187 beds in 1916 and more hospitals were now concentrated nearer the Reading War Hospital.

By 1917 a further six auxiliary hospitals became affiliated to the Reading War Hospital. Three could only provide a few beds. The White House in Basildon, with 12 beds, was lent by Colonel Morrison who had already lent part of his home, Basildon Park, to be used as a convalescent hospital for Guards officers. Colesburg in Caversham could accommodate eight patients and Sulhamstead House in Theale, the home of Lady Watson, could take 15. The three other hospitals were larger. Newtown House in Newbury could take up to 54 patients, Woodcote House could take 47 and the Red Cross Hospital at Stratton St Margaret's, opened in June 1917, could take over 60 patients.

Over 700 beds were provided by the 22 auxiliary hospitals affiliated to the Reading War Hospital and the highest number recorded was 738 occupied beds in November 1917.

The work of establishing and running these auxiliary hospitals was considerable. Once suitable premises were found the various Detachments had to raise funds to equip and staff them. Invariably the local population was most generous in its financial and practical support. Equipment such as beds, chairs, linen and cutlery was purchased, loaned or donated.

Top: Sutherlands; *Bottom*: Struan House

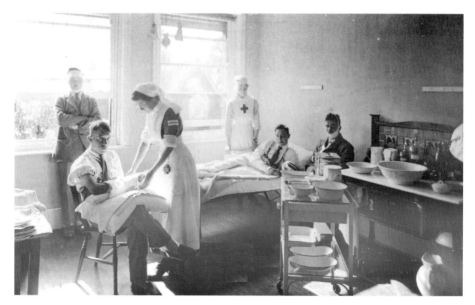

A ward at Inniscarra

Endless lists were made and accounts kept of everything that was obtained.

The Commandant of the Detachment which established an auxiliary hospital was in charge and under her a Quartermaster was appointed to be responsible for the stores. In many hospitals the Matron was provided by Headquarters if a suitably qualified person was not available within the Detachment. The nursing staff all came from among the members, with help from other Detachments if necessary. Local practitioners were asked to act as medical officers.

These hospitals were divided into two classes. Class A provided trained nurses and were suitably equipped. Class B admitted mainly convalescent patients who needed little or no hospital treatment. Practically all the hospitals affiliated to the Reading War Hospital were Class A, the exceptions being the White House in Basildon, Sulhamstead House and Colesburg in Caversham.

A War Office grant of between 3s and 3s 3d per day was paid for each military patient and later a small fee was also paid for each unoccupied bed. Hospitals which treated outpatients were given an allowance of between 6d and 1s 6d per patient per day. Local practitioners who acted as medical officers were given a fee per patient with a maximum total of 17s 6d per day for those attending patients in Class A hospitals and 12s per day for Class B hospitals.

Before the Reading War Hospital was opened in April 1915 the auxiliary hospitals at Buckhurst in Bracknell, Church House in Wokingham, Struan House and St Luke's Hall in Reading were treating sick soldiers billeted in Reading and the neighbourhood. Most were medical cases and many were extremely ill. They provided a sharp

St Luke's Hall

introduction for the nurses of what would follow in the years ahead. As soon as the War Hospital opened these hospitals received wounded from overseas and also treated outpatients.

The only complete records to have survived of the auxiliary hospitals affiliated to the Reading War Hospital are those of Church House in Wokingham, staffed by Berks. 28 VAD. They show the dedication of the staff and the extremely arduous work they undertook. The capitation grant was insufficient to cover costs and fundraising was a constant necessity. The rules were strict for patients and staff alike. Detailed records had to be kept and reports made to be sent weekly to the Reading War Hospital. Here monthly returns of all the hospitals were produced to show numbers admitted, discharged, remaining and the average number of days the patients were in the hospitals. War Office, Red Cross and Reading War Hospital orders, directives and circulars bombarded the hospital and added to the tasks of the staff and Medical Officer. The paperwork was almost endless.

One patient admitted to Church House on March 20th 1915, before the War Hospital was opened, was a case of suspected cerebro-spinal meningitis. Details of the case were recorded in the Report Book and the soldier was eventually transferred by motor ambulance to Aldershot.

Once the War Hospital opened wounded soldiers from overseas were sent to Church House. Most were surgical cases with gunshot wounds. There were also amputees who had recovered sufficiently to be moved from the main hospital. The Report Book recorded the treatment of septic wounds, noted tubes in wounds being shortened, cavities washed out with hydrogen peroxide and stitches removed. Pain was relieved with morphine.

Sutherlands dining and recreation room

A wide variety of medical cases was recorded including gas poisoning, dysentery, trench foot, rheumatic fever, bronchitis and pleurisy. Treatment included linseed and mustard poultices, gamgee jackets for patients with bronchitis, hydrogen peroxide for sore throats and, most importantly, massage to enable limbs to regain movement.

Several hospitals provided massage and some, like Woodclyffe in Wargrave, also provided electrical treatment. This was of great benefit to the outpatients who attended the auxiliary hospitals from convalescent homes nearby. Albion House in Newbury specialised in the treatment of cases of paralysis and this work was particularly praised.

The local medical officers at the various auxiliary hospitals were now having to treat cases, both medical and surgical, which were seldom if ever encountered in general practice. When problems arose the staff at the War Hospital were contacted and the medical officers were advised what to do and, if necessary, the patients were referred back to the War Hospital. The records of Church House include letters from Major L Joyce, by now the Registrar at the No 1 War Hospital, concerning patients and their treatment.

When fit enough patients were either discharged and sent on leave before returning to the front, or sent to the many convalescent homes which were opened locally. From here they could attend the War Hospital or the auxiliary hospitals as outpatients and receive any further treatment that was necessary. Among the convalescent homes opened at this time was one for officers at a large house called Dunedin on the Bath Road in Reading. This house, greatly extended, is now the BUPA Dunedin Hospital.

Top: Church House, Wokingham; *Bottom*: Church House Nurses

Visit of the King and Queen July 31st 1915

The King and Queen with Lieut-Col Hanly and Miss Willetts

Life at the War Hospital

On the afternoon of Saturday July 31st 1915 King George V and Queen Mary visited the No. 1 War Hospital. By this time the hospital had been open for just over three months and was working to full capacity. The visit had not been announced in advance but when the news leaked out crowds began to assemble in the streets to greet the royal family. This was the first time the King and Queen had visited Reading since their accession in 1910. The visit lasted two hours during which the royal couple toured the wards and talked to the patients, offering them sympathy and giving them encouragement. The medical and nursing staff were particularly pleased that the importance of their work was now widely recognised. When the King and Queen left the hospital large crowds were lining the route to wave and cheer the royal car on its way back to Windsor. They too were heartened by the visit and wished to demonstrate their loyalty and affection.

By now three of the Section Hospitals were receiving patients. As well as the 100 military beds at the Royal Berkshire Hospital, No. 4 War Hospital at Redlands School had been open for five weeks and No. 2 War Hospital at Battle School had been open for one month. It was no longer practical to send the wounded arriving in large convoys straight to the No. 1 War Hospital, so a new system was introduced. As soon as No.1 War Hospital was notified of the arrival of a convoy the Commanding Officer arranged for the dispersal of the wounded according to the beds available at the various hospitals. As the wounded left the train at Reading Station each man was given a ticket informing him of the hospital to which he would be taken. The ambulances outside were similarly labelled and took the wounded straight to the appropriate hospital.

The members of Berks. 13 VAD carried out their stretcher and transport work quickly and efficiently. All had retained their full-time employment and were able, with their employers' agreement, to leave their work whenever they were needed for convoy duty. As soon as the VADs were notified by telephone that a convoy was on its way, they left their work and assembled with their ambulances at the railway station. By the end of the war they had handled some 493 convoys.

No.1 War Hospital was now often called the Central War Hospital as this was the main hospital for administrative purposes. Here the daily routine was unrecognisable compared with the Workhouse days. The closure of the Tramp Wards had ended the daily procession of vagrants wanting accommodation for the night. Their absence was noted with satisfaction by the public. An undesirable nuisance had ended. The work of the farm, retained by the Guardians, did not affect the War Hospital but the grounds of the former Workhouse, with their lawns and walks, were appreciated by patients and staff alike. Inside the busy Hospital the work of the Care and Comforts Committee was to be seen everywhere. In the wards flowers, books and comforts were provided for the patients. Those who were fit enough went to the large dining hall for their meals. This

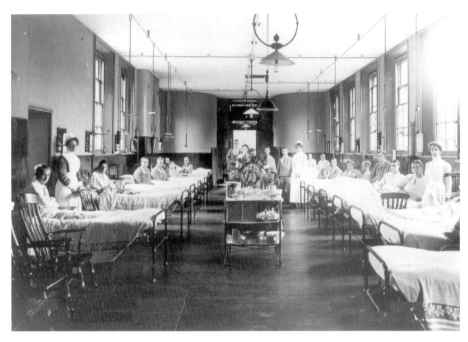

Royal Berkshire Hospital, No. 6 War Hospital. Benyon Ward

Redlands, No. 4 War Hospital. Ward 1 C Block

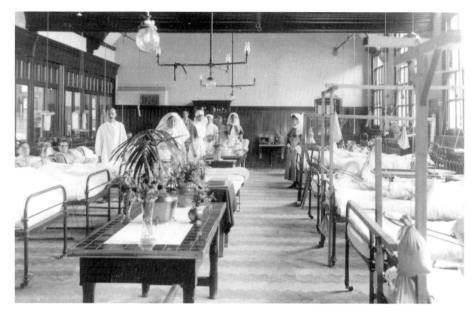

Battle, No. 2 War Hospital. Ward A 13

room was also used for concerts and entertainments organised by the Care and Comforts Committee. Soon weekly concerts were arranged and also whist drives and various other recreations including outings outside the Hospital. River trips were particularly popular in the warmer weather. Wounded servicemen, in their blue hospital uniform, became a familiar sight in the town.

Unlike the Workhouse days, a room was set aside in H Block as a Chapel which was open all day for those who wished to pray or to be quietly on their own. The Church of England Chaplain, the Revd F Gillmor, held Communion here on Sundays and Wednesdays and evening prayers on Sundays. A main Sunday morning service was held in the dining hall at 9.30am The Chaplain also regularly visited the wards and gave communion to those who could not leave their beds. The Roman Catholic Chaplain, the Revd Father Kernan, also visited the wards and patients who were fit enough were taken by car to attend Mass at St James' Church on Sunday mornings. Free Church services were held on Sundays in the dining hall at 8.30am for the Nonconformist patients.

The visits of relatives were most important and any who needed accommodation were given addresses and, if necessary, their expenses were paid out of funds raised by the Care and Comforts Committee. Those who were unable to visit were urged to state the Block and Ward on their letters to enable them to be delivered as quickly as possible. Photographers were allowed to produce picture postcards of the Hospital and soon photographs of the buildings, shut away from the public eye in the Workhouse days, were being sent all over the country and abroad. A

Motorbike outing 1915

valuable pictorial record was being made of the Hospital during the war years.

In January 1916 the first issue of a magazine called *The Ration* was produced by members of the RAMC Detachment working at the No. 1 War Hospital. Financed by the Commanding Officer, the officers, nursing staff and advertisements, it was sold at 1d per copy. Its aim was 'to entertain and amuse, to touch upon every side of the work of the Hospital'. The Editor informed readers in the first number that magazines published by war hospital staff throughout the country were sent to the British Museum 'to be used in the compilation of the most remarkable history the world has ever known'.

The Ration, published monthly, was a great success but with rising costs the price had to be increased to 2d a copy in June 1916. Sales still increased and the magazine remained as popular as ever. Thanks to the skilled Editor and gifted cartoonist, the mix of informative articles, stories, cartoons and illustrations provided something of interest for every reader. It also gave an insight into the lives of those working in the Hospital and described the formation of a male voice choir, cricket and football teams and the provision of gym facilities by the YMCA for the staff when they were not on duty. Not least it provided a record of life at the Reading War Hospital and highlighted the support that was given to the patients by the general public and the Care and Comforts Committee.

THE MARCH OF SCIENCE.

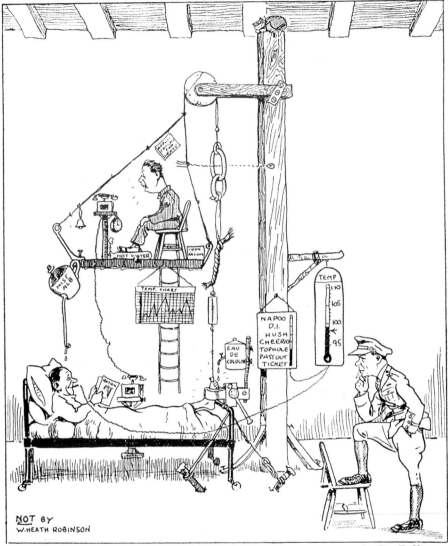

By Pte. E. Shaw.

Simple apparatus for securing extension in a case of fracture of the first phalanx of the big toe.

Cartoon from *The Ration*

Fewer issues were produced in 1918 and the one covering the months of May and June notified readers the price would rise to 3d a copy in future. There was only one further issue and this final copy came out six months later in January 1919, two months after the armistice had been signed and the war had officially ended. *The Ration* had entertained its readers for three years.

Medical Staff 1916

Front row L–R
Capt. G F Murrell, Capt. J L Joyce, Capt. G H R Holden, Major R Ritson, Major G S Abram, Lieut-Col W J Maurice, Lieut-Col E A Hanly, Lieut-Col W T Freeman, Major J A P Price, Major L M Guilding, Capt. W B Secretan, Capt. N B Clowes, Capt. H M Clarke.

Back row L–R
Lieut E Ward, Lieut G H Calverwell, Lieut A W Coventon, Lieut J F West, R H Cotton, Capt. Mackenzie, Lieut G A Bird, Lieut K E Xapier, (Liet G B Klein behind) W N Man, C B Tubbs, Capt. E W S Rowland, R Timberg, L Powell, R Donaldson, A Rhodes, R P Brooks, Lieut C W Beaumont.

The Work of the War Hospital

The War Hospital expanded rapidly as the various Section Hospitals were opened in 1915. A very large medical and nursing staff was needed to undertake the work of this greatly enlarged military Hospital. Shortly after the No. 1 War Hospital opened Captain J L Joyce, the Surgical Registrar at the Royal Berkshire Hospital, took over from Captain H M Clarke as Registrar. He remained in this position at the Hospital for the duration of the war, rising to the rank of Major in August 1917.

Each Section Hospital had its own medical and nursing staff with a Medical Officer in charge. Captain E W S Rowland was in charge of No. 2 War Hospital, Major Abram in charge of No. 3 War Hospital, Lieut-Col. Freeman in charge of No. 4 War Hospital, Lieut E F Clowes in charge of No. 5 War Hospital and Major L M Guilding in charge of the military wards at No. 6 War Hospital at the Royal Berkshire Hospital.

The nursing staff consisted of a core of well-trained and experienced nurses from Queen Alexandra's Imperial Military Nursing Service (QAIMNS) and Territorial Army nurses. These were assisted by

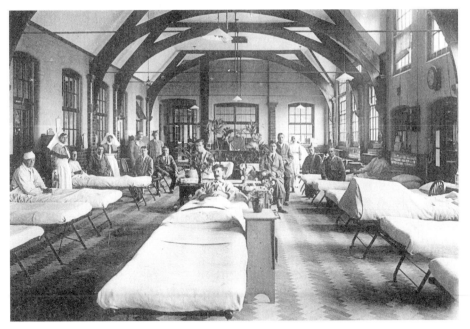

Top: Wilson, No. 3 War Hospital; *Bottom*: Ward

trained nurses from civilian life and Red Cross nurses who had only limited training and experience. Each Section Hospital had its own Matron and each ward had a Sister, an army wardmaster and as many nurses and orderlies as necessary. The majority of nurses had never seen a wounded or dying man before nor had they nursed the types of surgical and medical cases now filling the War Hospital. They soon showed they could rise to any challenge and their cheerfulness and good humour did much to ease the pain and suffering of their patients.

The number of wounded constantly arriving from France increased considerably following campaigns such as the Battle of the Somme in July 1916. More accommodation was needed and the West End Free Library in Oxford Road, not far from the No.1 War Hospital, was taken over to provide a further 350 beds for patients who were not too severely wounded. At the same time C Block at the No.1 Hospital, which had accommodated 150 wounded, was adapted to accommodate 110 officers.

The large number of wounded resulting from the onslaughts of Ypres and Paschendaele in 1917 meant even more beds were required. The Section Hospitals added as many beds as possible and the Royal Berkshire Hospital, now with 156 military beds, was receiving more military than civilian cases. More auxiliary hospitals were opened as the War Hospital expanded and these relieved the pressure on the main hospitals. Additional medical and nursing staff were required and the Red Cross asked for more nurses to volunteer for service in the military and auxiliary hospitals. By 1918 the War Hospital and its affiliated auxiliary hospitals were able to provide some 2,500 beds.

There were many changes in the staff as doctors and nurses were sent abroad. By the end of the war more than 300 other ranks, trained by the Reading War Hospital RAMC, had left for service overseas. At the No. 1 War Hospital the Matron, Miss Willetts RRC, QAIMNS, left for service overseas in May 1916. Her work had increased significantly as the Section Hospitals were opened. An Editorial in *The Ration* noted: 'The admirable way in which Miss Willetts dealt with the ever-increasing demands made upon her organising powers and administrative qualifications is beyond the praise of mere words.'

Miss L E C Steen RRC, QAIMNS, was appointed the new Matron. She had served through the South African War and had spent many years at various military hospitals abroad. At the outbreak of war in 1914 she was appointed Matron of the second hospital to be sent to France. Like her predecessor, she had been awarded the Royal Red Cross Class 1, the highest honour to be won in the nursing service. Miss Steen remained Matron of the War Hospital for the rest of the war.

Lieut-Col Hanly, who had done so much in establishing the War Hospital, became ill the following month. The death of his son, Lieut

Miss Steen

Medical Staff 1917

John Hanly, killed in action at the Battle of Jutland in May, had been a bitter blow. In December, when his health had not improved, he relinquished his Commission. Lieut-Col W J Maurice, who was in charge of the surgical division at the Hospital and also an Honorary Surgeon at the Royal Berkshire Hospital, was appointed Commanding Officer in his place. He retained this position for the duration of the war.

It is difficult to comprehend the magnitude of the work undertaken by the staff of the Reading War Hospital throughout the war. The reception of large convoys of up to 150 wounded at one time was a daunting task. A large proportion of the wounded were surgical cases suffering from gunshot and shrapnel wounds. There were also many medical cases and others who were victims of the horrors of trench warfare. All had received hasty treatment at the field hospitals and then had to endure train journeys of possibly up to five or six days before arriving at the War Hospital.

Once at the War Hospital the patients were assigned to the appropriate wards and treatment began. Each hospital was equipped with an X-ray department and every theatre was provided with anaesthetic equipment consisting of Clover's ether inhaler, nitrous oxide apparatus and Junker's chloroform inhaler. The surgeons, all experienced in civilian work, had to undertake operations they had seldom, if ever, encountered before.

Members of the Reading Pathological Society, who met monthly at the Royal Berkshire Hospital, were particularly interested in the work of the War Hospital and many were now serving there on the RAMC staff. In November 1915 the monthly meeting of the Society was held at the War Hospital and the members were shown the X-ray Department and the Pathological Laboratory. They were then shown several interesting cases undergoing treatment. These included patients with gunshot wounds to the lower jaw, the oesophagus and spine and others with injuries to the nerves. Various types of splints were demonstrated and X-ray photographs shown. Dr Donaldson, the Pathologist, produced bacteriological specimens which showed the differences in the various members of the colon-typhoid dysentery group.

Mr Secretan, an Assistant Surgeon at the Royal Berkshire Hospital and now working at the No. 1 War Hospital as Captain Secretan, noted in his autobiography *A Mixed Bag*: 'We did excellent work at the War Hospital, mostly dealing with bad compound fractures and other orthopaedic cases and nerve injuries.' The cases were more serious than those he later treated in France as the patients were usually 'rushed back to the base hospitals in England where more continuous and elaborate treatment was possible'. He also remarked on the time that was wasted on clerical work which would have been better spent on treating the patients.

The operations performed by Captain Joyce, later to be Major Joyce, were of particular interest and demonstrated the great advances that were being made in surgery, especially in nerve and plastic surgery. In April 1917 he showed members of the Pathological Society a patient who had a bullet removed from his brain one and three-quarters of an inch below the surface. The bone had been replaced by a bone graft from the shin. The patient had recovered completely and was left neither deaf nor paralysed.

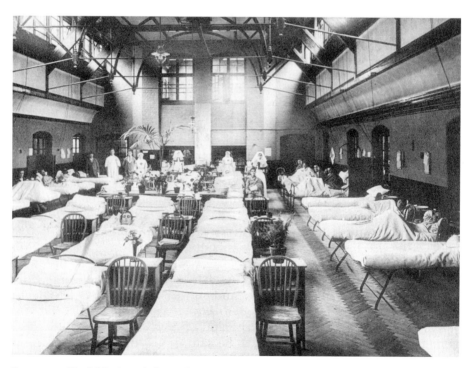

Katesgrove, No. 5 War Hospital. Ward A

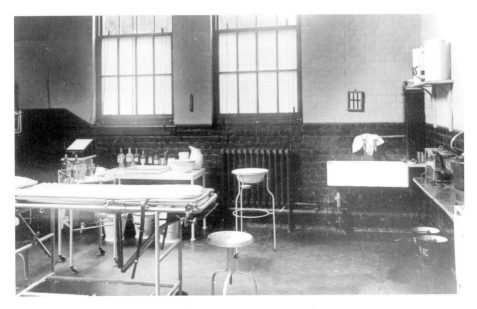

Top: Katesgrove, No. 5 War Hospital. Theatre; *Bottom*: Recreation room

The following month Captain Joyce showed patients with injuries to the peripheral nerves, some before and some after operative treatment. He then read a paper on '*Operative Treatment of Injuries to the Peripheral Nerves*' which he hoped to 'amplify and extend' and would probably publish after the war. In December the same year, now with the rank of Major, he showed a patient and described the operation he had performed to substitute a thumb by grafting two terminal phalanges of the ring finger

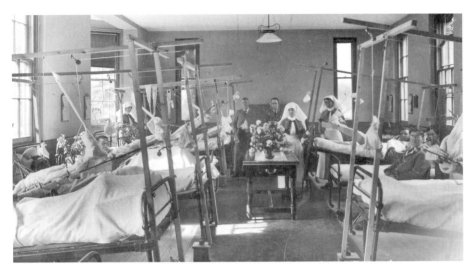

No. 1 War Hospital. Ward in F Block

of the left hand on to the metacarpal bone of the thumb of the right hand. The result was most impressive and he was congratulated.

Among the great variety of medical cases many were patients suffering from frostbite and others from trench foot. Cases of gas poisoning were also admitted. Patients with scarlet fever or diphtheria were sent to Park Hospital but cases of enteric fever, erysipelas and cerebral-spinal meningitis were treated in isolation at the War Hospital. There were also many cases of typhoid and paratyphoid fever and perforated typhoid and paratyphoid ulcers, all of which were of particular interest to Dr Donaldson, the Pathologist.

Dr Robert Donaldson had been appointed the Royal Berkshire Hospital's first Pathologist in 1912. In 1915 he was also appointed the Pathologist at the War Hospital with a laboratory at No. 1 War Hospital as well as his own laboratory at the Royal Berkshire Hospital. The War Hospital Laboratory was situated away from the main buildings behind D Block. It was divided into two parts known as 'the trench' and 'the dug-out'. The trench, the main laboratory, was long and narrow with shelves for bottles and others for incubators, sterilisers and a centrifuge. The dug-out was used for writing up the laboratory work.

The patients provided Dr Donaldson and his staff with a great variety of material for his pathological and bacteriological investigations which included work on cerebro-spinal meningitis and tubercular meningitis. He also produced papers on the colon-typhoid dysentery groups and on anaphylaxis. Some of his most important work was concerned with infections in wounds. At that time there were no antibiotics and infected wounds were usually treated with strong solutions of salt. Some cases did not respond to this treatment and Major Joyce noted certain particular

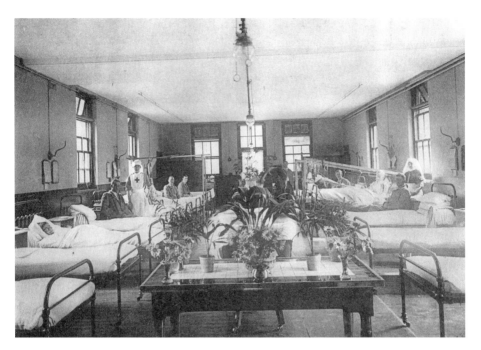

No. 1 War Hospital. Ward in B Block

differences in these and consulted Dr Donaldson.

Dr Donaldson's investigations on wound infections were described as being a model of skill with 'step following logical step to a convincing conclusion'. He obtained pure cultures from which he found a bacillus which he named the 'Reading' bacillus. When introduced to non-healing wounds this bacillus resulted in rapid cleansing. He and Major Joyce also found that the use of sphagnum moss on wounds was more effective and less painful than using saline solutions. Dr Donaldson and Major Joyce published their findings in the *Lancet* in 1917 and the following year Dr Donaldson published a paper on '*The Character and Properties of the Reading bacillus on which a new method of treating wounds has been based*'.

It became increasingly difficult to obtain assistants for the pathological laboratories at both the Royal Berkshire Hospital and the War Hospital. In December 1917 a new assistant was sent to help Dr Donaldson at the War Hospital. His name was Juda Hirsch Quastel, aged 18, a newly conscripted private at the Reading Barracks. He had stepped forward when his Sergeant asked if anyone knew how to use a microscope. He had temporarily worked at the laboratory of the Sheffield Public Analyst and was about to take up his scholarship at Imperial College, London when he was called up.

Juda Quastel described his work at the War Hospital Pathological Laboratory in his '*Short Autobiography*'. He had never seen dead and

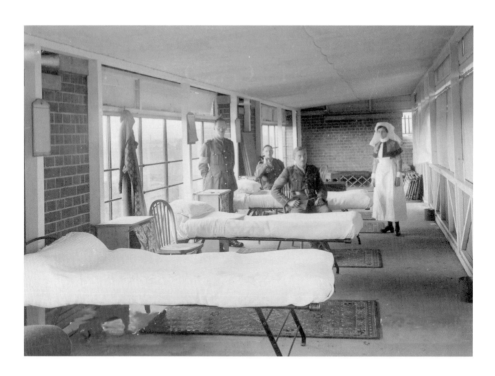

Top: No. 1 War Hospital. C Block Shelter; *Bottom*: Roof of C Block

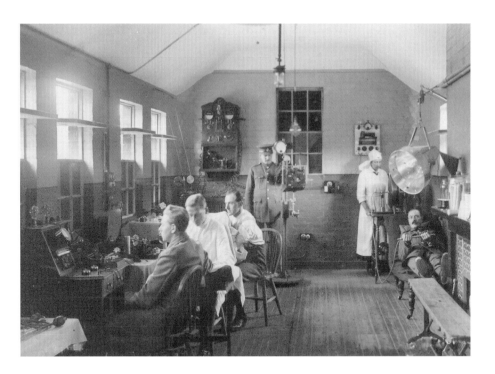

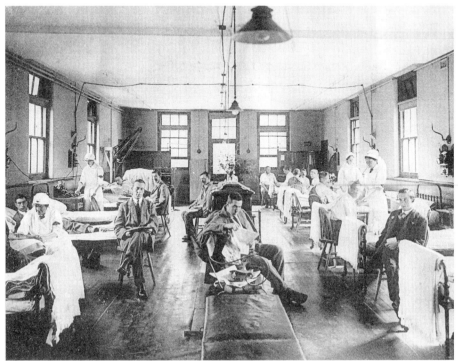

Top: No. 1 War Hospital. Electrical Department; *Bottom*: Massage Department

wounded soldiers before but Dr Donaldson was a good teacher and his assistant soon learnt 'to sterilise bacteriological media, to recognise and culture all manner of organisms, to make vaccines and to carry out Wassermann's reactions'. He helped with the many post-mortem examinations that were carried out and was shown how to run a bacteriological and pathological laboratory. Dr Donaldson impressed upon him how easy it was 'to make false diagnoses on too little data'. Juda Quastel remained at the War Hospital throughout 1918 during which time he and Dr Donaldson became firm friends.[1]

In addition to X-ray and Pathological Departments, Massage and Electrotherapy Departments were established at both the Royal Berkshire Hospital and at the No. 1 War Hospital. It was essential to provide treatment for the wounded to regain the use of their limbs. Nerve-testing, ionic, galvanic and faradic treatment and electrolysis were all provided as well as apparatus for mechano-therapeutics. Lieut-Col Freeman was put in charge of the new Department at the Royal Berkshire Hospital in March 1916 and later members of the Reading Pathological Society paid a special visit to the Department at the No. 1 War Hospital.

Inevitably there were numerous patients whose injuries resulted in amputations. These patients were given and taught how to use artificial limbs made by the workers at the Hospital Supplies Depot. When the King and Queen paid a second visit to the War Hospital on May 12th 1918 they examined a collection of surgical appliances which had been provided by the Depot. The work of the Hospital extended to providing psychotherapy and remarkable results were obtained for patients who had suffered shell shock. One case was noted of a patient who had become deaf and dumb. He was cured and able to hear a whisper at a distance of ten feet and could speak again quite normally. Curative Workshops were established to teach the wounded new trades and how to work with their disabilities.

The End of the War
The Armistice signed on November 11th 1918 brought an end to the war but not to the work of the War Hospital and its affiliated auxiliary hospitals. There were still many wounded to be treated and shattered lives to be repaired. The fervour of rejoicing that the war was over could not mask the dreadful epidemic of influenza that was sweeping the country.

Juda Quastel described the effect of the epidemic at the War Hospital. So many patients died suddenly that the bodies had to be put in a large marquee in the Hospital grounds as there was no room elsewhere. Dr Donaldson carried out numerous post-mortems and investigations and, in spite of taking few precautions, neither he nor Juda Quastel developed the illness. Dr Donaldson isolated an organism from specimens of sputa, blood, spinal fluid and enlarged glands. This he named 'D' and he then prepared a vaccine from it. He had first noticed this organism in the sputa of soldiers who had been gassed in France and were being treated at No. 4 War

ELECTRIC LIGHT BATHS.
Remarks on the Therapeutic application of heat generally. Other methods of producing Hyperæmia : Bier's Congestion, Klapp's Suction Cups.

DIFFERENT FORMS OF BATTERIES.
Use of Galvanic Current for Ionisation.
Muscle Testing and Treatment by the Galvanic and Faradic Current.
Lewis Jones' Condenser Apparatus.

SPLINTS.
A few specimens used for various forms of Paralysis.

SOME ADDITIONAL ELECTRICAL APPLIANCES.
Schnee Baths.
Diathermy.
High Frequency.
Violet Rays.

MECHANO–THERAPEUTICS.
Massage.
Passive Movements.
Active Movements.
Mechanical Appliances for Exercises.
Gymnastic Apparatus.
Class Exercises.

Printed by Patients in the Curative Workshops, Reading.

Equipment in Electrical and Massage Departments

Hospital at Redlands School. His findings were published in the *Lancet* and the *British Medical Journal*.

Fewer casualties were now arriving at the War Hospital and less accommodation was needed. Some of the auxiliary hospitals like Englefield House had already closed and others were gradually closed throughout 1919. In Reading Devonshire Lodge closed in December 1918. St Luke's Hall closed at the end of January 1919. Sutherlands closed in February only to reopen at the request of the Ministry of Pensions for the treatment of wounded pensioners. Inniscarra closed in March and Struan House in

Patients with artificial limbs (*The Ration*)

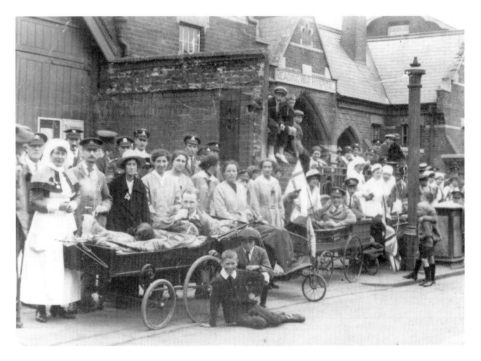

Waiting for the arrival of the King and Queen, May 12th 1918

Talking to a patient

No. 1 War Hospital Staff 1918

July. This was the last auxiliary hospital in the county to close. It had treated 1,980 patients. Each auxiliary hospital was sent a certificate of appreciation signed by the Secretary of State for War, Winston Churchill. The work of these hospitals had been invaluable.

The Section Hospitals were slower to close. No. 4 War Hospital at Redlands School was the first to close at the end of December 1918, only days after its Officer in Charge, Lieut-Col Freeman had died. It was believed his death had been accelerated by overwork and the strain of the past four years. The military wards at the Royal Berkshire Hospital, No. 6 War Hospital, were given up in March 1919. Nos. 2, 3 and 5 War Hospitals at Battle, Wilson, Katesgrove and Central Schools were closed between April and June 1919.

The No. 1 War Hospital was the only one to remain open. There were still patients to be treated and the Care and Comforts Committee continued its good work. There were no more convoys and the Transport Service had been disbanded. At Christmas 1919 only 58 patients were unable to go on leave during the holiday and over the next few months the numbers gradually decreased. In mid-April 1920 the last patient was moved elsewhere and, almost five years to the day since it opened in April 1915, the War Hospital closed. The *Reading Standard* wrote: 'No. 1 bore the distinction of being one of the best equipped war hospitals in the country.' At one time the Government had discussed retaining it as a military hospital but this had proved to be impractical. As soon as the War Office had removed its equipment the buildings would be returned to the Poor Law Guardians.

Outstanding work had been carried out at the Hospital throughout the war by the medical and nursing staff. The Care and Comforts Committee had carried on its excellent work until the end. The work of all

the voluntary services had been remarkable and all were thanked as they disbanded. The public had supported the Hospital in every way but now their thoughts were elsewhere and there was work of a different kind to be done. The War Hospital had opened with great publicity. Its closure was hardly noticed.

NOTES

1 This was the beginning of what was to become an eminent career in science and years later Juda Quastel was appointed Professor of Biochemistry at McGill University and Professor of Neurochemistry at the University of British Columbia. He died in 1987 aged 88. After the war Mr J L Joyce resumed his work as a surgeon at the Royal Berkshire Hospital in Reading. Douglas Bader was among the many patients to benefit from his skill. Mr Joyce died suddenly of a coronary thrombosis in 1939 aged 57. Dr Donaldson moved to St George's Hospital in London after the war and in 1928 he became Professor of Pathology at Guy's Hospital. He died of influenza in 1933.

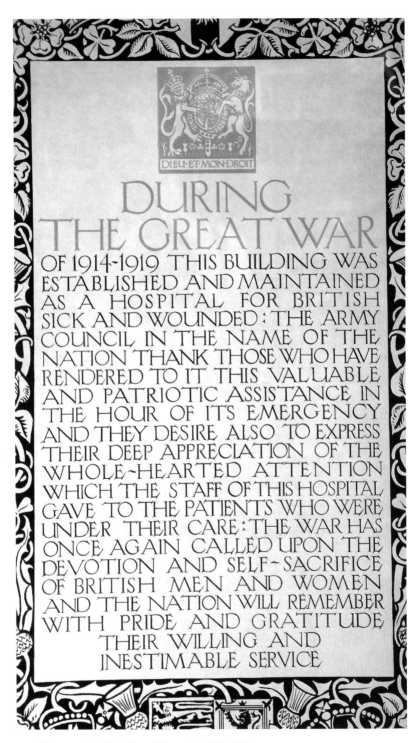

DIEU·ET·MON·DROIT

DURING THE GREAT WAR

OF 1914-1919 THIS BUILDING WAS
ESTABLISHED AND MAINTAINED
AS A HOSPITAL FOR BRITISH
SICK AND WOUNDED: THE ARMY
COUNCIL IN THE NAME OF THE
NATION THANK THOSE WHO HAVE
RENDERED TO IT THIS VALUABLE
AND PATRIOTIC ASSISTANCE IN
THE HOUR OF ITS EMERGENCY
AND THEY DESIRE ALSO TO EXPRESS
THEIR DEEP APPRECIATION OF THE
WHOLE-HEARTED ATTENTION
WHICH THE STAFF OF THIS HOSPITAL
GAVE TO THE PATIENTS WHO WERE
UNDER THEIR CARE: THE WAR HAS
ONCE AGAIN CALLED UPON THE
DEVOTION AND SELF-SACRIFICE
OF BRITISH MEN AND WOMEN
AND THE NATION WILL REMEMBER
WITH PRIDE AND GRATITUDE
THEIR WILLING AND
INESTIMABLE SERVICE

Certificate received by all Auxiliary Hospitals 1918

7

BATTLE INFIRMARY
1919–1930

The war years had been a particularly difficult time for the Reading Union Guardians. Their Workhouse premises in Oxford Road had been taken over by the military authorities for use as a war hospital. The inmates had been dispersed, many to neighbouring unions, others to Prospect Park Mansion and the sick to Grovelands School which had been adapted for use as an infirmary. The Workhouse nurses and officers had been accommodated in various properties across the town. All six staff at the Clerk's office had joined the army and, for the first time, women clerks had been employed in their place. Among the Workhouse staff 12 out of 15 had joined the army and a further three had been loaned to the military authorities at the War Hospital. It was not surprising that the Master, Mr Fryer, had had a breakdown.

Prices had risen alarmingly during the war. Fortunately the Guardians had retained the Workhouse farm. The produce, as well as helping the budget, became increasingly important in supplementing the inmates' diets when certain foods were rationed. The weekly cost of the maintenance of inmates had almost doubled from 9s 1d in 1914 to 17s 11½d in 1917.

By 1917 the Government had formed a Ministry of Reconstruction to consider reorganisation after the war was over. The Local Government Reconstruction Committee was one of many established under its authority and in 1917 this Committee published its proposals for the post-war years. Its suggestion that the functions of the Poor Law authorities should be transferred to borough and county councils caused great alarm. Boards of guardians throughout the country agreed to 'strenuously resist' such a move. It would mean their extinction and the local authorities, who would take over their duties, were already overburdened. Such a proposal had been included in the Report of the Royal Commission published in 1909 but, until now, had not been mentioned again.

Over the years boards of guardians and local authorities had taken on additional responsibilities. The former were now undertaking a wide variety of work associated with the welfare of those in the area of the union but not necessarily in receipt of poor relief. County and borough councils had been made responsible for certain aspects of public health such as child welfare and health visiting. Park Hospital, the smallpox hospital at Whitley and the Tuberculosis Dispensary were administered by the Reading Borough Council. Moulsford Asylum was the responsibility of the Berkshire County Council. Berkshire and Buckinghamshire County Councils were now jointly administering the Peppard Sanatorium which they had bought from Dr Carling in 1914.

By 1917 even more organisations had become involved with health care. Insurance committees, pension funds and welfare organisations were all concerned with the treatment and rehabilitation of the sick and wounded. Many people believed that a Minister of Health should be appointed to sort out the various duties now performed by different bodies. The Insurance Committees in particular were agitating for change. It was widely believed that a State medical service would be established after the war.

Berkshire County Council had mixed feelings on the subject. It agreed in principle to the public health services being unified under a Minister of Health but feared that control of the administration might be transferred to 'non-representative bodies incapable of dealing with the matter'.

The Voluntary Hospitals were alarmed at the prospect of a State medical service. In March 1917 a meeting was held at the Royal Berkshire Hospital where 32 members of the local medical profession agreed to form a committee 'to consider the best means of safeguarding the interests of the profession as far as they may be affected by future legislation'.

Early in 1919 the Government set to work on drafting the Ministry of Health Bill. It was widely assumed that the proposals of the Local Government Reconstruction Committee would be adopted and that boards of guardians would be abolished. It was a time of great uncertainty and in March the Berkshire County Council appointed a special committee to examine the proposals for the reform of the Poor Law as far as they might affect the Council. In July the Borough Council formed a Medical Services Committee under the chairmanship of Dr G S Abram, to reorganise and co-ordinate the various medical services in the town. Dr Abram, an active member of the Council, was also an Honorary Physician at the Royal Berkshire Hospital and, as Major Abram, had been in charge of No.3 War Hospital at Wilson School during the war.

In the event the Ministry of Health Act passed by Parliament fell short of the radical proposals so feared by boards of guardians. The new Ministry would combine the duties of the Local Government Board and the Health Insurance Commission under a Minister of Health. In future the Reading Board of Guardians would come under the authority of this new Ministry and, from their point of view, little would be changed by the Act. This, however, was but the first stage. In October 1919 the new Minister of Health set up a Consultative Council on Medical and Allied Services under the chairmanship of Lord Dawson, to consider and make recommendations for the provision of a comprehensive medical service for the country. Once again the future of boards of guardians was uncertain.

Throughout 1919 the work of the Reading Guardians continued much as usual. Gradually all the auxiliary hospitals and section hospitals were closed but the No.1 War Hospital was still treating the sick and wounded. There was no sign of the premises being returned to the Guardians. In August they requested the new Minister of Health to do everything possible to get the Army Council to vacate the Workhouse, but to no avail.

In April 1919 elections for Guardians were held for the first time since 1915. Mr E O Farrer, Chairman of the Board for the past six years, retired and Mr T Norris was elected in his place with Mr F E Moring elected the Vice-Chairman. The work of the Board continued as before with monthly meetings at which the reports of the various committees were considered.

The Emergency Committee, formed in August 1914, was still in operation and the others included three Relief Committees (one for each District), the Assessment Committee, the Dispensary Committee, the Finance and General Purposes Committee, the Building and Farm Committee, the Stores and Furnishing Committee, the Infant Poor Committee, the Asylums Visiting Committee and the House Committee, which consisted of the whole Board.

In addition the Guardians were represented on the boards of other bodies. These included the Poor Law Unions Association, the Court of the Royal Berkshire Hospital, the Executive Committee of the Reading Church Army Labour Home, the Reading Blind Aid Society, the Committee of the Queen Victoria Institute for Nursing the Sick Poor, the Caversham and District Nursing Association, the Berkshire Joint Vagrancy Committee, the Reading Council of Social Welfare, the Reading Tuberculosis Dispensary Committee and the Reading Distress Committee.

The Union officers and staff who had joined the armed forces were gradually demobilised. Dr Guilding, who as Major Guilding had been in charge of the military wards at the Royal Berkshire Hospital (No. 6 War Hospital) during the war, was demobilised in the middle of 1919 and resumed his duties as Medical Officer for the still dispersed inmates of the Workhouse. As he had reached retirement age he gave up his position as an Honorary Surgeon at the Royal Berkshire Hospital and was made a Consulting Surgeon. By October all the Union staff had returned to their pre-war duties with the exception of one, who had been killed in action.

In July the Finance Committee reported on the hours of work, salaries and duties of the Union staff. The administrative staff worked $36\frac{1}{2}$ hours per week, the indoor staff 77 hours and the Scattered Homes staff 99 hours per week. A 44-hour week was introduced with the working day not to exceed eight hours with one day's rest in seven and half a day off each week. This meant the infirmary staff would need to be increased by four probationers. There would then be the Superintendent Nurse (Miss Slack), two Charge Nurses and 15 Staff Nurses and probationers. All salaries would be increased. Miss Slack would receive £100 per year instead of £85 and Charge Nurses £60 instead of £50. It was suggested the probationers, now earning from £15 rising to £25 per year, should be paid £20 to £30 per year. It had been extremely difficult to obtain probationers and advertisements for applicants over 21 years of age, who were 'well-educated, strong and healthy', drew little response. It was hoped the proposed increase would produce a better result.

Changes had recently been made in the organisation of nurses nationally. In 1916 the College of Nursing had been established to 'secure uniformity of training and curriculum for nurses engaged in various branches of civil, military and naval practice'. This had been followed in 1919 by the formation of the General Nursing Council and the Nurses Registration Act. A more uniform and professional nursing service would evolve with higher standards and wider experience.

The Return of the Workhouse Premises

By 1920 there was still no sign of the military authorities moving out of the Workhouse premises and it was not until the end of March that the Guardians were informed that arrangements were now under way to vacate the buildings. The last patients were removed at the end of April and the premises vacated except for various military personnel. Dilapidations now had to be assessed and the Guardians appointed their architect, Mr W Roland Howell and the Union Clerk, Mr Oliver, to act on their behalf with the War Department Valuer.

The disposal of the surplus army stores at the No.1 War Hospital now had to be arranged. The Quartermaster, Major Exton, asked the Guardians if they wished to purchase any items for sale. Dr Guilding and the Dispenser selected drugs, dressings and surgical appliances priced at £803. The Guardians were not prepared to pay this amount and eventually a sale was agreed for £450. Furniture was also available and that in the Nurses' Home was purchased for £633 9s 10d. When the remaining furniture of interest to the Guardians was offered at £1,568 18s 9d they asked for a reduction. If this was not agreed they would buy 250 blankets at 9s each. Various fittings were bought for £451 as well as other items such as painters' materials, soap, soda, 1,500 yards of canvas and 75 'excellent' suits. Eventually, when the all the purchases were handed over, the Master had to ask for assistance as there were thousands of articles to examine, check and enter into the various inventories and account books.

The British Red Cross Society was also disposing of surplus equipment and opened a depot at 1, Bath Road to handle the many items. Rear Admiral Fleet notified the Guardians that the Society was offering to transfer the Windsor Red Cross ambulance to them for an experimental period of six months, provided it was not used for commercial purposes and would be available for the Society to use in an emergency or if the Red Cross ambulance broke down. If, after six months, the ambulance had not proved satisfactory, it could be returned. If retained there would be no conditions imposed upon its use. The offer was accepted gratefully as the horse ambulance was far from ideal. The motor ambulance would be received when the Workhouse was eventually reopened.

In May 1920 the Consultative Council on Medical and Allied Services, under the chairmanship of Lord Dawson, published an Interim Report. It was far-sighted and far-ranging and envisaged a comprehensive national health service available to all. It included preventative medicine and general practitioner services as well as primary and secondary health centres to be administered by a health authority in each area. Secondary health centres would be provided by hospitals in the larger towns to which general practitioners could refer their patients for specialist treatment. The method of funding was not fully considered, but a national insurance scheme was envisaged as a possibility with charges for hospital treatment except for those unable to pay.

Practically every aspect of the future National Health Service was included in the Report but the economic conditions after the war prevented its implementation at that time. Instead a slow step-by-step progression took place before the proposals of 1920 were eventually embodied in the National Health Service created in 1948. The work of the Poor Law guardians continued as before with those of the Reading Union now fully occupied in organising the return of their buildings. It would be several years before the first radical change was made and local authorities took over guardians' responsibilities.

In August the Board of Guardians received a certificate from the Secretary of State for War, Winston Churchill, thanking them on behalf of the Army Council for having made the Workhouse available for use as a war hospital during the Great War. The certificate was framed and placed in the Committee Room. Unfortunately this certificate has not survived but it was probably very similar to those sent to the auxiliary hospitals at the end of the war.

The buildings were handed back to the Guardians one by one as the military left but it was to be many months before the Workhouse was completely vacated. By this time the dilapidations had been assessed at £4,496 12s 8d, excluding outside painting, and it was now time to start the renovations and redecorate. It was hoped the Master's quarters and Nurses' Home could be handed over as soon as possible to enable the work to begin.

In the meantime, in anticipation of the return to the Workhouse premises, a massive reorganisation of the Workhouse staff was carried out through the initiative of Dr Guilding. In September 1920 he had reported to the Board that conditions had entirely changed since the war and it was now imperative that a full-time Medical Officer was appointed. The present part-time system was open to serious criticism, not only from the point of view of the patients but also regarding the training of the nurses and midwives. The nursing staff attended lectures at the Royal Berkshire Hospital but they were not able to receive the amount of detailed instruction that would be possible with a resident medical officer. The Central Midwives Board had said they would not take nurses from the Workhouse for short periods of training owing to the fact that they were not trained under a resident house surgeon. The appointment of a larger nursing staff following the adoption of a 44-hour week would mean more time was needed for their instruction. At present the nurses did not receive sufficient training.

Dr Guilding also advised that in future the imbecile block should be under the authority of the Medical Officer. It would, however, be far better if all the mental cases were removed and transferred to suitable licensed premises elsewhere, leaving accommodation for temporary cases only in the Workhouse. By now most epileptics were being cared for by the National Society of Epileptics and were no longer classified with the mental defectives and feeble-minded.

When asked if he would be prepared to be the full-time medical officer, Dr Guilding said he would consider the suggestion. It was then proposed that whoever was appointed should be in charge of the whole institution, thereby combining the duties of Medical Superintendent with those of Master. A Matron could be appointed who was also a fully-trained nurse and the Workhouse would thereby become a hospital. As the present Master and Matron now wished to retire, this would be an appropriate time to introduce a new system.

Dr Guilding had also been asked to advise on the nursing staff 'in consequence of the 44-hour week'. At first he had recommended there should be 46 nurses but, as this would be too expensive, he then recommended 32 nurses who would work a $44\frac{1}{2}$-hour week when on day duty and 50 hours per week when on night duty. Each nurse would have six months' day duty followed by three months' night duty. The day duty staff would then consist of one sister and eight nurses on the male side and a similar number on the female side, all working an eight-hour day making, with time off, a $44\frac{1}{2}$-hour week. There would be 11 night staff who would have three nights off per fortnight, making a working week of about 50 hours. The nursing staff would consist of three emergency nurses, 18 day nurses and 11 night nurses, making a total of 32 nurses. Dr Guilding's suggestions were approved and would be implemented when the Workhouse infirmary was returned to the Guardians.

Dr Guilding accepted the position of full-time resident Medical Superintendent and Master with a salary of £500 per year as Medical Superintendent and £200 per year as Master. He would now become the chief administrative officer of the institution in addition to his former medical duties. He would attend the children at the Scattered Homes and also the Workhouse staff. The unfurnished Master's quarters would be enlarged and he would be provided with the usual allowances of rations, coal, light and washing, valued at £200 per year. His wife and daughter would live with him but any rations drawn on their behalf must be paid for. Miss Emily Slack, the Superintendent Nurse, was now promoted to be

Matron with a salary of £300 per year with an apartment, the usual allowances and uniform valued at £100 per year.

The appointment of a non-resident visiting Medical Officer was agreed. He would act under the direction of the Medical Superintendent and assist him with the medical and administrative duties. He would attend the Workhouse daily and act for the Medical Superintendent in his absence. The appointment would be advertised in due course but did not need to be filled until the inmates had been returned to the Workhouse.

One other position was advertised to be filled as soon as practicable. Mr T J Farmer of 109 Elm Park Road, Reading was appointed from a list of 227 applicants to be the Medical Superintendent's Clerk and Steward. He would be paid £300 a year for this non-resident job and his duties would be to assist the Medical Superintendent generally in all duties relating to the office of Master and to be responsible for keeping all the stores and accounts. He would take up his duties at the end of the year. The appointment in January 1921 of Mr S G Davis as the Medical Superintendent's Book-keeper with a salary of £120 per year completed the staff appointments at the Workhouse.

The Engineer, Mr G Dummer, the Stoker, Mr W H Longhurst and the Painter, Mr J Willis, all returned to the service of the Guardians having been working at the No. 1 War Hospital since 1915. Mr Dummer's salary was increased to £320 per year and his assistant, Mr G Smith, who had been working at Grovelands School during the war, returned with a salary of £200 per year. Mr Longhurst's salary would be £200 per year and a temporary stoker would be appointed to assist him. Mr Willis would be paid £220 per year and would work under the supervision of the Engineer.

By the end of 1920 all the Workhouse buildings had been returned to the Guardians and the task of renovation and redecoration was under way. After almost six years the work of the Workhouse was about to be resumed.

The Return of the Inmates
It was to take several months before all the inmates returned to the Workhouse. The patients at Grovelands School were the first to come back early in January 1921 followed by some sick inmates boarded out at Newbury Workhouse. Only 80 beds were available but work was under way to bring the rest of Blocks A and B into operation as soon as possible.

By this time the nursing staff had been reorganised. Nurse Edith Frankum had been promoted to be Deputy Matron with a salary of £150 a year with the usual allowances and uniform. Nurse Scarlett was now Home Sister with a salary of £150 per year, the usual allowances and uniform. Nurse Parsons was Assistant Matron with a salary of £125 per year, allowances and uniform. Three senior probationer nurses had been promoted to become Charge Nurses on obtaining their three years' training certificates, with salaries of £40 per year and the usual allowances and uniform. Eight probationers in order of seniority were promoted to become Staff Nurses. Advertisements were placed for 12 probationer nurses with salaries starting at £20 per year and rising to £25 and then £30 in the third year. Once all these positions had been filled there would be 10 Staff Nurses and 25 probationers.

It was now agreed that the Workhouse should be renamed Battle Infirmary and the change was sanctioned by the Ministry of Health. All the buildings would be included as all the inmates were either sick or incapacitated in some way and needed care. Attitudes had changed over the years. The term 'pauper' was no longer used and the title 'Battle Infirmary' was now more appropriate than 'Workhouse'.

The question of accommodation for mental patients was raised again. Conditions at Battle Infirmary were unsuitable for such cases. There were 24 mental cases boarded out, 13 females and 11 males. Of these 11 had no known relatives and the Guardians considered sending them to the Stourbridge Union which was certified as a suitable institution under the Board of Control. As only one woman and four men could be accepted there the rest would come back to Battle, the women to be accommodated as before in D Block and the men in H Block.

The Ministry of Health had approved the reorganisation of the nursing staff but asked the Guardians to reconsider the 44-hour week when appointing additional nurses. They did not approve of a working week of under 48 hours and the Guardians agreed to amend this to a 52-hour limit. At the same time the staffing levels were reconsidered in view of the imminent return of the remaining boarded-out inmates. Excluding the professional nursing staff who would be working mainly in A and B Blocks, various additional staff would be needed for the rest of the Infirmary. One senior male nurse for the mental and sick wards, one male nurse for relief and general duties and two assistant porters and portresses for the main entrance and the Casual (Vagrants) Wards entrance were required. One assistant cook and baker was also needed.

There were 70 applicants for the non-resident post of Senior Male Nurse and Mr Digweed was appointed with a salary of £208 per year. There were 74 applicants for the non-resident post of male Relief Nurse and Mr Butler was appointed with a salary of £172 5s. The Assistant Porters and Portresses would also act as bath attendants. They should be under 30 years of age and, if required, would live at Battle Cottages. There were 146 applicants for Assistant Porters and Mr Goodwin and Mr Eggleton were appointed with salaries of £172 5s each. Miss Brittain and Mrs Tigwell were appointed the two Assistant Portresses with salaries of £140 per year each.

There were only three applicants in answer to the advertisement for Assistant Cook and Baker and Mr Lloyd was appointed with a salary of £130 per year. The three meals he was allowed each day he was on duty were valued at 16s 6d per week.

The inmates boarded out at Basingstoke Workhouse returned to Battle Infirmary in February 1921. Those from Wallingford Workhouse returned at the end of that month, followed by those at Hungerford

Workhouse in March and the remainder from Newbury Workhouse by the end of May. It was noted that the bedding returned from Wallingford was in a very bad condition, whereas that from Newbury had been well looked after.

In June, when all the boarded-out inmates had returned to Battle Infirmary, the non-resident Assistant Medical Officer was appointed. There were three candidates and Mr L C W Cane MRCS, LRCP was appointed with a salary of £125 per year.

Block D, the female imbecile wards, was reopened on May 27th. The Casual (Vagrant) Wards were reopened on August 1st. The rules of the Berks. Bucks. and Oxon. Joint Vagrancy Committee stipulated that casuals should be detained for two days as far as accommodation would allow. The Medical Superintendent, however, authorised all those genuinely seeking work to be discharged on the morning after their admission. The sheds used for the task work of wood chopping and bundling were now made ready for use. Block E, The Cottage, for the isolation of 'obnoxious or infectious cases' was not opened until September.

The Chaplain and Non-Conformist Religious Instructor
The Revd A N Halpin, Chaplain for 30 years, resigned at the end of 1920. The Guardians asked the Rural Dean to nominate three candidates in his place. A salary of £120 per year would be offered. The Reading Free Church Council was also asked to nominate three canciciates for the position of Non-Conformist Religious Instructor with a salary of £60 per year. Both positions would be part-time and subject to the approval of the Ministry of Health.

In February 1921 the Revd Frank Burnett was appointed the new Church of England Chaplain with the approval of both the Bishop of the Diocese and the Ministry of Health. He was the incumbent of St Mary's Church, Castle Street, Reading and wished to supplement his income 'in these hard times'. He had been Chaplain for $4\frac{1}{2}$ years at St Mary's parish, Colchester and, as Chaplain at Essex County Hospital, Hamilton Road Military Hospital, Colchester General Hospital and Colchester Union Infirmary he had much experience in hospital work.

Mr Barlow was appointed the Non-Conformist Religious Instructor. He was 64 years old, in excellent health and offered satisfactory references regarding his 'moral character and social qualifications'. He had a long connection with religious and temperance work in the town. For $17\frac{1}{2}$ years he had undertaken similar work on a voluntary basis for the Free Church Council as Superintendent of the Sunday afternoon services at the Workhouse. He had been a lay preacher for several years and had taken services in the absence of the Minister. His whole time could be devoted to his duties at Battle Infirmary.

By the time all the inmates had returned to the Infirmary both Mr Burnett and Mr Barlow had taken up their appointments. They produced monthly reports for the Board of Guardians and Mr Barlow in particular was quick to note bad behaviour and insolence among the inmates.

The Laundry

When the inmates were moved from the Workhouse in 1915 the Guardians had installed a temporary laundry at Grovelands School. The Battle Infirmary laundry, which had been used by the military authorities during the war, would not be large enough for the work it would have to undertake when all the inmates had returned. It was estimated that between 14,000 and 16,000 articles would have to be handled each week. A new laundry was out of the question as the Ministry of Health would not sanction capital expenditure at that time. The old laundry would have to continue as before but could be improved by using machinery removed from Grovelands School.

A more powerful 20hp electric motor was obtained for £307 11s. This expenditure would be offset by the savings made through only needing to use one boiler at a time. In July 1921 the laundry was in full working order but before long it would have to be completely replaced. With this in mind the Guardians paid £750 for a small plot of land used for allotments, measuring 2r 32p (just under three quarters of an acre), adjoining the east side of the Infirmary premises. It would be the ideal site for a new laundry.

Life of the Inmates

In many ways life at Battle Infirmary was easier than before the war. All the inmates were now referred to as 'patients' and more consideration was given to their comfort. Although discipline was still very strict, small alterations made the day-to-day routine less dreary. Part of the grounds were set aside for recreational purposes. Concerts and entertainments were frequently given. As a treat the women were allowed to eat sweets during concerts but a request that the men should be allowed to smoke was not granted. Later the elderly inmates were taken on day trips to the seaside. By now all inmate labour had been replaced by trained staff, distinctive clothing was no longer worn and the elderly were allowed to leave the Infirmary daily to visit relatives.

Very few cases were noted in the Punishment Book and these were usually for bad behaviour or insolence. Culprits were punished by having their privileges withdrawn. Frederick Hicks was a typical example. When he was reported for 'insulting and reviling' the Deputy Matron and Porter, he had his tobacco ration stopped for 14 days and his bread ration for one day.

The dietary was reconsidered and the diet tables simplified into six classes: Class 1 for adult males other than the infirm, Class 2 for infirm adult males, Class 3 for adult females other than infirm, Class 4 for infirm adult females, Class 5 for children under eight years, Class 6 for children over eight years.

The Medical Superintendent believed the diets were ample but monotonous and that 'considerable improvements could be made'. For a trial period all meat and vegetables authorised for each meal would be provided in bulk and, as soon as the patients had assembled, would be cut into slices and served on hot plates. The officers would then serve the meat and vegetables according to each individual's appetite and not by weight as before. Second helpings would be given.

The meals were to be made more appetising and no longer eaten in silence, as ordered before. The appearance of the dining hall should be improved so patients could sit facing each other rather than in lines. Table cloths should be provided, gravy supplied to each table and also cruets, baskets of bread and rolls. Meal times were to be made more pleasurable and relaxed. There is no record of whether the trial period was extended but in all probability the old system of grim, regimented meal times had ended for ever.

The Ambulance
The motor ambulance loaned to the Guardians had its limitations and in 1921 it was returned to the British Red Cross Society. A more suitable vehicle which would combine commercial and ambulance work would be more practical. The new ambulance should be able to take one stretcher case or not less than six passengers. It should be suitable for taking patients to the mental hospital and also able to be used as a commercial van. A quotation from Messrs Skerray's of Reading for the new Ford Commercial Utility Van with an ambulance body priced £355 16s 1d was accepted.

The gardener acted as ambulance driver until 1923 when Mr Eggleton, the Assistant Porter was appointed to combine his duties with those of Ambulance Driver. The Guardians were confident that he would be suitable as he had been 'tested by a firm of experts who had certified the he was able to carry out the duties of ambulance driver satisfactorily'.

In 1927, when it was five years old, the Ford Utility Van was pronounced unsafe and a second ambulance was obtained. The Great Western Motors provided a 1927 Bean Commercial chassis with a new body to be built to specification. It would have a four-speed gear box, electric lighting and starting, a 14hp engine and Dunlop tyres. The cost would be £400, it would be painted powder blue with 'Ambulance' in gold lettering surmounted by the Guardians' crest. The ambulance hut was adapted to hold both the old and new ambulances and the old horse ambulance was sold. Two years later the old Ford van was sold. It had now been pronounced dangerous and was replaced with a Morris shooting brake priced £310 from Messrs John Harrison of Reading.

The Nursing Department
By the end of 1920 the reorganisation of the nursing staff had been completed and the numbers were gradually made up to the agreed level. A and B Blocks were in full use a few months later and Dr Guilding was

able to report that the nursing staff had made splendid progress and their conduct was excellent. Since 1899 probationers had attended lectures at the Royal Berkshire Hospital but once Dr Guilding had been appointed the full-time resident Medical Superintendent all training was carried out at Battle Infirmary.

In 1921 Reading Borough Council purchased a house called Dellwood in Liebenrood Road and adapted it for use as a maternity home for cases which could not be delivered safely at home. The following year it was agreed that pupil midwives from Dellwood should attend a course of training at Battle Infirmary for the Central Midwives Board certificate. In return Battle nurses would go to Dellwood for 'practical instruction'.

Training was becoming more uniform and when the General Nursing Council drew up a draft examination syllabus Dr Guilding agreed 'it appeared to meet all requirements'. The age of probationer applicants was now reduced from 21 years to 19 years. It was hoped this would meet the demand for probationers, but there were still problems. Almost one third of the probationers did not complete the preliminary two months' trial and left either because they were unsuitable or were not strong enough. More attention was now being given to obtaining applicants whose standard of education was high enough to pass the nursing examinations. In 1923 Dr Guilding and Miss Frankum (Deputy Matron) were asked by the General Nursing Council to serve occasionally on the Board of Examiners.

In 1923 Battle Infirmary was approved as a Training School for nurses. At the same time the working hours of probationers was increased from 52 hours to 56 hours a week, with one day or night off each week. Understandably there were complaints especially among the male nurses and general staff whose hours had been increased to 60 hours per week.

The standard of training at Battle Infirmary was highly regarded and Dr Guilding agreed to allow registered sick children's nurses to attend, two at a time, for a two years' training in general nursing whenever there were vacancies. However when Bath Union asked if their probationers could be taken at Battle for further training after they had passed their preliminary examinations, he had to refuse as there were no vacancies.

Midwifery was rather different. There were only eight maternity beds and, as these probably did not provide the necessary experience, the Central Midwives Board would not approve the Infirmary for pupil midwives to receive their practical training. It was stressed that such training should be completed and Dellwood probably provided the necessary number of cases for the Infirmary midwives.

In 1925 the three Charge Nurses asked for their salaries of £40 a year to be increased. Enquiries at the Royal Berkshire Hospital and other Poor Law unions showed that salaries varied from £75 per year to £92 per year. Those at Battle were then increased to £50 a year which, with bonuses, would amount to £80 a year. It was also noted that Charge Nurses were now usually called Ward Sisters and the change in name was then adopted at Battle.

Unemployment

The problem of unemployment was to be the concern of the Guardians for many years. The change from war-time conditions to peace-time employment caused great distress. Many ex-servicemen found there were no jobs for them when they were demobilised and the change from a war-time economy was to take many years to accomplish. Since 1914 the Guardians had, from time to time, arranged with the Reading Distress Committee for unemployed men to level and improve the land behind the Infirmary.

By 1920 the number of unemployed had risen alarmingly. Dr Abram, now the Mayor of Reading, called for special efforts to be made to provide work for these men. He suggested additional work should be carried out on reclaiming the Guardians' land at Battle Infirmary. There were still some 5 acres left to be reclaimed, half of which was under water and part of the remainder was used as a Corporation rubbish tip.

It was estimated that the cost of complete reclamation would be about £4,000 and an application was made to the Treasury for a grant from the Development Commission. In March 1921, when no grant was forthcoming, application was made to the Town Council for a grant from the Unemployment Grants Committee.

The Guardians were in an extremely difficult position regarding the unemployed. They were responsible for paying relief to these families and as a result expenditure soared. A combination of circumstances now put the Union's financial position in a perilous state. The Army Council still owed the Guardians some of the money for dilapidations and there was also money outstanding for the claim of £48,559 11s for the war-time occupation of the Workhouse premises. Prices had continued to rise and the cost of administration was now £14,299 compared with £4,145 in 1914. Staffing levels had risen from 51 in 1914 to 98 in 1921. Additional money had to be raised from the overseers of the parish of Reading and a further £12,000 was required which brought the total contribution that year to £60,000. At this point the Government declared that the official date for the termination of the war was August 31st 1921 and the Guardians disbanded the Emergency Committee.

All applicants for unemployed relief now had to be interviewed by the Guardians rather than the District officers. A man and wife would receive 25s weekly, 5s for each child under 16 years, a reasonable rent allowance and one cwt of coal or its equivalent in gas. Single people over 16 years would receive 15s per week. If a married couple lived in their parents' house they would be treated as though in separate houses. Some relief would be given in the form of vouchers.

It would be far better if the unemployed were given work for which they could be paid. There was no serious unemployment among skilled workers but for the ordinary labourer it was very different. By July 1921 some 40 men, half of whom were ex-service men, were being employed on land reclamation at the Infirmary and a few months later an additional 50 men were taken on. A further 32 men were given work for the rest of the year on the farm and in the garden. Two unemployed carpenters and one bricklayer were employed on minor work on the buildings. The £1,500 cost was helped by grants from the Town Council and the Unemployment Grants Committee.

Guardians throughout the country were facing similar situations. All believed the Government should not rely on boards of guardians to pay relief for the unemployed out of the poor rates. A resolution to this effect was passed by the Reading Guardians and copies were sent to the Prime Minister, the Minister of Health and Lieut Col Wilson MP, but to no effect.

In January 1922, when it was proposed to reduce the scale of relief, a deputation of the unemployed asked to meet the Guardians but were refused. A large crowd then assembled outside the Guardians' offices at the monthly Board meeting to express their anger and made their presence known by playing martial music, blowing bugles, banging drums and singing songs. When the Guardians still refused to admit a deputation the crowd became threatening. Two Guardians who left early had to be escorted to safety by the police amid shouts of 'what about our starving children' and a shower of stones.

The Guardians were well aware of the position of the unemployed. They had already asked the Town Council to provide more work but nothing had been achieved. It was decided a deputation should go to the Ministry of Health to demand that the Town Council be allowed to carry out various projects to relieve the unemployment. Towards the end of the meeting a deputation of unemployed was admitted and the Guardians were told in no uncertain terms of the great hardship that was being endured. If the scale of relief were reduced there would be 'a general civil commotion'. In return the deputation was told that there were 3,000 unemployed in Reading who were receiving relief from the Guardians and there were many more in work who were not being paid as much as the unemployed.

This was not the end of the matter and at the next Board meeting relief measures were adopted in line with those approved by the Ministry of Health for the Metropolitan boards of guardians. Relief for a man and wife, or two adults living together, would not exceed 25s per week. For the first child under 16 years the relief would be 6s, the second and third children would receive 5s each and other children 4s each. Adults living with parents would receive 10s weekly and those living elsewhere 15s weekly. Relief up to 10s would be paid in kind and the remainder in money. No money would be paid to supplement strikes or lock-outs except when there would be hardship to children.

The distress continued and in December 1922 the Guardians helped unemployed marchers from Oxford by providing food, blankets and baths. In 1923 some 90 hunger marchers arrived in Reading and were accommodated at Silver Street School. Again the Guardians loaned blankets and crockery and provided tea, bread and cheese. Other groups of marchers were also helped and their distress brought home the desperate plight of the unemployed throughout the country.

In 1923 , because of the exceptional circumstances, it was decided to put into force Article X11 of the Relief Regulation Order of 1911 whereby applicants for unemployed relief would be put to work 'for such periods as the Board of Guardians may determine not exceeding four days per week'. The relief would be in accordance with the scale adopted by the Board for unemployment relief and at least half was to be paid in kind. These 'Labour Tests' entailed men performing one or more of four different tasks: wood chopping and bundling, farm work, land improvement or such other work as might be required on the premises. Men on test work would work for two days followed by two days off and would be required to sign on at the Labour Exchange on the days they were not employed. The approval of the Ministry of Health was required and could be requested for a period of three months at a time. Such were the problems of unemployment that the Guardians renewed the Labour Test every three months for the remainder of the decade.

Later in 1923 the scale of relief was reduced again. A man and wife would still receive 25s per week but allowances for children were cut to 4s per week for the first child under 16 years, 3s each for the second, third and fourth children and 2s each for any other children with a maximum of £2 2s allowed for the whole family. Unemployed youths now had to attend the juvenile employment centre to obtain relief.

The Guardians continued to employ as many men as they could but others gave up and emigrated to Canada and Australia. In 1924 the tipping of refuse ended. The tip was now full and work was given to 24 unemployed men to cover it over with top soil. Further work was carried out on reclaiming the land. Unemployment relief was now accounting for 88% of the poor rates. The pre-war rate had been 1s 3d in the pound, now it had risen to 3s 2d. By this time it had been decided to carry out necessary work on improvements at the Infirmary. Unemployed men would be given work wherever possible.

Improvements
Since the war only necessary repairs had been undertaken at the Infirmary and by 1923 a great deal needed to be done to bring the buildings up-to-date. The first work to be undertaken was to improve the heating and boiler services. A loan of £2,250 was obtained and the work was completed by the end of the year.

Eight schemes were suggested which, besides improving the property, would relieve unemployment in the months ahead.

Scheme 1. Work on the farm buildings.
Scheme 2. General work.
Scheme 3. Improvement to farm land.
Scheme 4. Improvement to lighting and ventilation in H Block.

Scheme 5. Improvement to lighting and ventilation in F Block.
Scheme 6. Stripping and re-roofing H Block.
Scheme 7. New laundry.
Scheme 8. Additions to Nurses' Home.

When application was made for grants to the Unemployment Grants Committee the Guardians were informed no grants would be considered for building work as there was a shortage of skilled workers in that trade. Grants of 60% of the wages up to £80 would be allowed for Scheme 3 to improve the farm land. Similar grants would be allowed for Schemes 4 and 5. The £1,513 5s 2d tender of Messrs Sheppard, Ryder and Taylor of Caversham was accepted to improve the lighting and ventilation in Blocks H and F.

Attention was then given to Schemes 7 and 8. The Nurses' Home, with 21 bedrooms, should be enlarged to 26 bedrooms, the three bathrooms increased to six and a much needed recreation room provided. The architect, Mr Roland Howell FRIBA, recommended building another storey. However, when it was pointed out that it was unlikely that consent would be given for additions to the Nurses' Home and also for a new laundry, it was agreed the latter was more urgently required.

By November 1924 Mr Howell's plans had been approved for a laundry constructed with a steel frame, concrete blocks and corrugated asbestos roof. No skilled labour would be required and there would be little need for bricklayers, carpenters and plasterers. Half the cost, estimated to be about £7,000, would be for labour for which a 75% grant was allowed. A Wardle drying machine and other new machinery would be installed and alterations made to existing equipment. It was then found that the heating plant was inadequate. The new laundry would be 250 feet away from the underground boiler house which had been installed 31 years earlier and additional steam and higher pressure were now required. A new boiler house, a central calorifier chamber and a new system of hot water pipes to supply new radiators were needed. It was estimated the work would cost about £29,650.

The new laundry was now urgently needed and when the Guardians were informed that work must start by June 6th 1925 in order to obtain the grant, it was decided to go ahead using temporary boilers and leave the new boiler house and additional work for later. The tender of Messrs George Lewis of Reading of £4,350 for the building and that of Messrs Haden and Sons of Trowbridge of £2,267 6s for the machinery were accepted. The problem of water pressure was solved by linking the Infirmary to the town's high pressure water system for an additional £1,000. A loan of £8,600 was obtained to cover all the costs. The Engineer, Mr Weight, was appointed Clerk of Works and at last the construction of the new laundry began.

It was to be almost one year before the new laundry was completed and in the meantime an important innovation was obtained for the

Parish of Reading.   Battle Infirmary.

⋅ ⋅ WIRELESS ⋅ ⋅

OFFICIAL OPENING, WEDNESDAY, 16th DECEMBER, 1925,

BY

Mrs. H. G. WILLIAMS,

Wife of the Borough Member of Parliament.

PROGRAMME OF ARRANGEMENTS.

4 p.m.   Visitors will assemble in the Committee Room situate at the entrance to Battle Infirmary, where the Chairman of the Board, (Mr. T. Norris) will give a brief explanation of the Wireless.

4.5 p.m.   Visitors will proceed to the Infirmary (Male Block A) where the Chairman will ask Mrs. Williams to set the Wireless in operation.

4.10 p.m.   Mrs. Williams will perform the Opening Ceremony.

4.15 p.m.   Visitors will accompany the Chairman of the Board to various parts of the Institution where the Wireless is installed, viz. :—Block B (Female Infirmary) and Block C (Aged and Infirm patients).

5 p.m.   Tea will be provided in the Sewing Room (Block F) where the Chairman will welcome all visitors.

5.20 p.m.   The Chairman will give a report concerning the Wireless Installation.

        The Chairman will propose and Mr. F. E. Moring Chairman of House Committee will second a vote of thanks to Mrs. Williams.

        Mrs. Williams will reply.

        Sir Stewart Abram, Deputy Mayor, will propose, and Mr. H. G. Williams, M.P. will second a vote of thanks to the Chairman of the Board.

        Mr. Norris will reply.

Wireless installation 1925

Infirmary. Wireless installations were now gradually being obtained for hospitals and similar institutions and in June 1925 Mr Norris, Chairman of the Board of Guardians, had been impressed by the system which had been installed at the Royal Berkshire Hospital. He immediately wrote to the Reading Standard asking for money to be raised for a similar installation at the Infirmary. The public responded readily with hundreds of small donations and within months £300 had been raised to enable a wireless system to be installed in A,B,C and D Blocks and also the Nurses' Home.

On December 16th Mrs Williams, wife of the local MP, performed the inaugural ceremony before an appreciative audience. The wireless would be a boon for all the patients, many of whom were there for years on end. It would relieve the tedium of their lives, keep them in touch with the outside world and give them an interest in life. One old lady aged 94, seen close to a loud speaker, was enthralled and wondered where the sound came from. It was hoped further subscriptions would enable the wireless to be installed throughout the Infirmary.

The new laundry was opened on May 27th 1926 by the Mayor, Mr Leonard Sutton CBE, accompanied by the Deputy Mayor, Sir Stewart Abram, before a large audience which included Lady Abram, Mr Williams MP, Mr A B Lowry, the Chief Inspector of the Ministry of Health, Mr Rogers, Chairman of the Royal Berkshire Hospital and members of the Board of Guardians. It had been hoped that the Prince of Wales would perform the opening ceremony in conjunction with the unveiling of the tablet at the New Bridge, but this had proved impossible to arrange.

The occasion was widely reported in the local newspapers with photographs of the new building and glowing accounts of the up-to-date machinery. The concrete blocks had been specially made using ballast dug from the Infirmary land. The light and airy building had glass partitions separating the receiving room, general wash house, foul wash house, ironing room, airing room and delivery room. The Architect, Mr Howell, was congratulated, the powerful machinery admired and all concerned were commended on their foresight. On a more sombre note Col Hybert, Chairman of the Building and Farm Committee, pointed out that when the time came for the Guardians to hand over the Institution to another authority, it would be 'complete in every particular'.

Work remained to be carried out on the heating, lighting and electric power. A consultant engineer, Mr Wayne-Morgan, had been asked to advise the Guardians but the Ministry of Health believed his scheme should be simplified and the estimated cost of nearly £30,000 considerably reduced. It was to be over one year before agreement was reached on a modified plan and tenders accepted for the work to be carried out. Loans of £18,850 were sanctioned and in September 1926 the work was under way with Collier and Catley converting the old laundry buildings into a power house, constructing subways and other building work, Poulton and Sons constructing a 120-foot chimney shaft and the economiser house, and Cash and Co of London undertaking the remaining work.

By October it was necessary to arrange for inmates to be boarded out at Wallingford and Basingstoke Unions while work was carried out in the various buildings. In January 1927, while the work was still under way, the Ministry of Health agreed electric light should now be installed

New Laundry 1926

Interior of Laundry

throughout the Infirmary. This would be undertaken as the heating and hot water systems were completed building by building and would be followed by painting and decorating.

The Resignation of Dr Guilding

Shortly before the opening of the new laundry Dr Guilding had sent the Board of Guardians a letter of resignation to take effect at the end of June 1926. He had been advised to resign on medical grounds and believed a younger man was needed for the position of Medical Superintendent and Master at Battle Infirmary. During the 32 years he had worked for the Guardians he had seen the Infirmary grow from a very small beginning 'to its present high state of efficiency'.

The sub-committee appointed to consider the appointment of a successor noted with appreciation all Dr Guilding's work over the years. His successor should fulfil the same duties, he should be fully qualified and registered, aged not over 40 years, be married and able to give his whole time to his duties which would include the training of probationer nurses. He would be required to enter a Bond of £500 with an approved Society, he would be paid a salary of £350 per year as Medical Superintendent and Medical Officer of the children's homes and £150 as Master with un-furnished accommodation and the usual allowances valued at £200 per year.

Advertisements placed in the medical journals, the Poor Law Officers' Journal and local newspapers produced 20 applicants, three of whom were selected to be interviewed. One withdrew his application leaving the choice between Dr W P Elford aged 32 from Coventry and Dr D C Thomas aged 27 from Cardiff. After the Guardians had carried out 'minute investigations' of both candidates 'regarding their qualifications and abilities', Dr Thomas was appointed as 'he appeared to have the greater experience of the two'.

Dr Thomas was a native of Swansea, the only son of the Revd D J Thomas, Rector of Canton, Cardiff. He was educated at Christ College, Brecon and went on to Cardiff Medical School and qualified MRCS, LRCP. He was appointed House Surgeon at the Middlesex Hospital, London and for a time was resident anaesthetist. For the past $3\frac{1}{2}$ years he had been the resident Medical Officer at City Lodge, Cardiff where there was accommodation for some 900 inmates including the sick. The Ministry of Health approved the appointment. Until Dr Thomas took up his duties in September, the Matron would be in charge of the Infirmary and Dr Cane would act as the temporary Medical Superintendent.

Mentally Defective Patients

It became increasingly evident throughout the 1920s that Poor Law institutions were not able to provide suitable accommodation for mentally defective patients. In 1920 Dr Guilding had suggested that those at Battle Infirmary should be removed to licensed premises elsewhere but only a few were transferred to Stourbridge and the majority remained where they were. When the Visiting Commissioner in Lunacy proposed that the premises should be certified under the Board of Control as an institution for mental defectives, Dr Guilding advised against taking such action. Once the Infirmary was licensed it was unlikely these patients would ever be removed.

In 1924 the Newbury Guardians proposed that all mentally defective patients should be moved from local unions and held in one institution where they could be looked after appropriately. The Reading Guardians supported the idea provided it extended over Berkshire, Buckinghamshire and Oxfordshire as this would be more economical to administer. At that time Battle Infirmary had 51 mental patients and their removal would relieve the pressure on beds. It was agreed that action had to be taken to remove these patients from mixed institutions and provide them with suitable accommodation elsewhere.

A year later, in March 1925, a special conference attended by 50 delegates from unions in Berkshire, Buckinghamshire and Oxfordshire, was held at Battle Infirmary to consider the matter further. The Board of Control agreed that better accommodation was urgently needed but, under the Mental Deficiency Act 1913, this should be provided by local authorities and not by boards of guardians. To date local authorities had done absolutely nothing in this direction and the Board of Control was now urging them to take action.

As the boards of guardians were powerless to initiate a suitable scheme, the Conference delegates passed a resolution which it was hoped would be effective. They noted the need for separate accommodation for the mentally defective patients 'where medical and nursing staff and trained attendants can be provided'. Local authorities should take immediate steps to provide such accommodation 'in accordance with the opinion expressed by the Board of Control'. If these patients could be removed from Poor Law institutions they could be placed in different categories and, where possible, be given tuition and instruction in various occupations and recreations which 'may render the lives of the mentally afflicted happier'. Copies of the Resolution were sent to the County Councils of Berkshire, Buckinghamshire and Oxfordshire, the Reading Borough Council, Oxford City Council and every board of guardians in the three counties.

This far-sighted idea fell on deaf ears and in the following years Battle Infirmary badly needed the wards occupied by mentally defective patients for ordinary cases. By 1929 the situation had not changed and even the exertions of the Ministry of Health and Board of Control had met with no response.

Casuals

The Casual Wards, previously called Tramp or Vagrant Wards, reopened in August 1921. At that time a large proportion of the casuals were ex-servicemen and these were allowed to leave early on the morning after admission without performing any task work. This concession was soon withdrawn and all casuals were detained until 11am regardless of previous military service.

The Casual Wards, built to accommodate 45 men and about 10 women and children, were soon found to be totally inadequate for the number of casuals now wanting accommodation. The problem became steadily worse following the Casual Poor (Relief) Order 1925 which came into operation on May 1st that year. Casuals now had to be detained for two nights instead of one and also on Sundays. A Relief Order Book had to be kept to record the number of admissions and other relevant information. Probably designed to ease the lot of the casuals, the Order had the opposite result. The number needing to be admitted rose and the inadequacy of the accommodation became all too obvious. It was noted that neighbouring unions were not detaining their casuals for two nights and this had increased the difficulties at Reading.

Within months conditions had become so difficult that the Reading Guardians asked the Ministry of Health to withdraw that part of the Order relating to two days' detention. Women casuals had now been removed from the Casual Wards to part of E Block in the Infirmary but even with their wards and the alteration of two cells into wards for men, there was still overcrowding and the conditions were becoming insanitary. Tickets were now being issued to enable casuals who could not be accommodated at the Casual Wards to obtain bed and breakfast at lodging houses in the town. The Ministry of Health noted the problem but replied by stating that several unions, such as Newbury, Wallingford, Hungerford and Easthampstead were extending their accommodation for casuals. Nothing was done about the two days' detention.

The Berks. Bucks. and Oxon. Joint Vagrancy Committee, which had been formed in 1908 to oversee the administration of poor relief to casuals in the three counties, was a voluntary body. The guardians of the various unions in the scheme contributed towards its costs and at that time this amounted to some £800 a year for the Reading Guardians. In 1924 the Committee had asked the Ministry of Health if it could be given statutory powers to enable it to become more effective. It was not until January 1926 that the Ministry of Health agreed to the suggestion, by which time the administration of casual relief had become increasingly difficult.

From April 1st 1926 the Vagrancy Committee would become a Joint Committee with statutory powers for an initial period of seven years, with a further term at the discretion of the Ministry of Health. Each union within the Berkshire, Buckinghamshire and Oxfordshire area would have three representatives on the Committee with a three-year period of office. The Committee would have the duty and power to provide for the reception and maintenance of any casual. It would be able to transfer to a general institution any sick, aged or infirm casual and to pay for his/her care and maintenance. It would be responsible for the care, maintenance and education of any child casual if necessary and would be able to remove any casual to his/her place of settlement. It would be able to provide premises or alter buildings for the accommodation of casuals. The Committee would arrange for the provision of mid-day meals at such places as might be desirable. It would provide way-tickets for casuals who were genuinely in search of work to enable them to reach their destination. It would assist in the repression of begging and sleeping out.

These powers did little in the short term to solve the problems at Reading. In desperation another deputation with five Guardians, the Clerk and the local MP, Mr H G Williams, had gone to the Ministry of Health. If neighbouring unions would detain their casuals for two nights it would relieve the pressure on Reading. It was not possible to extend the casual wards, nor did the Guardians wish to expend money on enlargement. Nothing was done and the numbers continued to rise.

In May 1926 some 575 casuals were admitted who had been detained for one night only at neighbouring unions and in the same period 261 lodging house tickets had been issued. The Guardians now decided that any casual in search of work would be detained for one night only, any with money on them or who were drunk and disorderly or abusive would not be admitted. Those in the know quickly hid their money somewhere away from the Casual Wards so it could be retrieved later, if it had not been stolen in the meantime. Conditions in the Wards had become very difficult and often the police had to be called to deal with rowdy men. Foul and abusive language was common.

One year later, in June 1927, an agreement was signed with the Joint Vagrancy Committee for uniformity of administration within the area of the Committee. It was, however, the report of the Medical Superintendent, Dr Thomas, in July that at last put the problem of casuals in perspective. His report was introduced by the statement that he had come to the conclusion that the presence of the Casual Wards at the Infirmary was 'very undesirable and at times dangerous'. The infirmary was now more a hospital than a workhouse and it was desirable to eradicate as far as possible 'all suggestions associated with the old idea of workhouses and pauperism'. The presence of casual wards was 'the greatest hinderance to fostering hospital ideas with the tramps waiting outside the gates in all their filth, disease and misfortune and sometimes intoxicated, noisy and obscene'. These wards gave rise to the risk of epidemics and infectious diseases. The accommodation could be put to better use.

Two months later the Joint Vagrancy Board asked the Guardians what accommodation was needed in Reading to meet the requirements for the detention of casuals for two nights and also on Sundays. At last action was being taken but by now even more decisions were having to be made regarding other aspects of Union work and Poor Law reform.

Moves Towards an Integrated Health Service
Although the proposals for an integrated health service made in 1920 by Lord Dawson's Committee could not be implemented at once, the first

tentative steps were taken throughout the decade. At that time Voluntary Hospitals, Poor Law Unions and Local Authorities were the main providers of health services. In Reading these were the Royal Berkshire Hospital, the Reading Union Guardians, Reading Borough Council and Berkshire County Council, and each worked independently of one another.

Attention was paid first to the Voluntary Hospitals and in 1921, following recommendations made by a committee chaired by Lord Cave, a Voluntary Hospitals Commission was established with regional committees representing every county or area. In 1922 the Regional Committee of the Voluntary Hospitals of Berkshire, Buckinghamshire and Oxfordshire was formed. Included among its members were two representatives from each County Council and one from each Borough Council.

Four years later, in 1926, the Minister of Health, Mr Neville Chamberlain, delivered a speech in Coventry in which he extended the ideas of Lord Cave's Regional Committees and asked for closer co-operation between the various hospitals including voluntary and municipal hospitals. There was need for 'a closer co-ordination of the institutions in any given area'. By this time the Reading Guardians and the Royal Berkshire Hospital were already discussing co-operating in two important matters.

The Guardians had asked if probationers who had passed their Preliminary Examinations might be allowed to attend the Hospital for training in the aural and orthopaedic departments. It was now essential that nurses sitting their State Examinations should have training in these special departments.

It had also been noticed that the Hospital had a list of 165 cases waiting for operations. If the Ministry of Health gave their approval, the Infirmary might be able to assist by making 12 surgical beds available (six for each sex) for such cases, on the understanding that the Hospital would pay £1 1s for each patient who was a member of their Contributory Scheme and a suitable fee for all others.

There was a delay of some months before the Hospital responded during which Dr Guilding tendered his resignation as Medical Superintendent. It had been through his efforts that the Infirmary nurses had attended lectures at the Hospital and no doubt they now wished to see who was appointed in his place before coming to any decision. Dr Thomas was appointed in June 1926 and shortly afterwards the Infirmary was notified that their probationers would be allowed to attend the aural and orthopaedic out-patients' departments. Two nurses could attend any one department at a time, they would be strictly under the control and supervision of the Sister in charge and any nurse who proved unsatisfactory would have to be withdrawn on request.

The Hospital also agreed in principle that Reading patients who were waiting for operations 'who may be considered suitable by a member of the surgical staff of the Royal Berkshire Hospital' would be offered the alternative of admission to Battle Infirmary 'to certain wards set aside exclusively for the purpose'. The arrangements could be terminated on three months' notice on either side and no case would be admitted which was unsuitable for treatment in a general hospital.

It was not until January 1928 that agreement had been reached on all points and the Ministry of Health gave their approval. The following month Mr Joyce, who had a very long waiting list, said he was not prepared to select any of his patients for admission to the Infirmary. However good the facilities might have been, the Infirmary, with its workhouse associations, was not considered equal to the Royal Berkshire Hospital. In March 1928 the first transfer of six patients was made to Battle Infirmary and out of a total of 103 operations carried out that year 36 were on patients sent from the Hospital. The Guardians noted the good co-operation they had with the Royal Berkshire Hospital and added that no-one in Reading who needed an operation now had to wait.

In the meantime a conference was held at the Royal Berkshire Hospital between its representatives and those of the Reading Guardians and Reading Borough Council to discuss 'the position of voluntary hospitals in a co-ordinated scheme of public heath service'. The Guardians had appointed their Chairman, Mr Norris, the Chairman of the House Committee, Col Hybert, and Dr Thomas, the Medical Superintendent, to be their representatives. The Borough Council had appointed Sir Stewart Abram, Cllr L C Quelch (who was also a Guardian) and Dr H J Milligan, the Medical Officer of Health. The Hospital had appointed Mr C E B Rogers (the Chairman), the Revd H W G Thursley (Chairman of the House Committee) and Major Norman Mackinnon (Treasurer). The first step had been taken in bringing the three main health service providers together.

By the time the first surgical patients had been transferred to Battle Infirmary in 1928 proposals had been made for the reform of the Poor Law. It was now evident that eventually the work of guardians would be transferred to local authorities. With this in mind the Borough Council suggested the Reading Guardians should form a Joint Committee with the Council to confer with the Council's Capital Expenditure Sub-Committee on 'questions of finance and other matters which materially affect the interests and welfare of the Borough'. The Guardians appointed four representatives including the Chairman, Mr Norris, and the Council appointed the Mayor, the Deputy Mayor and the Chairman and Vice-Chairman of the Finance and General Purposes Committee. The Local Government Bill was published later in 1928. The first stage in the integration of the health services was about to be carried out.

The Final Years of the Reading Guardians
The fundamental proposal of the Local Government Bill was that all the responsibilities undertaken by boards of guardians should be transferred to local authorities. It required each council to prepare an administrative

scheme for this transfer and, as far as possible, this should be considered in association with the terms of the Mental Deficiency Act 1913, the Maternity and Child Welfare Act 1918, the Blind Persons Act 1920, the Public Health (Tuberculosis) Act 1921 and the Education Act 1921. Each council should form a Public Assistance Committee, bearing in mind that all assistance which could be provided other than by way of Poor Law relief, should be so provided. It would only be a matter of time before the Bill was passed by Parliament and a date would be fixed for the Local Government Act to come into force.

While the Council was preparing an administrative scheme the Guardians were continuing to improve the Infirmary buildings and bring the facilities up to date. The new heating and hot water system was completed and this was followed by the installation of electric light throughout the Infirmary. The roads were resurfaced, an automatic telephone system was installed and 3a 1r 3p (about three and a quarter acres) and two small plots of land adjoining the Infirmary property on the east were purchased from the Saunders Estate for £1,750.

The Infant Poor Committee was renamed the Children's Welfare Committee and, as less accommodation was now needed for children, some Scattered Homes were sold. All outdoor relief was centralised at 40 Russell Street and a smaller number of staff was employed. In 1928 the three Relief Districts were reduced to two called East and West.

The most important work was connected with the accommodation and medical facilities at the Infirmary. Dr Thomas had proved to be an excellent Medical Superintendent and Master and, like Dr Guilding, he was able to direct the attention of the Guardians to the most important aspects of the Infirmary's needs. He pointed out that the Infirmary as a whole was too small. There was no spare capacity for the winter months. It was impossible to classify by Blocks or even within a Block. He noted: 'It is not desirable to have bedridden people and acute diseases together, or cancerous people and others together. Tuberculosis patients must be kept apart and these use up considerable space. The surgical wards have to be kept for operation cases. Infectious or suspicious cases must have a side ward.'

The sick men were partly in A Block and partly in H Block. The sick women were in B Block which was usually full, especially in winter. Sick children had no ward of their own and were distributed between A and B Blocks. C Block was overcrowded with infirm men and women and often there was no room for patients who should be transferred from A and B Blocks. The able-bodied men in H Block and able-bodied women in F Block were all afflicted in some way with either mental or physical disabilities. H Block was always full. The male mental cases were also in H Block and the mental women were in D Block. These wards could not be used for any other purpose. More beds were needed for senile and dementia cases. The accommodation for healthy children had been improved and beds were available for 18 infants under nine months and

15 beds for children under four years old. The accommodation for nurses and maids was distributed over various Blocks as well as in the Nurses' Home. The Casual Wards were overcrowded and posed 'unnecessary danger' of exposure to infection from scabies, vermin and filth. The tramps' washing had to be done in the Casual Wards and kept out of the laundry. These wards should be moved elsewhere, away from the Infirmary.

Additional building was not recommended through lack of space, besides which the unsettled position of Poor Law administration ' made it inadvisable'. The wards occupied by mental cases were badly needed for ordinary cases. If the Casual Wards could be moved elsewhere these too could be adapted for ordinary cases. For the time being some able-bodied inmates would be boarded out at Wallingford and Basingstoke Unions to ease the pressure.

By this time the Infirmary was being run as far as possible as a hospital. There had been a general increase in salary for all the staff. Miss Slack, the Matron, received a salary of £400 a year and Miss Frankum, the Deputy Matron, was paid £200 a year for a 56-hour week. Miss Scarlett, the Home Sister, was also paid £200 a year for a 56-hour week. Her duties included giving classes in invalid cookery and she was also in charge of the midwifery department. All three were regarded as administrative staff although they were trained nurses. The Ward Sisters were now paid £70 a year rising by £5 a year to a maximum of £80. Those who held a Central Midwives Board Certificate were paid an additional £5 a year. Probationers were paid £30 in their first year, £35 in their second year and £40 in their third year.

In 1927 when Dr Thomas had been at the Infirmary for one year, he applied for an increase in his salary of £500 a year. When the BMA advised that a salary of £800 a year was suitable for the dual responsibilities of Medical Superintendent and Master, the Guardians agreed. Dr Thomas had 'performed his duties satisfactorily'. He would receive an additional £100 in June 1927, a further increase of £100 in June 1928 and £50 in each of the following two years. In 1930 he would be receiving £800 a year which, with allowances, would be valued at £1,000.

The standard of nursing at the Infirmary was considered to be extremely good and nurses who took jobs elsewhere when they qualified were highly praised. The training of probationers had been extended to meet the examination demands. Teaching was now given on the wards as well as through lectures and demonstrations. New sick-record cards enabled probationers to acquire 'a systematic knowledge of disease'. Test examinations were introduced to be taken before candidates sat their State Examinations. The Committee Room was used for lectures and quiet study.

When off-duty the nurses were able to enjoy the Infirmary grounds and play tennis and bowls. It had not been possible to carry out the necessary extensions to the Nurses' Home. The bedrooms were unheated and the sitting room was also used as a dining room and recreation room. The accommodation was far from satisfactory.

Dr Thomas had ensured that the Infirmary was well-equipped with surgical instruments and appliances. All pathological work was undertaken by the Royal Berkshire Hospital and, when necessary, staff from the Hospital attended the Infirmary for consultations and to give anaesthetics. Among these were Mr Baxter, who assisted with two abdominal operations, Dr Price and Dr Rowland who gave anaesthetics, and Dr Norman May who was consulted over an 'obscure' skin case. All were paid £2 2s for each case. An efficient ambulance service was in operation and patients admitted for surgery now by-passed the receiving wards.

One serious handicap was the lack of X-ray equipment. Dr Thomas pointed out: 'We are placing ourselves in a false position by declaring ourselves ready to undertake acute work without this very necessary piece of equipment and it is certain that no hospital or infirmary can hope to be modern without it.' Patients who needed X-rays had to be taken to the Royal Berkshire Hospital and the difficulties in moving them often outweighed the advantages. The Guardians agreed this equipment must be obtained.

Another necessary piece of equipment was a sun-lamp for ultra-violet treatment. By March 1928 it had been obtained from Messrs Allen and Hanbury for £40 3s 6d, complete with goggles. It took far longer to install the X-ray equipment and during this time Dr Thomas took a refresher course at an Edinburgh hospital and also a two-week course in X-ray treatment. In his absence Mr Joyce performed 18 operations at the Infirmary and Dr Price and Dr Rowland gave anaesthetics.

It was not until the end of 1928 that plans had been approved for an X-ray building to be installed in the central section between A and B Blocks. Mr Forder, the Radiologist at the Royal Berkshire Hospital, had been asked to advise on the equipment. There were several delays and a year later, in September 1929, several months after the Local Government Act had been passed by Parliament, the installation was finally completed. The total cost had been just over £1,000. Mr Forder had been a great help and would assist Dr Thomas until he was accustomed to working the 'modern plant'.

The passing of the Local Government Act gave urgency to the Guardians' work. Their responsibilities would be transferred to the Local Authorities on April 1st 1930 and much remained to be done in the ensuing year. Continuity would be maintained after that date by four Guardians serving on the Reading Assessment Committee and two serving on the Committee for the Care of the Mentally Defective. Other Guardians who were Councillors would also ensure that the change would operate smoothly.

During the past few months the Revd Bernard Pater, Chaplain since 1922, had resigned following a disagreement about an armistice service. The Revd A G Parham, Vicar of St Mary's Church, Reading had been appointed in his place in January 1929 with a salary of £120 a year. Mr T Norris, the Chairman, died the following month. He had been a Guardian for 14 years and Chairman of the Board since 1919. His work had been much appreciated. The Vice-Chairman, Col F R Hybert, was elected Chairman in his place and Mr F C Moring became the Vice-Chairman.

It had been agreed in 1927 that new Casual Wards should be built outside the Borough and in June 1928 a 12-acre site had been found just off the Bath Road at Woodley. It was for sale at £1,650. As the Joint Vagrancy Committee now proposed to close the Casual Wards at Windsor, Easthampstead, Maidenhead, Wokingham and Henley, the Casual Wards at Reading would be in even greater demand. The site at Woodley would be most convenient. Tramps leaving the Eton Union Casual wards at Slough would have a 21-mile walk along the Bath Road to Reading after which they could go on to either Newbury (17 miles) or Wallingford (16 miles). A sub-committee of the Building and Farm Committee was formed to be in charge of the scheme. Mr Roland Howell, the Architect, Mr Wayne-Morgan, the Consultant Engineer, and Professor Herbert L Hawkins, Professor of Geology at the University of Reading were asked to submit reports. By the time the Local Government Act was passed plans were being prepared and in May 1929 the Ministry of Health was asked to sanction a loan of £1,650 to buy the site.

The prospect of Casual Wards being built in Woodley provoked strenuous opposition. The Woodley Parish Council held several public meetings where the objections of the residents were made known. They were supported by the Wokingham Rural District Council. The Casual Wards would be in a 'particularly attractive' part of the parish and in a residential area. Tramps, a 'most undesirable class of individual', would cause 'serious depreciation of the value of property' and would be 'a menace to the health of the community' and 'a disturbance to the peace'.

The Reading Standard supported the Guardians and, despite the protests, the Ministry of Health authorised the Guardians to proceed. The plans submitted to the Ministry of Health and the Berkshire County Council, showed the building to be roughly in the shape of a cross with an administrative block, wards and cells, a labour master's house and a labour ward with sheds and stores. It was sited some 200 yards from the entrance on the Woodley Road. The total cost was estimated to be about £25,000.

During the following months, while waiting for the plans to be approved, the Guardians turned their attention to improving the facilities at the Infirmary. This included building permanent Vita-glass shelters in place of the wooden structures on the roof of C Block for the use of tuberculosis patients. The narrow entrance to the Infirmary from Oxford Road was proving a problem. The piers at either side had been removed in 1925 but the entrance was narrow with insufficient headroom. The entrance should be widened, the height increased and two gates installed which could be operated from the Porter's lodge. The Guardians accepted the tender of £397 from Messrs G S Lewis and Son to carry out the work.

An ambitious scheme was undertaken to make an out-patients' department at the Infirmary. The Union Dispensary at Friar Street would be closed and the premises adapted as Relief Offices. The offices at 40, Russell Street would be sold. All Dispensary services would be sited at the Infirmary. A lady Dispenser, Miss Elsie Inglis aged 21, was appointed from among 22 candidates to the non-resident post with a salary of £160 rising to £200 a year. She was highly qualified, a Member of the Pharmaceutical Society and a fully-qualified chemist. In addition to her dispensary work she would help in the X-ray department, develop and print the photographs and assist with the ultra-violet treatment. The appointment of a lady dispenser was believed to be more appropriate than a man as she would be required to assist female patients to prepare for their treatments.

Arrangements were then made to provide an out-patient department at the Infirmary. The waiting room at the entrance to Battle was converted for use as a temporary out-patients' dispensary, the front room behind the Porter's office was adapted to be the waiting room and the adjoining office was divided to provide a doctor's room and a dispensary. Once the new Casual Wards had been built those formerly used at Battle could be converted into an out-patients' department and a residence for the Assistant Medical Officer.

The three Poor Law District Medical Officers had reached retirement age and their appointments were terminated on September 30th. The Assistant Medical Officer at the Infirmary, Dr Cane, would now include attendance at the out-patient department among his duties and his salary would be increased from £125 to £175 a year. Dr Thomas would visit out-patients at their homes. He would receive an additional £100 a year and a car allowance of £70. The Caversham District was omitted from the arrangements and Dr Cheney, the Medical Officer for the District, would continue and have a surgery at 2 Bridge Street, Caversham for his patients.

The new out-patient department was opened on October 1st 1929 and after a month it was working 'satisfactorily'. There had been 134 attendances, Dr Thomas had made 66 home visits and Dr Cane had made 12. Three chemists were appointed to dispense prescriptions for the convenience of patients living in the outlying parts of the town.

Objections to building the new Casual Wards remained as strong as ever. Wokingham Rural District Council refused to pass the plans and stated the Wards would spoil the amenities of the District and would cause very serious and disastrous consequences to the village and community of Woodley. The residents wanted to send a petition to Parliament. A deputation from the Berkshire Federation of Women's Institutes told the Guardians they feared for the safety of women alone in their homes and of girls going along the road with tramps around. The Guardians assured them that adequate policing and lighting would be arranged.

In the meantime it was learnt that the whole of the Bulmershe Estate, some $109\frac{1}{2}$ acres, was for sale for under £5,000. The Guardians had noted that Battle Infirmary would eventually be required for sick and infirm patients only and accommodation would have to be found elsewhere for ordinary Poor Law cases. The land at Bulmershe would provide an ideal site for the erection of new buildings for those inmates who were unsuitable to be admitted to a hospital. Reading Town Council was consulted and supported the suggestion. There were certain building restrictions attached to the land but if an adjoining 32½ acres belonging to Mr Costin, called the Larches, were bought, the restrictions might be lifted. The whole area of just under 150 acres might be purchased for £5,800. When it was found it would be difficult to lift the building restrictions the Guardians and Town Council were advised not to proceed. Instead about three acres of land with a frontage to Woodley Lane, belonging to Mr Budd of Caversham, could be purchased if the vendor could demolish the Elizabethan cottage on the site and remove the materials for his own use.

Col Hybert, the Chairman of the Board of Guardians, died in January 1930, only weeks before the Local Government Act would come into force. Mr F E Moring was made Chairman and Mr G W Cook the Vice-Chairman for the remainder of the Guardians' term of office. Two months later the Ministry of Health approved the plans for the new Casual Wards and sanctioned the expenditure of £1,650 for the purchase of the site and £2,840 for Mr Budd's land. Tenders had been invited for the buildings and that of Collier and Catley for £18,967 had been accepted. The Ministry of Health sanctioned the further expenditure of £21,350 for the building work and allowed loans to be taken out to cover all the costs. The Joint Vagrancy Committee had agreed to contribute £1,125 annually for 30 years. As the Wokingham Rural District Council still refused to pass the plans, the Ministry of Health firmly over-rode their decision. The building was necessary, the site was convenient and no other equally suitable site could be found.

The Board of Guardians held two meetings in March 1930. At the first the Guardians recorded their regret that 'with the time at their disposal' they had not been able to provide separate accommodation for sick children at the Infirmary and they had not been able to carry out the enlargement of the Nurses' Home. They asked that the attention of the Town Council should be drawn to these matters and referred to the appropriate committees.

In addition to the usual business the Medical Superintendent and Matron thanked the Guardians on behalf of themselves and the nursing staff for their many kindnesses. They would look back upon the association with pleasure and were very sorry it would soon be severed.

The final meeting was held on March 31st. Besides the Chairman and Vice-Chairman there were 24 Guardians present. One item alone was considered. Dr Thomas had asked that a resident Medical Assistant should be appointed. Too much of his time was taken up with routine work and there was no one on the staff to whom this could be delegated. He was 'tied to the Infirmary by day and night' as cases were admitted at all hours. He

Last Board of Guardians 1930

believed he could not face another winter without additional help. The Guardians agreed to pass on this urgent request to the Town Council.

Several officers had asked for testimonials and these would be given. Framed photographs of former Chairmen, Mr G R Smith and Mr S J Vinden, were then presented and Mr Moring presented a photograph of himself before reading a report of the past work of the Board.

Mr Moring expressed his appreciation of the work of all the staff and especially that of the Clerk, Mr Oliver. He had been one of 83 applicants for the position of Assistant Clerk in 1905. In 1907 he was made Clerk and had held this position for $22\frac{1}{2}$ years. He had an unrivalled knowledge of the Poor Laws and he undertook his work with urbanity and courtesy. It was hoped the Guardians' successors would ratify the decision that Mr Oliver should receive an increase in salary of £150 a year.

Mr Oliver in his reply noted the innovations the Guardians had introduced over the years and ended by saying: 'The extent and variety of the work of the Board of Guardians has been little known, little appreciated and often misunderstood. The proper public recognition of the gratuitous service rendered by them, which has meant considerable expenditure of time and money, has not been given.' Mr Oliver then presented a framed photograph of the whole Board to be hung in the Board Room.

The Minutes record that a 'very hearty' vote of thanks was given to the Chairman after which the Guardians, 'in order of seniority, filed passed the Chairman, Vice-Chairman, Clerk and Assistant Clerk, shook hands with each of them in turn, and wished them good-bye'.

So ended the final meeting of the Reading Board of Guardians. It had been almost 95 years since the Reading Union had been formed and the first Board of Guardians had been elected in August 1835 following the passing of the Poor Law Amendment Act. Over the years subsequent Boards had carried out their responsibilities with diligence and gradually the harsh measures of the Victorian era had given way to a more enlightened attitude towards the poor and needy.

The Guardians were handing over an Infirmary with 580 beds and some 36 acres of garden, recreation ground and a farm, all of which had been established and maintained by public rates. The hospital side had 279 beds in the charge of an excellent Medical Superintendent and Matron. It was recognised as a Training School for nurses and provided up-to-date facilities for its patients. There had been 1,044 admissions in 1929 and 155 operations had been carried out. Remarkable progress had been achieved in recent years to provide the facilities required of a hospital. Its future development now lay in the hands of the local authorities and under them it would be steered towards the final integration of the health services.

PART II

BATTLE HOSPITAL

by

MARSHALL BARR

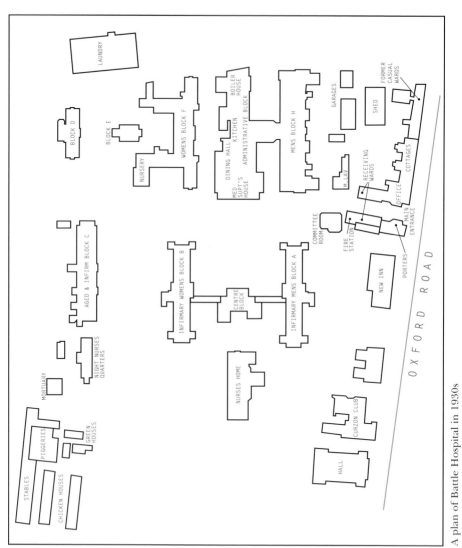

A plan of Battle Hospital in 1930s

1

THE MUNICIPAL HOSPITAL IN THE 1930s

An Eventful First Year

The two final communications from the Board of Guardians regarding unfinished business at Battle Infirmary were a mere politeness. Reading Borough Council knew very well about the Guardians' 'inability to complete before 1st April schemes for the provision of separate accommodation required for the treatment of sick children and accommodation for housing the nursing staff'. They were also well aware of the need for a Resident Medical Officer to assist Dr Thomas. The Medical Officer of Health Dr Milligan had overview of all health matters within the Borough. Some Guardians served on the Council, while any of the Board's plans had usually involved one or more of the Corporation's various committees. It had been the Maternity and Child Welfare Committee, for example, who had requested the Board when 'considering

Oxford Road entrance, 1930

243

their scheme for alteration and reconstruction of the Casual Wards for the purpose of an out-patient department to consider the possible use of the building for infant welfare purposes' and the Highways and Lighting Committee had approved the plans to improve the Oxford Road entrance. The Board had expressed disappointment at the failure to co-opt members to the Council's Public Assistance Committee and angry correspondence in the *Berkshire Chronicle* had demanded to know who would have the necessary experience to take over the work of the Board of Guardians. In fact, although 'strictly the Poor Law side fell under the purview of public assistance' as the Medical Officer of Health noted, management of the whole institution was given to the Council's Health Committee, and two members of this Committee, Mr Quelch the Vice-Chairman and Mrs Wheeler, had been members of the final Board of Guardians.

The formal communications from the Ministry of Health in March 1930 were more in the nature of a directive to the Council than courteous hand-over information:

'Local Government Act 1929.
On the understanding that steps will be taken to ensure that the duty of the Council to supply the necessary relief to the destitute and sick is discharged, the Minister is prepared to agree to the appropriation by the Council of the hospital portion of the Institution of the Parish of Reading for the purpose of services under the Public Health Acts...
If it is proposed to use the hospital for the treatment of patients under the Council's tuberculosis scheme or under their scheme for the diagnosis and treatment of venereal disease, it will be necessary to obtain the Minister's approval. The Council are no doubt aware that the accommodation to be transferred to them from the Guardians is barely sufficient at the present time to meet the purposes for which it was provided and the Minister hopes that they will give early consideration to the question of providing further accommodation.'

This was followed by final notification of approval for 'appropriation by the Council of certain parts of Battle Infirmary for hospital purposes'.

Taking over the hospital portion of Battle and its constitution as a hospital under the Public Health Act meant that the new hospital was no longer subject to the provisions of the Poor Law and that patients admitted were no longer Poor Law patients. However, there would still be much bureaucracy, supervision and direction from the Ministry of Health and Battle was clearly going to be an expensive undertaking even before the Corporation got on with its own plans for the hospital.

So most of the background information was already in place when the Town Clerk addressed the Health Committee to give an outline of their additional duties associated with the take-over. The Council were required by the Act to consult with the local Voluntary Hospital to co-ordinate provision of hospital services and a committee had already been formed for conferring with the Royal Berkshire Hospital. As with similar cases elsewhere, all the existing officers of the Poor Law Authority would be transferred on the appointed day, 1st April 1930, to become officers of the Council. The Clerk to the Guardians was to become the Council's Public Assistance Officer, mainly within the province of the Public Assistance Committee. The Medical Superintendent and Master would continue to perform his duties under the general direction of the Health Committee and the Medical Officer of Health.

The Health Committee comprised the Mayor, three aldermen and 14 councillors with Councillor G H R Holden MD as Chairman. The Committee was already committed to 'transact and have charge of all matters relating to the health of the district of this Borough', a huge responsibility involving Park Hospital, Whitley Smallpox Hospital, Dellwood Maternity Home and various clinics, together with activities as diverse as food supplies, immunisation, canals and slaughterhouses. It is certain from their optimistic early resolutions that the members were delighted to take on Battle Infirmary as well. This was the opportunity to develop a fully-staffed and well-equipped municipal hospital which would be run along the lines they wanted. The Committee agreed to continue meeting twice a month on Mondays at 5pm, but the site of their meetings would now alternate between the Town Hall and Battle. Half an hour prior to each Battle meeting the members were to gather there and 'inspect in groups the various portions of the hospital'. Since the pauper side was really the concern of the Public Assistance Committee, its Chairman was invited to attend the Health Committee meetings to secure close co-operation on all Battle matters. (An immediate resolution in April 1930 was that the bathing rules relating to the Poor Law side of the infirmary be amended 'so as to permit of the inmates being bathed as often as required and at least once a week'.)

Most of the major early decisions were of course financial. In accordance with Section 16 of the Local Government Act 1929 it was necessary for the Council to take steps to recover maintenance expenses in respect of persons admitted for treatment to the hospital side of Battle Infirmary. A sub-committee was appointed immediately to deal with this, but first the Health Committee wanted a new name to distinguish their new style of hospital. With much enthusiasm they recommended to the Council that in future Battle Infirmary be known as Reading Municipal Hospital. The collective wisdom of the Council suggested a reconsideration and at the next meeting it was agreed that the new title should be Battle Hospital. Few would have guessed when that decision was made that Battle Hospital's life span was to be just 75 years.

The patients of the Local Authority Hospital would be somewhat different from those of the old Infirmary. Aside from the transferred surgical patients (and the Medical Officer of Health reported that the Royal Berkshire Hospital was willing to continue the arrangement for admission to Battle of cases on the Hospital's waiting list), it would not be mainly paupers admitted to Battle. In October the Health Committee resolved that 'the Medical Officer of Health give notice to all medical practitioners within the borough that it is no longer necessary to make application to the Relieving Officers for the admission to Battle Hospital of cases requiring treatment there but that application may now be made direct to the Medical Superintendent'. A charge would be made, subject to assessment of the patient's circumstances.

By June 1931 new negotiations were in progress regarding the payments in respect of treatment at Battle of contributors to the Great Western Railway Hospital Savings Association and Huntley and Palmers Employees' Hospital Fund. At that time the Association was paying 15s a week for six weeks, then 10s a week up to another four weeks. However, for their surgical patients the Royal Berkshire Hospital was paying 21s per week. Before revising arrangements with the private firms the Recovery of Expenses Sub-committee cannily negotiated for an increase in the amount paid for maintenance of Royal Berkshire Hospital patients transferred to Battle. The movement of hospital patients was however two-way, and this was the start of many years' repeated wangling between the Borough Council and the Royal Berkshire Hospital Board of Management as their financial advisers kept seeking better deals. A joint conference was held with representatives of both Hospitals and the Royal Berks' offer of 24s10d per week was accepted for maintenance of patients who were members of the Hospital contributory scheme. This was a very welcome increase, but the proviso negotiated for the Board of Management was that the Council would then be 'prepared to accept responsibility for non-members of the scheme who are also transferred'.

While their sub-committee was bargaining to boost Battle's income, the Health Committee and the Finance Committee were authorising some of the expenditure needed if Battle was to advance. The question of an Assistant Medical Officer was referred for report by the Chairman, Vice-Chairman, Medical Officer of Health and Dr Thomas, the Medical Superintendent. This small committee quickly agreed that such an appointment was indeed necessary; it was what Dr Thomas had been asking for. They recommended that the appointment should be for one year in the first instance, and that the salary be £300 per annum with furnished quarters, rations, coal, light, laundry and attendance. When the appointment was made it would be 'possible to dispense with the services of Dr Cane who now acts as Assistant Medical Officer and assists in the outdoor relief service'. Dr Cane, notified of this intention, at once began a quest for compensation.

The first advertisement sent for insertion in the *British Medical Journal* was rejected. The British Medical Association felt that the appointment should be a temporary one in the nature of a house surgeonship and the person appointed should not be called upon to perform outdoor work (that is, outdoor medical relief and other work outside the Hospital). A revised advertisement was accepted and Mr Clarence Poniedel of Selly Oak Hospital, Birmingham was appointed, starting duties on 14th September 1930. An allocation of £50 covered alterations in C Block to provide his quarters and it was agreed that a servant allowance of 5s a week should be made to the Assistant Resident Medical Officer for payment in respect of services rendered to him by an inmate of the institution. The nearly rejected Dr Cane had his appointment confirmed to assist with the outdoor work. In the meantime a clerk was appointed for service in the Medical Superintendent's office and the formal application required for the treatment of tuberculosis was made and approved. In July Dr H R Minkley was appointed consulting Medical Officer for tuberculosis patients at Battle and for the certification of those persons receiving assistance in their own home.

There were strings attached to the Minister's approval for the treatment of tuberculosis at Battle. He was 'of the opinion that the accommodation proposed to be used is not altogether satisfactory... if at any time there is pressure for additional TB beds, such beds should be provided at outside institutions. He however approves the use of the beds temporarily, subject to certain conditions. The balconies should be used for the accommodation of not more than four patients. Very advanced cases or cases with bronchial complications should only be treated in the balconies if suitable heating is arranged. Patients suffering from pulmonary tuberculosis should not be treated on the general wards.' The Medical Officer of Health observed that these conditions were being complied with. Heating for the balconies was installed in September at a cost of £75.

Although money was being spent on improving the hospital service, the Corporation were careful to avoid any extravagance. An allowance of 6d per week was made to inmates whose old age pension was being claimed as part of the cost of their maintenance. Nor would there be much splashing out on celebrations for the Battle inmates' first Christmas under their new regime. In considering arrangements for Christmas Day the Health Committee decided the usual fare was to be provided with Matron empowered to spend not more than £10 on ward decorations, a policy and budget unchanged for more than 10 years.

The Medical Officer of Health's Annual Report provides a picture of Battle Hospital in 1930/31. Dr Milligan took the opportunity to review the recent Hospital history. He noted on the pauper side that in the last few years 'the element of repression was rapidly vanishing in the light of the knowledge that much of the destitution with which the Guardians were called upon to deal arose as the immediate result of sickness'. Appropriation of the hospital portion and its constitution as a hospital under the Public Health Act meant hospital cases were no longer subject to the provisions of the Poor Law.

The distribution of beds remained as at the hand-over. Block A had 83 beds for sick men, Centre Block the operating theatre suite, a maternity department of eight beds, the X-ray department, Dispensary and administrative offices. B Block had 82 beds for sick women. C Block, for the aged and infirm, housed 62 males and 44 females. It also provided the temporary quarters for the Assistant Resident Medical Officer and a roof overflow flat for night nurses. The mortuary and post mortem room were a separate, secluded, well-designed unit. The Nurses' Home housed Matron and 23 day nurses. A separate temporary building housed 14 night nurses. (This was a hut just to the west of C Block). All the permanent buildings he described as modern and well laid out. The Casual Wards (formerly known as the Tramp Wards) were now closed. H Block had 114 beds for 'so-called able-bodied men, most of whom have some disability' as well as mental wards of 38 beds and general offices. The Administrative Block contained the Medical Superintendent's home, dining hall, kitchens, bakehouse, stores, boiler house and fitting shop. F Block was for 102 'able-bodied' women. 'Nearly all show some physical or mental disability.' It also had the linen stores and sewing room. Block D of 30 beds was for female lunatics. The laundry block, newly built and equipped, dealt with 9,693 articles per week. The main entrance was flanked on either side by receiving wards. The remainder of the site was reclaimed marshland laid out as a market garden and recreation grounds, which served the purpose of 'keeping occupied such persons as are able to work' and also supplied fresh eggs and garden produce. Any surplus was sold at current market prices.

The Medical Superintendent regarded the Hospital as well equipped for general medicine, surgery, midwifery and diseases of women. There were no established beds for sick children and no specialist departments for ear, nose and throat, eyes, orthopaedics and conditions requiring massage and electrical treatment. The Borough Council had special arrangements at the Royal Berkshire Hospital for treatment of venereal disease, complications of pregnancy and parturition, and for operative treatment of enlarged tonsils and adenoids. Although no agreement existed, all the orthopaedic cases which come to the knowledge of the Maternity and Child Welfare and the Education Committees were treated at the Orthopaedic Clinic and special examinations were undertaken at the Pathology Department. The medical work was mainly of the chronic variety but there was a decided increase in the amount of acute work. The Hospital had been a full training school for nurses recognised by the General Nursing Council for some years. During the last five years, of 38 nurses entered for the final examination 31 had succeeded at the first attempt.

Payments made for additional services during Battle Hospital's first year give some insight into the medical activity at that time. Consultations by outside doctors were rare. Mr S C Alcock was paid 10s 6d for consultation on one patient. Fees of £2 2s 0d were paid to Mr Alcock and to Mr Cane for the administration by each of a 'special anaesthetic' to patients at Battle Hospital. Mr Joyce, Assistant Surgeon at the Royal

Berkshire Hospital, was reimbursed £2 2s 0d for providing surgical assistance for Dr Thomas. In July 1931 during the absence of Dr Thomas on holiday the other Assistant Surgeon, Mr Baxter, was paid 30 guineas for services rendered and Mr Forder, the Senior Radiographer at the Royal Berkshire Hospital received five guineas for 10 X-ray cases. Although no case notes or other records have survived, it is clear that the Medical Superintendent did most of the surgery and X-raying himself as well as the routine medical work and that he rarely felt the need to call for assistance in special cases. When you add his administrative responsibility for both the hospital and the pauper activities Dr Thomas's work load must have been punishing in the extreme.

Since the Council's policy was now to admit many more patients the Assistant Resident Medical Officer post was also going to prove a busy one. During the Medical Superintendent's absence on holiday the very junior Mr Poniedel was empowered to call on Mr Baxter and Mr Lambert to assist him at operations. When the Assistant Resident Medical Officer himself went on holiday later in the year his contribution was missed and Mr Cane had the satisfaction of being paid 14 guineas for extra assistance. Mr Poniedel's appointment as Battle's first Assistant Resident Medical Officer was obviously a great success: despite the British Medical Association's strong line on the post being temporary he was re-appointed in 1931 for a second year.

The most significant event of 1931 for Battle was undoubtedly the early removal of the Casual Wards to purpose-built accommodation at Woodley. In this depression era overnight lodging of vagrants was a big problem. The tramps were very well remembered by Mr Bob Eggleton, who became Administrator of the Child Psychiatry and Mental Handicap Unit of the West Berkshire Health Authority. The young Eggleton lived alongside the Casual Wards, at 332 Oxford Road; his father was the Battle ambulance driver. The tramps had to apply for admission before 5pm. They could not take in more than one penny or they had to pay for lodgings, so they hid their valuables under turf in a grassy bank at the bottom of Valentia Road, identifying the spot with their individual mark. The local boys amused themselves by switching the contents of the hiding places. If penniless, the tramps were deloused in the reception area and admitted to the Casual Ward to sleep on iron beds with straw mattresses. They could stay two nights with a day's work in between, cutting firewood or breaking stones which were used for road making.

Transfer of the Tramp Wards to Woodley was thrice beneficial: it eased some of the increasing burden, the vacated space was available for development of the out-patient services and removal of the tramps greatly improved the Hospital's image. To quote Dr Milligan: 'The congregation of tramps outside the institution has probably done more than any other one thing to perpetuate the workhouse atmosphere.' The Public Assistance Committee had agreed that the new Casual Wards should be managed entirely separately from Battle, yet Dr Thomas was asked to provide medical cover. That he immediately agreed seems a remarkable decision, particularly considering his strongly worded 1927 report. He could surely have pleaded increasing pressure of work at Battle and a local GP could more conveniently have looked after the tramps at Woodley. One suspects the answer is that despite the intoxicated, the noisy and the obscene, Dr Thomas really enjoyed contact with the rich variety of characters on the road. Bob Eggleton says: 'They were genuine tramps, not layabouts, and many were charming people.' Whatever his reasons, Dr Thomas was appointed Medical Officer of the Casual Wards at Woodley; in his unavoidable absence the Assistant Medical Officer at Battle would take his place.

Many other connections remained between Battle and the new tramp accommodation. Renewal of clothing, bedding, linen, hardware and food would be requisitioned from Battle stores. Able-bodied Battle inmates would be employed to work at the new Casual Wards. Mr Digweed, the Senior Male Nurse and his wife were appointed Casual Wards Superintendent and Matron. While the posts of Labour Master and Mistress were to be advertised, Mr E A Toovey, Assistant Porter at Battle, was appointed Assistant Labour Master. The positions of Mr and Mrs Penny, Casual Ward Porter and Portress were deferred due to Mrs Penny's ill health. At the next Health Committee meeting it was agreed that Mrs Penny was incapable of discharging her duties owing to her present state of health and retirement was suggested.

On 27th March 1931 the Revd Dr L R Phelps, Chairman of the Joint Vagrancy Committee, opened the newly named Woodley Institution. The tramps were moved on the same day, marking an important milestone on Battle's long journey from Poor Law institution to modern hospital.

Problems and Progress
In November 1931 the Recovery of Expenses Sub-committee reviewed the figures and found that the 24s10d per week agreed for surgical patients from the Royal Berkshire Hospital and contributors to the Hospital Funds was less than the actual cost of maintenance, now estimated at 31s 2d. The private institutions were warned and at the start of the next financial year the Contributory Funds agreed that the ascertained cost would be paid. In return they achieved the concession that contributors would have the use of the Corporation's motor ambulance at no charge for their conveyance to Battle Hospital for admission.

Negotiations with the Royal Berkshire Hospital were more complicated because a new deal was required on patient transfers in the reverse direction. The Corporation had proposed a grant of £200 per annum for the maintenance of non-pulmonary tuberculosis cases treated by the Royal Berks. The Voluntary Hospital's financial people disliked this concept of a fixed sum for an unknown number of patients. Their counter-proposal was 8s per patient per day, that is 56s a week or nearly twice the Battle

Hospital rate; they would 'defer considering the request from the Council for the ascertained cost of maintenance for members of the Hospital contributory scheme until receiving a reply'. The response was an alternative suggestion: the Council would increase the grant to £400 per annum and ask the Hospital Board in view of this increase 'to undertake to extend treatment to all orthopaedic cases for which the local authority are responsible in addition to non-pulmonary tuberculosis', thus formalising the ad hoc orthopaedic arrangements.

The background to these proposals was the increasing problem of TB affecting the bones and joints. Such patients needed skilled surgical treatment and long bed-rest convalescence. The Royal Berkshire Hospital had built Blagrave Branch Hospital, opened in 1930, specifically to care for the orthopaedic TB cases and for other patients requiring prolonged convalescence, particularly following surgery for osteomyelitis (infection of bones by other bacteria). The other cases, usually referred from the Maternity and Child Welfare Committee or the Education Committee, were mainly the orthopaedic problems resulting from congenital defects and birth trauma, such as club foot and cerebral palsy. The Royal Berkshire Hospital agreed to the £400 proposal, 'subject to review in 12 months in the light of experience gained and to approval by the Minister of the Blagrave Branch for the treatment of such cases'. The Board now agreed that they too would pay the ascertained cost of 31s 2d for Royal Berks patients at Battle.

A year later a new set of negotiations resulted in agreement to a different arrangement, reverting to a charge per patient: £2 2s 0d per week would be paid to the Royal Berkshire Hospital for each non-pulmonary TB patient and orthopaedic case treated. This was accompanied by a similar change to the previous system of payment for difficult maternity cases. Instead of the grant of £50 hitherto paid annually for the treatment of complicated labours, a payment of £4 would be made for each case admitted. With these figures accepted, the Royal Berks agreed to continue paying the actual cost of maintenance for patients transferred to Battle. Considering all these hard-fought business negotiations it is surprising that no payment was demanded when permission was given to Mr P O Collier of 13 Thames Side, Reading in November 1932 to take photographs of the grounds of Battle Hospital 'for reproduction on postcards intended for sale in shops'. On the other hand the postcards would be a fine advertisement of civic pride in Reading's municipal hospital. Perhaps the Council felt that the publicity would be adequate recompense.

The Health Committee was now asked about patient transfers of a completely different nature and in the saddest of circumstances. In 1932, a letter was received from HM Inspector of Anatomy, presumably to confirm with the Hospital's new management the arrangement finally agreed with the Anatomy Department at Oxford University in 1892. Again the request was for facilities to be provided whereby unclaimed bodies at

Battle Hospital could be placed at the disposal of the University of Oxford for anatomical purposes. The University was experiencing difficulty in securing enough bodies for anatomy classes. The Health Committee rightly agreed. Anatomical dissection was a hugely important part of medical training. But the members must surely have reflected on the tragedy of lives ending at Battle in abject poverty, without a soul knowing or caring.

On a brighter note, in June 1932 a report following the visit of officers of the Department of Health was generally favourable. The Visitors did make two specific points. The first was that the Nurses' Home was too small and the nurses had no adequate rest room. This was hardly new information; inadequate accommodation for the nurses had been one of the main comments by both the Guardians and the Ministry at hand-over. But something was now expected to be done about it. The second observation was a suggestion for making Block C more efficient. If lifts were provided, all the floors could be used for nursing acute cases and the flat roofs brought into use.

A small extension to the Nurses' Home was quickly designed to provide the rest room. It was ready by May 1933 and a wireless set for the nurses was installed at the considerable cost of £20. Nothing was done about a lift for C Block and the question was raised again in 1933 by the Minister when he sent his annual letter continuing the conditional approval for treatment of tuberculosis. A memorandum with this letter suggested that the third and fourth storey and the roof space of C Block might be used for advanced cases of TB when lifts were provided. The Medical Officer of Health was not enthused: 'The top storey and roof were previously used for TB patients and were found to be unsuitable. The isolation and inaccessibility had a very bad psychological effect on the patients. The Block is always fully occupied by aged and infirm patients and the nursing staff is untrained.'[1] Regarding the lift, Dr Milligan commented: 'The building generally has not proved to be particularly suitable and it is doubtful if provision of a lift would remedy all the defects.' (A lift would eventually be installed in 1952 and C Block with all its deficiencies would serve until the Hospital finally closed.)

A completely new problem was reported to the Public Assistance Committee in August 1933. The Medical Superintendent had received a letter from the Reading Branch of the National Unemployed Workers Movement stating that unless the foreman supervising the work performed at Battle Hospital by men in receipt of unemployment relief was withdrawn their members would refuse to return to work. They also demanded a suitable place for meals and washing. The Committee stoutly and successfully resisted this mini-mutiny. They refused a demand that officials of the Movement be allowed to attend a Public Assistance Committee meeting to discuss their grievances. They noted that only fully able-bodied men were set to work and suggested that as many as possible should work at Woodley. They recorded confidence in the manner in

Christmas 1933. Child patients in men's ward. Nurse Ann Jones came from South Wales to train at Battle

which the Medical Superintendent carried out his duties with control and management of the men in receipt of unemployment relief – the nine men who had refused to work had been sent to work at Woodley. In future if any man refused to perform his allotted task the Relieving Officer was authorised and directed to discontinue the relief.

Shortage of accommodation for children, again noted in the hand-over by the Guardians, was at last addressed in 1934. The Medical Officer of Health reported that the Nursery had been overcrowded for years, unsuitable for more than a dozen children. There was neither accommodation nor staff for sick children and numbers were dealt with in side wards and among adult beds. He gave figures showing the increase in under 16s admitted: 128 in 1924 and 140 in 1925 had risen since the changeover to 164 children in 1932, of whom 133 were sick and in the last year 298, of whom 235 were sick. He recommended adding to the present Nursery a room for nursing mothers and additional sanitary accommodation and also the setting aside of Ward A6 with its balcony as a ward for sick children. This would mean the move of 14 bed-ridden men to Block C and of 14 aged and infirm from Block C to Block H and the old isolation cottage. Staffing on C would have to be increased by one day and one night attendant. The full scheme received Health Committee approval.

Since 1930, the total number of beds had stayed the same at 580. With the establishment of the children's ward in A Block the hospital beds, as distinct from pauper inmate numbers, had risen from 279 to 292. And of course the sick children were only part of the increase in hospital activity. Admissions went up as the average stay for hospital patients was reduced from 13 weeks to 10 weeks in 1934. The number of operations fluctuated. In 1930 it had been 134 (76 from the Royal Berkshire Hospital); for the next four years the operation figures were 163, 104, 141 and 136. X-ray examinations were rapidly increasing, jumping from 108 in 1933 to 155 in the following year. Maternity cases had risen in four years from 16 to 31, out-patient attendances from 1,207 to 2,134. The number of mental patients admitted rose from 54 to 104; of these, 44 were sent on to the Berkshire Mental Hospital (later Fairmile Hospital) in 1930, only 36 in 1934. Since there was no increase in long-stay mental beds, the figures must reflect an improved selection of patients, and the admission of many with short-term episodes of mental illness who were able to return home. There were two small counterbalances to the increased hospital activity: domiciliary medical visits decreased from 529 to 401, while Borocourt, the Joint Institution of the local authorities of Buckinghamshire, Berkshire, Reading and Oxfordshire, opened in 1933, allowing transfer from Battle of several mentally handicapped children.

At the end of 1933 the Clerk and Steward Mr T J Farmer requested an increase in salary, well justified since he was managing without any increase in administrative staff. The medical staffing seems to have coped smoothly with the extra clinical work, despite several changes in personnel. In April 1932 Mr Poniedel was appointed Junior Assistant Medical Officer at Middleton Sanatorium near Ilkley, doubtless thanks to his experience with the 30 to 40 TB patients admitted to Battle during his tenure. His replacement on May 16th was Dr W E McIlroy of Basingstoke. For services required in the interim, payments were made to Mr Joyce, to Dr Parry Price (Anaesthetist at the Royal Berkshire Hospital) and to Dr Cane. Dr McIlroy was reappointed Assistant Resident Medical Officer for another 12 months from May 1933 and reimbursed for travelling expenses incurred 'in connection with his district and institutional visits'. It would seem that the British Medical Association restrictions on outdoor work were also being quietly ignored. In May 1934 Dr McIlroy was reappointed for a further three months, but then went on sick leave. Dr L P Fitch was appointed temporary Assistant Resident Medical Officer at £6 per week plus travelling expenses until September, when a local young man, John Charles Thomas aged 22 of Reading, took over the post.

Increasing Costs
Increased clinical activity brought to light problems with the laundry, reported on by the Borough Surveyor in May 1934. The drying room was inadequate, being just a screened-off central area; the ventilation was defective; in the event of a breakdown of the steam plant all laundry

operations had to cease till repairs were effected. The Health Committee authorised him to prepare schemes for a new drying room with separate sorting room attached to the north end of the laundry, a mechanical ventilation system and an emergency electric drive for the machinery.

By December, the Borough Surveyor had prepared costed schemes for the nursery and the laundry additions, both more ambitious than the original recommendations. The children's block would have a two-storey extension. On the ground floor there would be an extension to the day room, with adjoining kitchenette, a sink room, children's bathroom containing two baths, a room with six small WCs specially for children, two WCs for mothers, a separation ward, staircase, entrance lobby and corridor. The upper floor would provide a large eight-bed dormitory for mothers, a two-bed separate ward, a mothers' bathroom, two WCs, a sink room, landing and corridor. Constructed of red brick facings and slated roof, in general appearance similar to adjoining buildings, the estimated cost was £2,700. For the laundry a single-storey building would be attached to the north end, having three large rooms: an airing room where clothes would receive their final airing by steam- heated grids at floor level, another room for storing after airing and a third for sorting and dispatch. Construction would be of brick walls rendered in cement to match the existing building, with a flat concrete roof. The estimated cost was £950. In addition an electrically operated fan would be installed at the gable end of the existing building costing £45, an electric stand-by motor would be provided for £175 and at the request of Matron, a separate finishing machine for drawsheets was included for £200. The total cost with sundries amounted to the very significant sum of £4,370. Both the Health Committee and the Public Assistance Committee concurred with this expenditure and the Finance and General Purposes Committee meeting in February 1935 agreed, adding also £100 which had been requested for repair of the Porter's lodge and its adaptation for use as a gynaecology clinic.

The Porter's lodge at the Hospital entrance became available because Mr J Cooper, Porter and Mrs Agnes Cooper, Head Portress, left on 24th November after 24 years' service, Mr Cooper having attained 65 years. The Medical Superintendent felt it was not now necessary to have a resident porter, so the lodge could be adapted. This seems not to have happened; the Porter's quarters were converted to become Matron's flat. The clinic was probably held in the Out-patient Department on the other side of the Hospital entrance.

The formation of a gynaecology clinic happened with remarkable swiftness. In July 1934 the Maternity and Child Welfare Committee asked for favourable consideration to be given to establishing such a clinic at Battle. In November the Health Committee agreed that the clinic should be provided on half a day a week and that Mr C B Baxter OBE, FRCS, MCOG be appointed Visiting Gynaecologist at a salary of £125 per annum. Referring practitioners would be asked to provide the patient with a medical history and a letter of introduction. Patients from the Council's other hospitals and clinics might be referred. The Visiting Gynaecologist would be empowered to recommend patients for admission to Battle and to treat them there. The clinic sessions began on New Year's Day, Tuesday 1st Jan 1935.

With Mr Baxter now having admitting rights to the Hospital for gynaecology patients it was felt to be time to advance Battle's maternity service. The Health Committee informed the Maternity and Child Welfare Committee that they were prepared to receive into Battle Hospital any applicants in excess of the maximum number (which was currently 24) who could be accommodated in Dellwood Maternity Home.

To fill the porter vacancies Matron asked for approval for Miss Hunt, Head Attendant of C Block to become Head Portress. Miss Beken, an Attendant on C Block, was promoted to Head Attendant at a salary of £115 rising to £125 a year. There were also adjustments to the male staff: Mr Saunders, Porter, was given an increase in wages from £2 17s 6d to £3 weekly; Mr R Watts, Attendant, was promoted to Assistant Male Nurse at £2 15s a week. These changes heralded a review of other staff salaries in February 1935: Sisters, currently on an annual salary of £85, were put on a scale of £80 to £90 over two years. With the maternity work increasing, an additional £5 per annum would still be paid for possession of the Cental Midwives Board certificate. Miss E Scarlett, who at this time was both Home and Maternity Sister, would have been pleased to be getting skilled assistance. Miss M F Price SRN, CMB, was engaged as Night Sister in November.

The probationer nurses' rates of £30, £35 and £40 for their three years in training were deemed satisfactory, although probably not by the student nurses. Owing to the size of A and B Blocks, it was agreed that the staff should be strengthened by the appointment of nurses capable of taking more responsibility than a probationer. Three additional staff nurses at a salary of £70 rising to £75 a year would meet this difficulty. The first was Nurse Chapman, whose promotion in March after passing her final examinations thus nearly doubled her income. The added work in the Nurses' Home was recognised when Mrs Eadington was appointed Housemaid at a salary increased from £35 to £45 per annum and the Home Cook Miss A Russell's salary rose from £55 to £65. Their pay and certainly that of the trained nurses seem low in comparison with the £2 15s per week (equivalent to £140 a year) received by two additional porters taken on in April 1935, although the porters of course were non-resident.

There were many other wage increases during the year, which throw light on the level of staffing and the perceived worth of various positions. Mr A G W Cowdery, the Hospital Engineer, had been appointed on probation in February 1934 to replace Mr A E Weight who retired due to ill health. Mr Cowdery's starting salary was £4 10s a week. His appointment was confirmed in June 1935 and now increments were added up to £5 5s. The income of Mr G E Hunt, the Foreman Gardener, rose

Nurses in Battle wheat field 1930s

from £2 17s 6d to £3 per week. Rates for the Porter, Mr J D Macfarlane, the Night Porter Mr W J Butler, Mr A E Head Assistant Attendant, Mr R R Gosden, Assistant Infirm Attendant and an unnamed window cleaner and handyman, all increased from £2 10s to £2 15s a week, and Mr P Fewell, poultryman and farm worker, received an increase from £2 4s to £2 10s. In October Miss Pollock the second laundress was promoted to Head Laundress at £2, rising to £2 10s.

It is also of interest that in September 1935 the Finance and General Purposes Committee, referring to a decision made in 1927, granted Junior Clerk L Wicks a gratuity of £5, when he passed the final examination of the Poor Law Examinations Board for Institution Officers. A later beneficiary of this award would be Miss Dell the Dispenser who in 1937 also received £5 when she passed the exam to become a member of the Society of Radiographers.

Coping with Diphtheria

In the summer of 1935 a diphtheria outbreak occurred in Reading, posing a problem in finding enough beds for affected children. The vacated

Casual Wards were still empty and it was quickly agreed to renovate the area as a children's isolation ward. By September the Medical Officer of Health reported that the Borough had 82 cases of diphtheria under care, with eight children in the old Casual Wards. In October he reviewed the epidemic for the Health Committee. For the past 10 years the average number of cases annually had been 64. The total number for this year so far was 165, of which 141 had been in the present epidemic since June. There had been seven deaths. The increased prevalence was probably accentuated by the large new child population on the Whitley Estate where an undue proportion of cases had occurred. There were now 74 patients under treatment, 68 at Park and six at Battle. The current number of beds available for new cases was eight at Park Hospital and 12 in the Casual Wards at Battle.

Use of the Casual Wards had provided an ample margin. The Medical Officer of Health offered reassurance to the Committee: 'I should state there is no danger whatsoever to the other inmates at Battle.' There would be little danger in nursing cases in different wards in the same block, he said, which was commonly done elsewhere. The Casual Wards were in a different enclosure with separate entrance, kitchens and staff accommodation.

Although horrifying to the modern generation, there was no great alarm associated with this epidemic. Only 70 years ago diphtheria outbreaks were not unusual. It had however been the worst epidemic since 1911 with a real problem in coping with the sudden demand for isolation beds. In July there had been 27 new cases in two weeks. When the 1935 outbreak gradually petered out Battle could be congratulated on having played a significant part in the Borough's effective management of several difficult months. In October, rather belatedly, the Council established a clinic for diphtheria immunisation at the School Clinic.

A New Matron and New Challenges
Matron Miss E B Slack would reach retirement at 65 years in October 1936 and her long service to the Hospital was recognised in the most practical manner. Having regard to her ill health during the winter months the Health Committee granted her sick leave from July 1st for the last three months. The Finance and General Purposes Committee was equally sympathetic. Miss Slack asked for her superannuation allowance to include some recognition of her service as Superintendent Nurse at Battle from 1910 to 1920 even though she had contracted out of the provisions of the Act. The Committee agreed to add five years.

The Appointments Sub-committee recommended that Theatre Sister Miss Edith Sarah Frankum be appointed on probation from 1st July as Acting Matron at an annual salary of £240 rising to £270. A successor to Miss Frankum should be appointed at £140 rising to £160, and should be known as Senior Sister and Tutor Sister. On 25th October Miss Frankum's appointment to succeed Matron Slack was confirmed. Meanwhile in June,

Miss Dorothy Elizabeth Brace SRN, CMB, of the St Nicholas' Hospital of London County Council, had been appointed Senior Sister and Sister Tutor. Five years previously this young Welsh nurse had cared for RAF pilot Douglas Bader at the Royal Berkshire Hospital following his leg amputations; after the war she would become famous as 'Brace' in the book and film *Reach for the Sky*. For now, the 32-year old Miss Brace was starting a new phase in her career and she was destined to remain at Battle until her retirement.

The new Matron and Senior Sister took on their responsibilities in a hospital still facing many challenges. Firstly costs were continuing to rise and the financial relationships with the Royal Berkshire Hospital were about to change dramatically. In 1937 the Borough Accountant assessed the cost of maintenance in the 'public health wards' as £1 14s 6d per week, over 40% higher than in 1931. This was to be the charge for Royal Berkshire Hospital and the private firms' Contributory Funds. Other patients and liable relatives were to be charged the equivalent sum of 4s 11d per day. But in May 1937 a letter from the Secretary of the Royal Berkshire Hospital gave notice that the Board of Management wished to 'terminate the arrangement entered into in 1927 respecting treatment of certain surgical cases at Battle' and requested negotiations for a revised arrangement. A new sub-committee was formed to confer with the high-powered Royal Berks representatives, Ophthalmic Surgeon Mr Cashell, Treasurer Col Krabbé and future Treasurer Mr H H Wilder. After several meetings they reported in November on agreed arrangements with the Royal Berkshire and Associated Hospitals Contributory Scheme in respect of patients recommended for surgical treatment at Battle. The Council accepted figures which were astonishingly favourable to the Voluntary Hospital – for the first six weeks the charge would be just 15s per week for the contributor, 10s for each dependant and 5s for each child under 16. The amounts would then be scaled down for the next four weeks to 10s, 7s 6d and 2s 6d, and subsequently to only 5s, 5s and 2s 6d. The sub-committee noted it would be necessary to adjust the payments made by the Huntley and Palmer's Work People's Hospital Fund and the funds of other firms who were at present paying the Corporation the ascertained cost of maintenance. The loss of revenue was estimated at £1,300 a year.

Regarding payments to the Royal Berkshire Hospital, the Education Committee accepted responsibility for non-TB orthopaedic cases of school age children and the Maternity and Child Welfare Committee for those under school age, whether or not the parents were members of the Hospital Contributory Scheme, paying a fee of £2 2s per week with a reduction of 5s if the parents were members. The Corporation also would pay the Board £2 2s per week for each adult non-pulmonary TB case admitted for which the local authority was responsible. Finally, when informed that its annual subscription of £100 to the Royal Berkshire Hospital was low compared with similar subscriptions in other towns, the Council agreed to double that sum.

There is no mention in the various committee minutes as to why these generous amounts were agreed. If the Council were simply supporting the Royal Berkshire Hospital's Centenary Appeal it was an expensive gesture because the rate for the Royal Berks determined that of the other Contributory Funds. Presumably the Board of Management had spelled out to the Corporation just how severe were their underlying financial difficulties. The future for Battle, overworked and with inadequate facilities, depended inextricably on the specialist services provided by the Royal Berkshire Hospital, so extraordinary measures were justified to help prevent the Voluntary Hospital from plunging into crisis.

Another difficulty was the problem of image, the attitude of both the public and the health professions to Battle as an institution. Alongside the increasing acute activities there were still the chronic sick, the long-term mental patients overseen by the Board of Control and, most visibly, the paupers. When I came to Reading in the 1970s I quizzed Bob Eggleton and the late Frank Cheadle, who also lived pre-war in the Hospital's Oxford Road cottages, about the Battle they knew as children. They painted a most vivid picture of life there in the 1930s. A great distinction was made between hospital patients and the 'Workhouse people'. The Workhouse men wore tweed suits with a straw hat in summer and a cap in winter. The women had blue print dresses, coarse aprons, black stockings and black hats. Many were 'fallen' women whose illegitimate children were kept in the nursery while they worked in the laundry. Frank Cheadle particularly remembered the depressing, steam-filled atmosphere in the big wash-house and the dejected, prematurely wrinkled faces of those unfortunate young women. The men, the youngest aged about 40, worked on the farm and as porters and groundsmen in the hospital. The life of the paupers was dominated by the rules of the establishment and regulated by the bell above H Block. They were 'pretty well locked in although their actual treatment was usually with kindness'. Neither Mr Cheadle or Mr Eggleton remembered any brutality, but together with the old people in Block C and until 1931 the Tramp Wards, the Battle environment was very oppressive.

The hospital side, despite the best efforts of the medical and nursing staff, still carried the stigma of being somehow second-class and most suited for dealing with the chronic sick. Gordon Bohn, who dropped surgical rank to come from Barts in 1937 to be Mr Joyce's House-surgeon at the Royal Berkshire Hospital describes the attitude, very little changed from that expressed a decade earlier by Mr Joyce:

'We looked down on Battle, very definitely, to the great resentment of Dr Thomas. "Look", he would say, "we are a very good hospital in our own right." But we used to dump patients on them. We had very strict standards as to what age of patient was fit, who could withstand an operation. If for instance a man came in unable to pass his water and he was over, say 75, he was just sent straight down to Battle because he was a "chronic sick". This was the attitude, we can't do anything for him, he goes down to Battle, and it was a very sore point. That poor old boy would arrive down there with his bladder distended up to the umbilicus. Dr Thomas would inject some local anaesthetic and stab into the bladder to put in a tube which would remain for the rest of his days, although he would very soon die. But up at the Royal Berks we would take out the patient's prostate, and he would usually die even quicker.'

Surprisingly, Battle's medical staffing remained very stable. While the Medical Superintendent soldiered on, the Assistant Resident Medical Officer post was consistently filled by a succession of capable young doctors. John Charles Thomas served his full year, followed by Mr Gavin Chapman Gordon MB, BCh (Glasgow) for two years from 1935, then Dr W H Hood of the Royal Victoria Hospital, Belfast took over in September 1937.

From the summer of 1935 the Medical Superintendent persuaded the Health Committee to appoint Dr Cane to act as Medical Superintendent during his holidays. As well as the Hospital itself and the work at Woodley (where in 1934 some 450 casuals were examined), Battle was also providing the medical services to children's homes in London Road and Milman Road and to the remand home. In addition there were the Poor Law district medical services for the whole of the Borough except Caversham. Dr Thomas produced three sound reasons why it was important to pay out the locum fee of 5 guineas a week: 'So that a senior clinical opinion with knowledge of the Hospital shall be available, to assist with district visits and other institutions and to release the Assistant Medical Officer for recreation.'

During this period Mr Baxter's gynaecology clinic and operating work steadily increased. In 1937 his remuneration was raised by £100 a year, this sum 'to cover all operations performed by him'. Consultations from outside, at first needed only a few times each year, increased in 1937 to at least twice a month. The chief recipients during these years were Drs Cane, Alcock, and Ratcliff (these three were in GP partnership), and surgeons Mr Aitken Walker and Mr Joyce, also Ophthalmologist Mr Cashell, ENT surgeon Mr Powell, physician Dr Le Marquand , and Radiographer Mr Forder.

Some recognition for the hard-working Assistant Medical Officers came from the Reading Pathological Society, the local doctors' prestigious club which was based in the Library at the Royal Berkshire Hospital. On Mr Baxter's suggestion, in 1938 the Society's rules were changed to make the Assistant Medical Officer at Battle Hospital an ex-officio member, as was the privilege of the resident medical officers to the Royal Berkshire Hospital. Dr Hood was thus the first junior doctor from Battle to attend meetings of the Reading Pathological Society. Dr Hood was replaced in September 1938 by Mr William Bradford Foster MB, BS (London), who was the first Resident Assistant Medical Officer not to serve at least twelve months. He resigned and was succeeded in June 1939 by Mr David Frederick Rees MRCS, LRCP of Middlesex.

Achieving a steady supply of nurses was never going to be so easy. Not only was the Hospital perceived as less than first-rate, the Nurses' Home was still crowded and lacking in modern amenities. The paradoxical situation was that any additional staff meant more pressure on already inferior accommodation. It is not surprising that in February 1937 Miss Scarlett, the Home Sister, was granted two months' sick leave and retired due to permanent ill health. Miss I W Morris, Ward Sister, was promoted to replace her on a new scale of salary – £183 to £209, including emoluments valued at £75.

In 1936 attention had at last turned towards a proper resolution of this long-standing problem, which meant getting support from the Ministry. The Minister of Health had already agreed to the Council borrowing £5,471 for the laundry extensions and children's accommodation. With those works under way, by local contractors Messrs Collier and Catley for the Nursery and Messrs Canning and Sargeant Ltd of Wokingham for the laundry, a new sub-committee was formed to consider again the question of an extension to the Nurses' Home. They quickly reported that an extension was not practicable. An additional building was recommended comprising at least 15 bedrooms to accommodate day nurses and domestic staff. Their attention had also been drawn to accommodation for night staff. 'We consider the present wooden building should be replaced by one of brick construction comprising at least 20 bedrooms.' The Council agreed. Outline plans were costed, major additional nursing accommodation went into the list of schemes for the next 10 years and an application was made for consent to borrow £25,480 for the project.

In the meantime during 1937 and 1938 several trained nurses left and more were recruited. Miss Price switched to day duties, and was replaced as Night Sister by Miss F E Jones before being herself replaced by Sister M Stevens; Sister M Llewellyn replaced Sister Davis; Miss E McCarthy changed from Relief Sister to Theatre Sister (to relieve Miss Brace who had been acting as Theatre Sister in addition to her roles as Assistant Matron, Senior Sister and Tutor Sister). Miss Catherine McCarthy and Miss Aeron Mary Davies were appointed Sisters: the Battle Hospital Sub-committee had recommended two additional appointments on discovering that the ward sisters at Battle had charge of far more patients than at the Royal Berkshire Hospital. Having completed her training, Miss D M Condrick was re-engaged as a temporary Staff Nurse and Miss Frances Mary Parsons' position as Staff Nurse was confirmed. The preponderance of Welsh names may indicate some influence by Dr Thomas, but it is more likely that Assistant Matron Brace had useful contacts. She was a Welsh woman who, says Betty Eggleton (Nurse Elizabeth Thomas 1941–1944), had come to Battle because her brother was a policeman in Reading.

Nurse staffing nevertheless remained under strength. In September 1938 two staff nurses had to be employed temporarily from the Nurses' Co-operation in Bath Road. And the recruitment/accommodation paradox persisted: it became necessary to use the upper floor of the new addition to the Nursery for sleeping accommodation for probationer nurses and by October 1938 the Medical Superintendent had to arrange for certain nurses to be boarded out at a cost of 27s 6d per week.

It was not only a problem of trained staff. The difficulty in recruiting sufficient probationers was uppermost in the Battle Sub-committee's thoughts when they considered the General Nursing Council proposal to set up a test educational examination for nurses to start in January 1938. 'Probably some who would otherwise be suitable will fail to satisfy the required standard of education,' they noted, and recommended that the Medical Superintendent 'be empowered to continue to engage certain probationers who fail to pass the test educational examination and to train them as assistant nurses for two years'. If found to be efficient, they should be granted the usual certificate. It was a sensible policy. The Medical Superintendent had drawn attention to the increasing number of chronic sick cases who were now occupying beds in C Block and the necessity of staffing the Block in the near future with assistant nurses in place of male attendants.

Against this background, debate on the question of introducing the three-shift (eight-hour) system for nursing staff was almost a waste of time. The Sub-committee was in favour of reducing the hours worked, but it could only be achieved by increasing staff. There was general difficulty in obtaining nurses and probationers owing to shortage in the profession. As an inducement (and probably as a sop to those demanding an end to split shifts) annual holidays were increased, for sisters from three to four weeks and for probationers from two to three weeks.

And the staffing difficulties of the late 1930s were not only due to a shortage of nurses. That most useful source of cheap labour, the able-bodied pauper inmates, were dwindling in number. Dr Thomas was not complaining about this, indeed he was urging the Public Assistance Committee 'to relieve Battle of the necessity of providing for men who are neither sick or infirm'. His goal was still the expansion of the hospital service. In March 1937 he proposed to appoint two domestic servants for duty in the Nurses' Home 'to replace certain inmate labour not now available'. This was approved. When Mrs King was engaged as a daily domestic help at a wage of approximately £90 per annum it was noted that the post 'for the last 10 years had been filled by an inmate who has taken her discharge'. By June Matron Frankum was empowered to engage additional assistance, but was still finding it difficult to run the laundry efficiently owing to a shortage of inmate workers. The following year, again to replace inmate labour, she was forced to employ additional workers on the wards.

While Battle waited hopefully for its new Nurses' Home to be finally approved another major undertaking, the long-delayed conversion of the

Casual Block, did go ahead. In September 1937 a letter from the Minister approved 'the appropriation of certain land and premises at Battle Hospital formerly used as casual wards for hospital purposes under the Public Health Act'. Since it was now two years after the Block had been used for diphtheria patients, this was perhaps a little late. The new plan was for an Out-patient Department, a TB Dispensary and Infant Welfare Clinic. However, from the records available it would seem that only the Out-patient Clinic eventuated.

Some unwelcome news came in 1937 from the Borough Surveyor. He reported that the existing coal fire apparatus for cooking was worn out. The Electricity Department had quoted for replacements consisting of three ovens with hot plates, one treble steamer oven and one canopy. The cost, including installation and wiring, was £410 2s 6d. The suggestion of using electricity for cooking brought up the question of adequacy of the supply to all the Battle premises; the Electricity Department's Engineer stated that existing service cables were not of sufficient capacity to deal with the additional load. He proposed laying a high-pressure cable to the Hospital premises with a transformer being housed in a building near the laundry. He thought his Department would supply this without cost to the Hospital if the building for the transformer were provided. The Borough Surveyor felt that quite apart from the question of electric cooking, the service cables were fully loaded and the increasing demand for lighting, heating and power would make it necessary in the near future to provide a high-pressure supply.

The first of these increased demands came with a proposal to supply electric lighting to K Block, as the old Casual Block was now called. Hopes of improvements in the kitchen and K Block were soon dashed when the Council had to avoid a potential overspend. The Health Committee's estimate for the next year was cut by £1,250. The electric cooking apparatus, the transformer house and electrical installation in K Block were all deleted.

Some improvements and a celebration were sneaked in before the financial clamp-down. A new incinerator was installed for £115 and £90 was spent on refrigerators in both A and B blocks. For George VI's Coronation celebrations the same pattern was followed as for as his father's Silver Jubilee: high tea for all patients, gifts of tobacco and oranges to the men, souvenir boxes of chocolates and oranges to women and children, plus souvenir tins of biscuits for the children. All those able to go out were allowed a half-day's holiday.

Despite the restrictions on smaller spending, things at first looked promising for the new Nurses' Home. The Ministry had not rejected the plans; instead they produced a string of queries, some nit-picking, which were responded to by Mr Howell, the Council's architect: *The dining room should not serve as a corridor connecting other rooms on the ground floor.* Howell agreed and produced a new plan, moving the dining room and kitchen block to the north end of building. *The cloakroom and lavatory could be better placed near the probationers' recreation room.* The architect disagreed. All the staff would be employed in buildings to the south of the home so the main entrance, cloakroom and lavatories should remain on the south side. *It was preferable for the Assistant Matron's and Home Sister's suites to be on the first floor, arranged so they could share one bathroom.* Agreed. *Two rooms in the existing Nurses' Home were allocated for the teaching of invalid cookery, but there was no lecture or demonstration room.* The Committee Room was used for lectures; if necessary the Visitors' Room in the Home might be used. *It would be preferable for accommodation for sick staff to be provided in the Hospital and not the Nurses' Home.* Here the architect showed traces of exasperation. There was no spare room in the Hospital. The accommodation for sick staff was in the Home chiefly to be used by the night nurses. If the Hospital were extended, these rooms could be used for more night nurses and accommodation for sick nurses included in the Hospital additions.

The exchanges of correspondence were all taking time and for Battle, as for Britain, time was running out. Another war with Germany, no longer unthinkable, was becoming almost inevitable and 'the bomber would always get through'. During April 1937 Dr Thomas had been sent to an Air Raid Precaution Department course of instruction at the Civilian Anti-Gas School, Falfield. In October a public meeting on air raid precautions was held at Reading Town Hall; by November a draft plan had been prepared for the organisation of Battle on a national emergency basis and in July 1938 Ministry of Health recommendations were sent to the Hospital on the fitting and storage of gas respirators. It was not a propitious time for Battle's capital expenditure bids for 1938/39, which included the new Nurses' Home, modernisation of the kitchen, more work on the laundry, a new steam boiler, a new operating theatre and renewal of the X-ray plant.

In January 1939 Emergency Medical Services Memorandum No 1 was issued by the Ministry of Health, referring to structural and other precautions against air raids. Now the Ministry demanded that the Nurses' Home plans be changed again to include steel frame construction. The architect disagreed, but it was an argument of academic interest only. Civilian construction projects were losing priority as the country prepared for major conflict and Battle's nurses would not get their new Home in the foreseeable future. In March the Corporation received a letter from the Ministry summarising the part which Battle Hospital would be expected to play in the event of war.

NOTES

1. In April 1933 Miss M E Hunt, Assistant Portress, was appointed Attendant in charge of the infirm block at a salary of £125 per annum. Following an enquiry about temporary employees, the Health Committee noted 'many employees are too old for the permanent staff yet their very age makes them all the more suitable for the work they have to do such as attendance on the aged and infirm in Blocks C, D, F and H, more particularly in regard to night duty'.

2

THE EMERGENCY MEDICAL SERVICE HOSPITAL

On the outbreak of war in September 1939 the Government's Emergency Medical Service came into force, organised on a regional basis. The Emergency Hospital Service was aimed to meet expected demands from air raid casualties, from refugee populations and from other hospitals destroyed by air raids. Throughout the country beds were reserved in voluntary and municipal hospitals for Emergency Medical Service purposes and paid for by the Exchequer; additional beds were provided and considerable financial help was given for the extra facilities likely to be needed. Reading was regarded as a key area, already coping with refugees from London and expecting tens of thousands more fugitives and casualties from air raids on the capital. The old attitudes and jealousies between Battle and the Royal Berkshire Hospital were replaced by a spirit of willing co-operation in adversity.

On the financial front the Corporation acceded to new Royal Berkshire Hospital requests for increased payments covering tonsil and adenoid operations, complicated labour and surgical tuberculosis cases, including liability for their follow-up out-patient treatment. When in 1940 the County Hospital was in dire difficulty, both Berkshire County Council and Reading Borough Council agreed to help with serious levels of funding. This time the Corporation had some not unreasonable conditions: the Royal Berkshire Hospital must offer them five members on the Board of Management excluding the Mayor (an ex-officio member), and those serving on the Board in a private capacity. Not less than one Corporation member should be on the important House Committee and on the Finance Committee. The Royal Berkshire Hospital must provide all information asked for, including access to all books, records and accounts. A grant would then be given, payable in half- yearly instalments, related to the deficiency shown in the difference between approved expenditure and income for the year. The Voluntary Hospital swallowed its pride and agreed. In February 1941 a payment of £2,500 was made to the Berks., Bucks. and Oxon. Regional Council, earmarked for the Royal Berkshire Hospital.

While these local financial arrangements were being negotiated, the Royal Berks and Battle had taken on their wartime appearance and their

Austin ambulance

functions under the Emergency Medical Service. At Battle more than 150
beds were reserved and arrangements made to increase accommodation in
an emergency by turning rooms and corridors into wards. A grant under
the Civil Defence Act provided the necessary additional services, water and
sanitation. Steel sheeting was supplied for the operating theatre roof and
the theatre was protected with a wall of sandbags, filled by volunteer
labour. The basement of the Nurses' Home and other cellars were
strengthened to serve as shelters. A First Aid Post was established in the
Out-patients Department, members of staff were formed into a Fire
Brigade and the Steward and the Engineer were both provided with a
home telephone. A new ambulance was needed: the Council's Transport
Manager and Engineer reported that the 'BEAN' ambulance was now
about 12 years old and in a very worn-out condition; spare parts could not
be obtained and it ought to be scrapped. From a list of quotations the
Austin 'B' type vehicle from local agent Vincent's of Reading was selected
at £830 and a further £90 was spent on refinements.

Staffing Problems
Soon the Hospital was under severe strain from the flood of extra patients
– evacuees, war-workers and service people – and the loss of staff to war
duties. As a Territorial, Mr Baxter had been mobilised immediately for
military service. Under the Emergency Medical Service scheme the GP
surgeon Mr A N Hooper was to act at Battle during his absence, with
Mr Aitken Walker as Surgical Consultant to be available once a week. Dr
Thomas's Assistant, Dr Rees, was certain to be called up (all doctors under

41 years were liable for military duty); Dr K W B Rostron of Halifax was appointed as a temporary Assistant Resident Medical Officer until the Ministry agreed on Battle's full-time medical staffing. That decision came in October 1940. The recommendation was for the Medical Superintendent to have two B1 Medical Officers (one medical, one surgical) and two junior B2 Medical Officers. A GP could also be employed on a sessional basis. Dr Rostron was promoted from B2 to B1 (medical) at £350 plus emoluments valued at £100. Dr Rees remained at B2 on £300 plus emoluments, and Dr W J Tindall of Theale was engaged for two sessions a week at £1 11s 6d per session.

Filling the junior posts at this stage did not prove difficult: Mr C A Forssander of Weymouth and District Hospital started in November and Mr Louis Hamilton replaced Dr Rees when he was called up in December. But advertising produced no suitable applicant for the Resident Assistant Surgical Officer position and Dr Thomas wanted for the time being simply to employ local consultants on a sessional basis. The Ministry of Health disagreed. Their view was that 'in the event of air raids on Reading the Medical Superintendent would be unable to deal with all the casualties and would be too dependent on surgical staff at the Royal Berkshire Hospital for assistance which might not be forthcoming owing to commitments elsewhere'. An appointment should be made to comply with the Emergency Medical Service scheme and they were prepared to raise the salary from £400 to £500 plus emoluments. Quarters were also prepared for this appointment by 'adapting the Medical Superintendent residence'.

Even though Reading was to suffer only one serious air raid, there is no doubt that the men from the Ministry were right. As the war progressed the general surgical staffing at the Royal Berks was severely depleted. Mr Joyce had died in 1939, Messrs Wheeler, Reid and Bohn were all eventually called up, leaving just Mr Aitken Walker who did not go because he was unfit with a damaged knee. According to Mr Bohn 'the Hospital would have ceased to exist if he hadn't been there'. At Battle, Mr A Dill-Russell took the Emergency Medical Service assistant surgical post until he too was called up in 1942, and replaced by Mr J J Evans FRCS.

During 1940 Dr Thomas had twice applied for an increase in salary. The Health Committee, 'while fully appreciating the services rendered by Dr Thomas,' did not feel able to accede to his request. In May 1941 when the Medical Superintendent's salary was again on the agenda, Chairman McIlroy for reasons not explained absented himself from the discussion. It was agreed that the current £900 be increased by annual increments of £50 for the next two years and 'the amount so reached with emoluments amounting to £200 be the maximum salary for the post'.

The Medical Superintendent was not alone in seeking an improved income under the stresses of wartime working. In March 1940 the National Union of County Officers asked for 'consideration of the remuneration in cash and kind for hospital employees', a deputation informing the Health Committee that the financial position of members of the Reading Branch was becoming acute. The matter was referred to the Wages Committee and the Medical Superintendent was asked to prepare a report as to the wages, hours and conditions of employment of all those in receipt of a weekly wage. One hopes Dr Thomas was able to delegate that time-consuming task. A welcome result was finally achieved for Battle's employees in the form of a War Bonus added to all salaries and wages.

Wartime exceptions were made to many employment rules. For example, Miss Parsons, Assistant to the Matron, was permitted to continue in service for 12 months after reaching 65 in June 1940. Mr J D Macfarlane, by now the Head Porter, had his basic wage increased to £3 2s 6d a week. Mental Attendant Mrs Taylor was now paid a weekly wage of £2 2s instead of an hourly rate. In October 1943 she would replace Mrs Wootten as Head Mental Attendant. When Mrs Bennett in the sewing room became unable to put in a full day's employment Mrs Vickers was put in charge in the afternoons for an extra 5s a week. In some cases, as with Hospital Engineer Cowdery, the Corporation refused to release key workers to join HM Forces.

More needed to be done also to retain vital nursing staff. Probationers finishing their training were immediately engaged as Staff Nurses, but the turnover in wartime was high and by December 1941 only two Staff Nurses remained. Dr Thomas asked for an urgent increase to bring the nursing salaries into line with current advertisements. The Staff Nurses went up to £90–£100 a year, Ward Sisters to £105–£115 with £5 for the Central Midwives Board certificate, cost of living bonus and residential emoluments. He also secured a raise for the Theatre Sister and Night Sister. They were brought up to the new Ward Sisters' scale with the current holders put on the maximum, plus an extra £15 per annum for the added responsibilities of these two posts. These moves were effective to the extent that resignations fell away and during the next year several new Staff Nurses and two Sisters were appointed. However, there was still a deficit and doubtless overwork was the cause of some dissatisfaction. In September 1942 representations were made on behalf of the Battle nurses by the National Union of Public Employees. The complaints were dealt with fairly briskly by the Battle and Park Hospitals Committee:

1. Relaxation has been made to provide for the three-month probation period being included in the nurses' three years' training.
2. No change can be made in the present procedure of paying the nursing staff monthly by cheque, but arrangements can be made for cheques to be cashed through the Steward at the Hospital.
3. Annual leave will be allowed as for the maximum in peacetime, provided the Medical Superintendent is satisfied prevailing conditions will permit this.

4. There will be no departure from the existing condition that members of the nursing staff desirous of being examined by a doctor either at the Hospital or outside must first report to the Home Sister.
5. No variation will be made in the system of late passes issued by Matron.
6. Owing to shortage of staff the Hospital cannot consider abolition of the shift system. As far as possible lectures are given during nurses' hours of duty. It is not possible to arrange for lectures to be held in continuity till the result of previous exams are known.

The National Union of Public Employees was firmly informed that the allegation that Matron had taken a census on whether nursing staff belonged to the Union or supported the representations was entirely without foundation. It was found that a census had been taken by a member of staff on her own initiative without the knowledge of the Medical Superintendent or of the Matron.

Another important cause for discontent was of course the unresolved problem of lack of nursing accommodation. The Hospital Committee felt it was now necessary either to provide temporary huts within the grounds or to requisition an adjacent building. With Reading's population bursting at the seams no suitable building could be found nearby and after prolonged discussions, in July 1943 the Senior Regional Officer of the Ministry approved the provision of two huts for nurses. Owing to the call for materials and labour for the fighting Forces these would be of Ministry of Works standard type, pre-fabricated huts approximately 60ft x 18ft 6in to accommodate 20–25 nurses. Since the Council had intended before the war to provide additional accommodation, it should pay 30% of the costs. This was readily agreed, but needing accommodation for closer to 50 nurses, the Health Committee asked for three huts each with 16 cubicles. The Senior Regional Officer refused; he could only sanction a total cost of £2,000 in total, which was 'best done by two huts of only 12 cubicles each'. The huts were erected by Messrs McCarthy E Fitt at a final cost of £1,550, plus some £900 for beds, bedding, furniture and floor covering.

They were still far from luxurious. Barbara White had one of the tiny rooms as a pupil midwife in the 1950s. 'It was very cold. The first one up in the morning used to go and turn the tap on in the bathroom because by the time the next one arrived the water might just be coming through warm. One morning soon after Christmas I woke and found the glass of water on the bedside table had frozen.' As with so many 'temporary' wartime constructions, the huts had a long life, remaining in use (one became the studios of Hospital Radio Reading in 1978) until Battle finally closed.

New Appointments, New Matron, Increasing Work Load
In December 1942 it had been accepted that Assistant Matron Brace could no longer do the Sister Tutor work. Mrs V Crofts, who had been Sister at

the First Aid Post, was appointed. As a married woman she lived out! Matron Frankum retired in September 1943 after 36 years' service with the Guardians and the Corporation. The Health Committee recorded their appreciation of the able and efficient manner in which Miss Frankum had served, especially since her appointment as Matron in 1936, and wished her good health in well-earned retirement. Miss Dorothy Brace was promoted to Matron in January 1944; Mrs Richards SRN, CMB, previously the Theatre Sister, became Assistant Matron. On the new Rushcliffe salary scale Matron Brace was paid £350 rising to £530, plus £50 for her Public Assistance duties and emoluments valued at £200. Betty Eggleton remembers that while Matron Frankum was a fierce disciplinarian: 'Brace was very good, embodying the old and the new order.'

In July Miss O James was appointed in charge of the Maternity Ward and in September Miss M Wilks became Staff Nurse Midwife. Reading's rising birth rate meant that the Maternity Department was becoming a significant part of Battle's growing work load. The Caversham Grove Maternity Home in Emmer Green had been established specifically for the evacuees, but they constituted only part of the local wartime baby boom. In the first six months of 1943 Dellwood had to refuse 65 applications from Reading residents, most of whom were then delivered at Battle. The statistics for 1944 showed that of 3,138 patients admitted to Battle, 380 went to Maternity with 345 deliveries by midwives and 31 by doctors. During the year the staff took 3,322 X-rays and performed 676 operations. For the first time figures were given for massage (245 patients, 4,206 treatments) and for rehabilitation (373 patients, 506 sessions). In the Oxford Road Out-patients Block 3,942 accident cases were seen and there were 1,260 attendances at normal out-patient clinics. In addition the Gynaecology Clinic still flourished with 496 consultations (Mr Baxter had been demobilised). A Scabies Clinic was also introduced to help deal with a major infestation. Between the School Clinic, Battle and six other dedicated clinics set up in the town's First Aid Posts, nearly 1,500 cases of scabies were reported for the year.

Coping with all the wartime hospital work could not have been made easy by repeated changes of medical staff. Dr Minkley, the specialist in tuberculosis, retired in 1941. A succession of young doctors filled the junior B2 posts – Drs Alhadeff, Mumford, Timothy (who reappeared as a B1 after RAF service), Davis, Hamilton and Guilfoyle. Owing to the urgent need of medical officers for the Services, the policy of the Central Medical War Committee was that all fit B2 Medical Officers would be recruited after six months in post. Now a few refugee doctors began to appear as the strict regulations on aliens were relaxed: from Poland Dr Richard Blitsztejn MD (Paris), from Austria Drs Paul Strykes and Walter Hausmann, from Germany Dr Martin Grieffenberg MD (Halle), who took a junior post at 63 years of age. The key appointment in relation to Battle Hospital's future was that of Dr Hausmann. He had qualified in Vienna in

Borough of Reading.

BATTLE HOSPITAL.

This is to Certify that *Margaret B. Alder entered the service of the Reading Corporation as a Probationer Nurse on the* Seventh *day of* January *1942, and finished the course of three years training as prescribed by the General Nursing Council of England and Wales, on the* Seventh *day of* January *1945*

Signed *F. E. Brace*.

Matron,

P. Alwyn Smith

Medical Superintendent.

1935 and had come to Britain in 1938, only to be interned on the outbreak of war. This outstanding young physician was then shuttled through junior hospital jobs, coming to Battle from the County Hospital, Otley, in Yorkshire in 1944 at the age of 35. Throughout the war the hard-pressed Royal Berkshire Hospital doctors were able to provide occasional help for the medical newcomers at Battle and eventually in June 1944 anaesthetist Dr Basil Hill was employed to give anaesthetics on a sessional basis and for emergencies.

The nursing scene at Battle is vividly recalled by Mrs Margaret Pilgrim, who began training as Nurse Alder in January 1942. Her quarters were above the Out-patients Department[1] but she was asked to live at home because accommodation was so short. The lectures by Sister Crofts were given in the Boardroom, gynaecology lectures were by Mr Hooper at the Royal Berks, dietetics and cookery at the University. The military patients came from all three Services, not with war wounds but accidents, hernias and varicose veins. The theatre had a Sister and Staff Nurse only; others were drawn from the wards when required. Regular theatre sessions were on Monday, Wednesday and Friday mornings, emergencies being done as they came in. Convoys would come up from Haslar Naval Hospital, as many as 60 patients, usually with gastric problems. 'A diet of milk 1 oz every two hours sorted out the malingerers,' said Mrs Pilgrim. On night duty there were two nurses to a ward looking after more than 50 patients. Because of staff shortages, help came from voluntary workers, particularly from the Red Cross and St John's. Some girls joined the Civil Nursing Reserve, took a course of instruction and worked full time, but although they were at Battle perhaps over three years they never became State Registered.

Dr Thomas was a strict disciplinarian. From his house opposite B Block if he saw a nurse idle he would ring the ward and ask if there was any work to do there. 'Pop' Evans, the surgeon, was an ex-Army man who wore the crest of Jersey on his braces: his home in the Channel Islands was being used as a German Headquarters. Everyone recognised that Dr Hausmann was brilliant. One patient who gave his occupation as 'civil servant' was admitted as having rheumatic fever but was not responding and Dr Hausmann was asked to see him. He enquired of the patient: 'Have you ever been bitten by a rat?' 'Yes,' he said, 'I am a Rodent Officer.' Dr Hausmann had seen a similar case of Weil's Disease in Vienna.[2]

The small children's ward was above the Nursery. The sick children, mostly with chest infections, were not allowed visitors, Mrs Pilgrim sadly recalls. Of the paupers working on the farm and in the Hospital she best remembers John, with one leg and on crutches, who was a great help cleaning instruments in the theatre. Off-duty nurses used to stroll round the farm in the evening past the mortuary, the piggery and chicken sheds to the wheat fields and grazing sheep. The mortuary steps were a favourite place for courting. A group of nurses, including Nurse Alder, got Matron's permission to hold a small sale to fund some 'extras' for the Nurses' Home. With items collected from friends and families they set up a table outside the Home on a Saturday and were pleasantly surprised at the response. The following year they did it again and raised enough to buy a sewing machine, most useful for their 'make do and mend' exploits with the wartime clothing shortage. The Hospital's large sewing room was where Sunday church services were held. Nurse Alder, a keen Baptist, was most impressed with the ministry of both the Church of England and the Free Church Chaplains.

This was in the middle period of the somewhat curious development of religious attendances at Battle. When the war started, Canon A G Parham of St Mary's Vicarage, Reading had been acting as Chaplain for over 10 years at £120 per annum. His request in 1939 for an increase was ignored by the Health Committee. In 1944 the Revd B W Mason, Vicar of St George's, became the Church of England Chaplain. Meanwhile in May 1937 Mr A Barlow, the 'Religious Instructor' had died in harness at the age of 80. The minutes record that a successor 'be appointed as non-conformist Religious Instructor at £60 a year for the purpose of giving religious assistance and instruction to the inmates of the institution on the understanding that no inmate be required to attend any service which may be celebrated in a manner contrary to his religious principles'. The

Reading and District Evangelical Free Church Council nominated the Revd J Wilford Murray.

Nurse Alder most remembers the Revd W E Booth Taylor who took the post of Non-Conformist Chaplain in 1942. He was replaced by the Revd John R Palmer and finally in his turn by the Revd W W M White in May 1948. The salary had by then reached £75 per annum. It was not until this year that the question of a Roman Catholic Chaplain was considered. In February 1948 the Health Committee received a letter from Canon B Morris: 'As the number of patients in Battle Hospital of Roman Catholic denomination has increased it would be to their benefit and also to the priest concerned if the official recognition afforded the Chaplains of other denominations at the Hospital could also be extended to the Catholic Church.' The Health Committee adjourned this item 'for further particulars'. In March 1948 Canon Morris was appointed Roman Catholic Chaplain, only to leave Reading three months later. The Revd J Welsh, his successor at the Church of the English Martyrs, took up the Hospital post. The salary for the Catholic Chaplain was £40 a year.

Wartime Benefits

One positive benefit from the increased work load was the chance, as the war went on, to get more facilities from the Emergency Medical Service finance and other sources. The First Aid Post in the Out-patients Department had been financed by the Ministry. (Perhaps this included the electrical wiring for K Block, since by the war's end there was certainly an electric heater in the waiting room). The First Aid Post of course brought more work, becoming in reality a Casualty Department which the medical staff had to cover. After a year of war the Medical Superintendent had reported the need for a portable X-ray machine. Battle was admitting all accident cases from the western half of town; some were heavy and included 'patients not fit to be trundled repeatedly to and from the X-ray Department'. A portable X-ray machine was needed. On at least two occasions a small machine was hired from Dunedin Nursing Home before the Emergency Hospital Service provided a field service X-ray unit free of charge.

In 1943 the Ministry decided it would be advantageous to carry out dental treatment for Service patients while in hospital. Battle was one of the hospitals selected and a dental surgery was equipped by the Emergency Medical Service in a room adjacent to the operating theatre. Local dentists Mr Williams and Mr Nicholls did occasional sessions here, with some extractions under general anaesthesia. The theatre itself received a share of many case-loads of surgical dressings donated by the American Red Cross Society and later was equipped with an American operating table. The Emergency Medical Service also paid to improve the air raid defences of the theatre complex, sanctioning expenditure to replace the by now defective sandbagging with hollow concrete blocks filled with sand to protect the theatre, X-ray room and Matron's office in Centre Block.

Battle's pathology laboratory service owed its beginnings to a 1942 decree by the Emergency Hospital Service that a hospital laboratory must be created. Finance was provided to convert a store building behind F Block; the service was to be organised by Dr John Mills, the salaried pathologist at the Royal Berkshire Hospital. According to Mr Bohn, Dr Mills was a 'fiery quarrelsome Yorkshireman'. His particular concern was the number of patients who died, mostly in medical wards, who could have been saved by a massive transfusion. Before the war he established his own transfusion service. He designed and invented all the equipment, did all the blood taking himself and did all the propaganda, going around talking to the mothers and Women's Institutes. Before long enormous numbers of transfusions were being given in the modern manner. For Reading it was a very retrograde step when Oxford took over a Regional Transfusion Service. 'We couldn't get the blood as fresh as we had before and the new service had all sorts of teething troubles.'

Dr Mills knew Battle well. Before the war he had given several transfusions there. (In March 1939, for example, the Royal Berkshire Hospital was paid £25 4s for six blood transfusions for a 'Mrs P'.) He set up the Battle laboratory with equipment for bacteriological and blood testing and a refrigerator, and he put his young technician Ernest Ingarfill in charge. 'I went down to Battle every afternoon on my bicycle and did lab tests', said Mr Ingarfill. 'If I found anything exciting, I used to have to ring up the Berks and Dr Mills or one of his medics would come down to confirm what I had found or decide what to do. We kept some blood in the fridge, group '0' for emergency use.' In January 1943 this small unit was recognised as an Area Pathology Laboratory under the Emergency Hospital Service.

The wartime largesse was not confined solely to clinical activities. In 1941 for instance, a deal was done to obtain a new ironing machine for the laundry, the cost to be shared equally between the Council and the Ministry. Some help was badly needed, the laundry having run into new difficulties. It had been struggling pre-war with a shortage of staff, trying to cope with laundry from the Council's childrens' homes and infant welfare centres on top of the Hospital demand. By late 1938 the Medical Superintendent had to ask for the infant centre work to be contracted out. Then early in the war a Rest Centre was established at Oxford Hall in nearby Eaton Place and Dr Thomas reluctantly agreed as an emergency measure that washing from the Hall could be done by the Battle laundry, despite inadequate equipment and further depletion of the inmate staff. Next the Divisional Food Officer approved the establishment of a British Restaurant at the Oxford Hall. It stayed open from 7.30am to 8.30pm and all the laundry just kept coming to Battle. The Medical Superintendent had to demand that they use a commercial laundry. In 1944 the Battle Hospital Committee officially investigated the laundry working conditions. Head Laundress Miss Paddick was granted an immediate increase to £3 17s 6d a week plus bonus, a temporary female assistant was taken on

Battle Hospital   *John Guy*

Christmas Greetings

Wartime Christmas card

and instructions given that 'as soon as practicable, owing to the heavy nature of the work, a man be engaged'.

Inmate Welfare

Extra patients meant extra congestion, notably in the mid-war years when F Block became particularly busy. In 1942 Miss E Farley, Attendant in charge of the chronic wards in F Block, had her salary increased to £80 per annum plus bonus. A temporary emergency attendant was employed 'owing to increase of work in F Block and the Nursery' and 15-year old Violet Chapman was engaged for domestic work in the block at £1 per week. It would obviously be helpful if the Nursery work could be reduced; outside placements for the unmarried mothers were a matter of co-operation between the Chief Health Visitor, Probation Officer, Public Assistance Officers and the Hospital, with suitable cases recommended for transfer to special hostels such as that run by the Salvation Army in London.

During 1944 the Nursery admitted 15 destitute mothers (13 evacuees, two from Reading) and their illegitimate children, but at the end of the year only two of these were still resident. There was much discussion too between the Public Assistance, Health and Education Committees about the benefit of transferring Nursery children above two years to the Council's Children's Nursery at 14 St Peters Hill, Caversham. Eventually those children between two and three years old were removed. But Dr Thomas found on his next round of Home visits in October 1944 that the Nursery had been closed and the children 'crowded into Bailey Home'. He ordered their immediate return to Battle.

For the children permanently living in the Nursery and for Battle's other long-standing inmates there could have been little enough cheer as the war dragged on. The visiting hours of Sunday 2–3pm and Wednesday 3–4pm had been marginally extended, firstly from 3pm to 3.20pm on Sunday 'for the benefit of persons residing at Tilehurst', then in November 1942, 'to meet the needs of war workers', a half-hour (6.30 to 7pm) was added on the Visiting Day evenings. The Old Age Pensioners' 1s per week for additional comforts was raised to 2s in 1943 and some effort was made at Christmas. That year, through the kindness of the Mayor, who ran McIlroy's Department Store, the shop's 'Santa Claus' visited the Hospital and presented a gift to each patient. On Christmas Day the Chairman of the Health Committee, Councillor E R Jackson, accompanied by the Matron and the Medical Superintendent made a tour of the wards. Donations and gifts were received from Councillor Jackson, the Berks and Wilts Toy Guild, Messrs Huntley and Palmers Ltd, King's Road Baptist Sunday School, American troops including the Military Police, Messrs Woolworth, pupils of Kendrick Girls School and of Malvern Home School, the Royal Army Pay Corps and Messrs Heelas Workrooms. There were several personal donations as well as this splendidly eclectic range of benefactors, but it must be said that many more contributions were made for patients at the Royal Berkshire Hospital.

The Emergency Hospital Service kept some watch on the welfare side of the hospitals under its wing. It was not, however, until October 1944 that officers of the Ministry of Health visited Battle to inspect the food storage, distribution and dietary of staff and patients, having first given a month's notice! Battle would certainly have tried to put on a good show, since their Emergency Hospital Service annual grant was over £20,000. The Visitors' report was that the diet for staff and patients was well planned and appeared to be adequate, the main kitchen was clean and well ventilated, the equipment was satisfactory (instead of electric cooking, an Aga system had been installed at half the cost early in the war). The only comment was that 'consideration be given to replace the rather obsolescent hot water tins used to convey food with a more modern type'.

COUNTDOWN TO A NATIONAL HEALTH SERVICE

War's End

By early 1945 it was obvious that the war would be won by the Allies. The threat of invasion was long past, the Luftwaffe's efforts were concentrated on defending their homeland. Hitler's V1 flying bombs and V2 rockets had caused serious damage in London and the south-east but the last 'vengeance' missile had fallen in March. It was time to start winding down the emergency services which meant many changes for Battle Hospital. Some were big: the Emergency Hospital Service instructed Reading Borough Council that only 130 beds need be reserved, which the Accountant estimated would mean a reduction in funding for the year of £10,883. Some were small: Battle was given foodstuffs from the supplies provided by American Red Cross War Relief for Reading's Emergency Rest Centres, and bought the refrigerator at Dellwood Rescue Depot for £25, transferring it to the Nursery Block.

In September the war was over at last. With the future for world peace still uncertain the Emergency Hospital Service cautiously reduced the reserved beds to 75. 'Should it be necessary to encroach upon the beds to extend the facilities available for ordinary civilian patients, the Hospital was at liberty to do so with agreement of the Regional or Sector Hospital Officer.' The number was reduced to 40 in April 1946 and to 20 later that year. When the First Aid Post was dispensed with it remained a civilian Casualty Department, although Dr Thomas argued against keeping this going. It would be 'giving attention to patients who are already in the main contributors to the Royal Berkshire Hospital'. The only arguments in favour were 'those of distance and the training of nurses'.

Payment of patient costs between the two Hospitals still carried on, irrespective of the annual Council grant to the Royal Berks which had risen to £4,000. (The following year the Regional Health Council brought this into line with the system of other local authority grants in the region, which were paid to hospitals in proportion to the number of the authorities' patients treated and the grade of hospital treating them). For 1945 the Royal Berkshire Hospital's daily cost per patient was 17s 4d, applied as usual to surgical TB, complicated maternity cases and tonsils and adenoids. Battle's maintenance rate was only 8s 2d per day. The disparities were no longer of great importance since Reading's two large hospitals were moving ever closer together. The Corporation still had significant influence on the Royal Berks with Aldermen Bale and Cusden, Alice Jenkins and Councillors Jackson and Lewis on the Board of Management, the Regional Health Council was working towards more local co-ordination, while Prime Minister Attlee's new Labour Government was pushing rapidly ahead with the plans for a National Health Service.

Among the many difficulties at the war's end there was a national problem in obtaining nursing and domestic staff for hospitals. In January 1945 the Medical Superintendent had complained bitterly: 'The Ministry of Labour is directing nurses as soon as they pass their final exam and are eligible for posts as staff nurses to institutions for chronic sick, mental nursing, cripple homes and the like. This applies to nursing staff trained by us and is being carried out without regard to the number of staff nurses remaining at the Hospital to carry on the work. The position today, 5th Jan 1945, would have been well below danger level had I not fought every possible type of delaying action. Even now there are only 10 staff nurses in

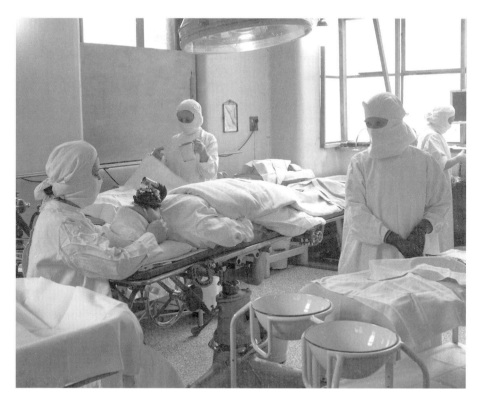

Operating Theatre 1945

all, three restricted by the Ministry of Labour to the Maternity Department
and two may be withdrawn at any moment ... The Matron and I feel that
leaving wards in the care of probationers creates an opportunity for
serious and even fatal errors. In view of the fact that we actually train staff
nurses I recommend the Minister of Labour and Minister of Health be
informed that it will be the policy of this Authority to close wards if and
when the Medical Superintendent reports that the staffing position is such
that patients cannot be nursed in them with benefit and safety.' No wonder
the Health Committee agreed to an increase in salary for Matron and all
the Sisters and applied it retrospectively.

The situation with student nurses was similarly acute. By September
Dr Thomas noted 'new entrants are practically non-existent'. In March
1946 Matron received a communication from the Director of Colonial
Scholars of the Colonial Office Welfare Department regarding
arrangements for submission of applications for Colonial candidates
(excluding women from India and the Dominions) who wished to
undertake nursing training in the UK. The Health Committee empowered
the Medical Superintendent and Matron 'to make such arrangements as
they consider desirable to enable a limited number of applicants to train at
Battle Hospital on the understanding that such an arrangement is in the

first instance in the nature of an experiment'. Although it is not recorded whether any Colonials were then taken on, these curiously worded passages are of some interest. Here we see the hesitant first steps toward acceptance of staff from overseas, the workforce sector which in a few years would become essential to Battle and to the National Health Service.

A combined campaign to recruit nurses locally was mounted by the Reading Division of the Regional Hospitals Council and the individual hospitals. For a week in May there were nursing exhibitions, special meetings, publicity posters and newspaper advertisements all stressing the need for more nurses. The Medical Officer of Health had to report that this effort did little to aid immediate needs. Rather hopefully he added that it 'undoubtedly was very useful in a long-term campaign for nurse recruitment'.

Things were somewhat better on the medical staffing side. The junior Assistant Resident Medical Officers Drs Grieffenberg and Hausmann had stayed in their posts by having their six-month appointments repeatedly renewed. In March 1945 Dr P Alwyn Smith was appointed to the medical B1 post, but surgically there was soon a problem. Mr Evans left in July 1945 and Dr I H Meyer took the post of Resident Surgical Officer (Emergency Medical Service) temporarily while the appointment was advertised. In September one candidate attended for interview but then withdrew his application. The Emergency Medical Service was unable to help and all the local Medical War Committee could do was press for the release of at least one of Reading's surgeons.

Retirement of Dr Thomas

It was during this difficult time that Dr Thomas, the Medical Superintendent, for so long Battle's surgical mainstay, had to take sick leave. In June 1945 the Health Committee minutes record: 'On the return to duty of Dr Thomas, the Medical Superintendent, Chairman, Vice-Chairman and Medical Officer of Health be empowered to make arrangements to release him of the duty of performing routine and emergency surgical operations.' Later in the year he was relieved of another burden when the medical supervision of the Children's Homes was taken over by the School Medical Officer, with local practitioners to be called in for emergencies. In September Dr Thomas informed the Council that owing to continuing ill health he would have to relinquish his appointment. 'Being cognisant of the fact that appointment of a successor to the post would necessarily take some time', he would for the time being leave open the actual date on which his duties would be terminated. The Council recorded with regret the 'necessity which has compelled Dr Thomas to arrive at his decision' and applied to the Ministry of Health for consent to a temporary appointment.

By every account, Dr Thomas was a competent surgeon and an excellent administrator, although very strict as Medical Superintendent. It is sad and strange that the service of one who had given so much for so long should end in a cold, ungracious fashion. Dr Thomas complained to the Finance Committee in December about the value of the emoluments of £200 per annum (on which he had been paying superannuation contributions) in connection with the house provided. Since June 1941 part had been converted to a self-contained flat for use by other Medical Officers. 'They have been charged for accommodation while the Medical Superintendent's emolument was not altered, both he and others being charged for the same accommodation.' A cash payment of £50 a year from June 1941 was somewhat brusquely granted and his retirement date was fixed as 6th January 1946, before the arrival of his successor. The Medical Officer of Health's Report for 1946 simply stated that Dr Thomas, after 20 years' service as Medical Superintendent, was forced to retire owing to ill health. In none of the Committee minutes was there any expression of praise for Dr Thomas, nor even of gratitude.

The advertisement for the post of Resident Medical Superintendent attracted 30 applications and Dr J C Harvey, 35 years old, Acting Medical Superintendent of Dorking County Hospital, was appointed. His contract required three months' notice to terminate, so Dr Alwyn Smith acted as Superintendent until 1st April. Although Dr Smith's B1 contract in fact should have ended on 1st March, he agreed to continue for yet another month to 'advise the new Medical Superintendent on future staffing'. In the interim the surgical situation improved with the appointment in February 1946 of Mr J W Bone to the B1 surgical post, with a living-out allowance of £100! The Health Committee expressed thanks to Mr Baxter and reimbursed him £150 for services rendered in responding to 45 emergency calls and performing 83 operations during the period in which Dr Thomas was unable to operate and the Hospital was without a resident surgeon.

Battle had got its new surgeon by being accepted as one of the hospitals providing posts under the scheme for postgraduate education of Medical Officers released from the Forces. The B1 surgical vacancy was notified to the Post Graduate Education Committee, who recommended Dr Bone as an ex-RAMC surgeon. Originally the salaries of such officers were payable by the employing authority, with reimbursement by the Ministry of Health if Emergency Medical Service beds were staffed. Tenure was for six months only.

Shaping for the Future
Within a month of Dr Harvey taking up his duties, the Medical Officer of Health, Dr Milligan, was succeeded by Dr Sidney Lawrence Wright MD, MRCP, DPH. The attention of both new incumbents was immediately given towards shaping the future of Battle and its relationship to the medical services of the town. The Battle Committee observed that the problem of staffing could not be delayed. Some immediate decisions must be made to implement the Council's decision to upgrade the Hospital and to plan a structure to be included with the least possible disturbance in a

co-ordinated service for the whole district. Battle could be regarded as comprising three specialised and two general divisions: the special divisions were acute medicine, including children (102 beds), surgery (60) and maternity and diseases of women (61), totalling 229 beds. The general divisions, chronic sick (155) and mental observation, public assistance and nursery (119), occupied 274 beds. Each Special Division would require a whole time Senior and whole time Junior Medical Officer. The work of the general divisions, Out-patients and Casualty Departments could be distributed throughout the staff. The resident establishment immediately required was one Medical Superintendent specialising in obstetrics, one Deputy Medical Superintendent specialising in surgery, one Senior Assistant Medical Officer B1 (medicine) and three Junior Assistant Medical Officers B2 (medicine).

The permitted establishment as laid down by the Central Medical War Committee still had only two B2 posts but in November Dr Harvey got an extra member of staff, at least temporarily. When the Health Committee recommended that Dr Bone's employment be continued, the Post Graduate Committee put forward Dr J C Lloyd as a supernumerary B1 with his salary chargeable to the Ministry of Health. Perhaps it was the solution of the surgical difficulties which persuaded the new Medical Superintendent to accept Edinburgh medical student Mr D Griffiths as a clinical dresser for five weeks in August/September, 'without remuneration but with resident hospitality' – Battle's first clinical medical student placement. Dr Hausmann was promoted to the B1 (Medicine) post and Dr Harvey's life was made even easier when Dr Ratcliff volunteered to make regular visits to the sick children's ward without remuneration, an offer accepted with best thanks.

The long pairing of Drs Hausmann and Grieffenberg ended when the German reached retirement age and resigned in early 1946. Another succession of names then appeared in the junior posts: Drs W M Gibson, G Gilford, J W G Evans, T E Hayden, Wyn Roberts and Dr McNaught. Restrictions on staff numbers had been eased but lack of suitable quarters hindered recruitment of a third Junior Assistant Medical Officer, even with Drs Bone and Hausmann now living out. The problem of insufficient accommodation was still the major stumbling-block to the Council's plans for upgrading and expansion; but of course the effect was greatest on nurse staffing.

The General Nursing Council's Inspectors of Training Schools visited Battle in early 1946 and a Report followed from the Acting Registrar. The Report noted that many wards were staffed by assistant nurses and that Enrolled Nurses were in charge of the chronic wards in which there were no trained staff. The accommodation for the nursing staff was far from satisfactory. The Education and Examination Committee were prepared to continue approval of Battle Hospital as a complete training school of general nurses for a further six months on condition that wards in which student nurses receive their training were adequately supervised by registered nurses, and that student nurses should not be required to work on wards staffed by assistant nurses. The situation would be reviewed in six months. If conditions were still unsatisfactory, approval as a training school for nurses for admission to the Register would need to be withdrawn. If such was the case in all probability it would be possible for an application to be made for approval as a training school for assistant nurses. The last point referred to the policy that from 31st December 1947 admission to the Roll of Assistant Nurses would be made by examination only. Unqualified persons entering non-training establishments would not be able to use any title including the word 'nurse'. (As an expedient, until there

Matron Brace

Medical Superintendent's residence. Assistant Matron Mrs Richards with group in foreground. Behind, with children, Matron Brace

was an adequate flow of qualified assistant nurses, the period when two years training or experience would be eligible for enrolment would be extended for a further 12 months). As well as asking for the accommodation to be improved and expanded, the Report wanted the children's work to be increased and the general conditions of that block improved. Finally, gas sterilisers for ward equipment should be placed elsewhere than in the ward kitchen.

The Health Committee hastened to make improvements. Moving the sterilisers was relatively simple. To make more room for treating sick children they began moves to have all the healthy Nursery children admitted to other institutions under the control of the Corporation. The methods of staffing were altered to comply with the General Nursing Council standards. The Committee also enquired about the possibility of establishing training facilities for pupil Assistant Nurses in addition to the present courses.

As for accommodation, a joint statement by the Minister of Health and the Minister of Labour and National Service on the national nursing crisis had recognised that accommodation was a key factor and recommended standards. Every nurse should have her own well-furnished room with adequate ventilation, heating and lighting; in all new buildings a space of at least 100sq ft should be allowed for each nurse's room. All very well in theory!

The Health Committee asked for a revision to the scheme for a new Nurses' Home which had had to be abandoned at the outbreak of war, pointing out that this should be calculated on the number of nurses required in connection with the upgrading of the Hospital and should be accorded first priority. They also wanted to expand the kitchen in the existing Nurses' Home and to convert the basement into a dining room for the nursing staff. This small latter project was approved and completed by mid-1946, but progress on the major building work was not so simple.

In March 1946 the Health Committee noted: 'Owing to the impending National Health Service Bill it is impossible to plan at the moment with any degree of assurance. The present staff in round numbers is 60 resident and 40 non-resident nurses and 50 non-resident domestics. The additional staff required to fully staff the available beds is 60. Of the total, Matron computes that about 120 should and would be resident if accommodation were available. Available now is 24 in the existing Home, 24 of doubtful utility in the new huts and 25 purely makeshift. A new Home of at least 100 beds must be provided without delay.'

The application to the Ministry for building priority received a reply in June. The Ministry 'approved in principle the scheme for nursing accommodation but were not in a position to decide priority for labour and materials'. They requested that Forms C.L.1136A and Py (N.B.P.)2 be completed and returned in duplicate with a copy of the specification for the work, together with a list of materials shown in Forms A, B, C, and D! Very sensibly, the Health Committee looked for another way forward.

Investigation began on possible lease or purchase of the large property at 42 Bath Road, previously Reading Blue Coat School. This may not have been conveniently close but it was available. The Finance Committee agreed to defray the cost of purchase, at once informing the Ministry of Health 'to be sure of an early decision on borrowing the amount required'. That amount, £11,000, was not needed until November 1947 when the sale was finalised. In the meantime, however, rental at £480 a year had been agreed and in June 1947 Mr Hunt, the gardener at Battle, was appointed Caretaker of 42 Bath Road (in addition to his other duties). Mrs Hunt was made temporary Assistant Caretaker and Housekeeper. The ex-school could house some 40 nurses, and a significant advance had been made from the accommodation impasse.

Battle's small training school for nurses was still struggling along. A Group Preliminary Training School had been established at the Royal Berkshire Hospital in 1943 and the Corporation agreed to pay a fee of £6 6s per nurse for new Battle nurses to undergo their eight weeks of preliminary training there, but the arrangement was terminated four months later due to transport and other difficulties. Tutor Sister Crofts had managed to do the Part I exam of the Diploma of Nursing Examinations in 1944, but the Hospitals Yearbook for 1945/6 records that the Battle Tutor was not on the roll of qualified Sister Tutors of the College of Nursing. Sister Crofts and Matron Brace were having to run a Preliminary Training School for the few new recruits, a three-year academic course, without adequate classroom and study facilities and a full clinical training programme, hampered by lack of trained staff, by bed closures due to staffing problems and the rigid regulations of the College. In 1947 some improvements were made to the training facilities in H Block and Miss M G R Gregory is recorded as Assistant Sister Tutor (unqualified). Students from the Berkshire Mental Hospital were accepted that year to take the courses of the Preliminary Training School.

In January 1948 the General Nursing Council agreed that Battle Hospital be approved provisionally as a complete training school for male nurses with the number of students limited to a maximum of 12 at any one time, probably a very optimistic figure. In April, Miss Hammond SRN, SCM, aged 49, was appointed Sister Tutor, but now the National Health Service was less than three months away. It is no surprise that Matron was instructed to discuss with the Royal Berkshire Hospital Matron the possibilities of a combined training school between the two Hospitals.

Despite the continual lack of nursing staff, the training problems, and the inadequate accommodation for nursing and medical staff, Battle Hospital had been making solid post-war progress, in close co-operation with the Royal Berkshire Hospital. During 1947 the Hospital admitted 3,638 patients and performed 1,087 operations. This figure was 'for the main theatre only' and represented many patients from the Royal Berks waiting lists for surgery and gynaecology. During the year the Maternity Ward had 581 deliveries, 73 by doctors. The dramatic increase in maternity work was doubtless due to Dr Harvey's interest in obstetrics. Bob Eggleton remembers him as a genial man who was more concerned with clinical matters than administration. Within a month of his arrival the new Medical Superintendent had established a weekly ante-natal and post-natal clinic in the former First Aid Post, under his personal direction. These clinics served all patients in West Reading, whether they were booked for confinement at Battle, at one of the other municipal maternity homes or by the Corporation's domiciliary midwives. In the Maternity Ward two Junior Sisters were appointed for day and night duty and the Medical Superintendent invited assistance from part-time midwives and from volunteers for maternity duty. Sister James in charge of the Ward was refunded £6 6s for attending a special course in gas and air analgesia at Plymouth, although the Health Committee did wonder whether courses could not be held in Reading. In November an additional gas and air machine[3] was purchased for the Ward.

In October 1946 plans were introduced for the adaption of C Block to provide a full maternity unit which it was hoped would become a training school. The Central Midwives Board, however, informed the Medical Officer of Health that 'as the Maternity Department does not conduct over 500 confinements per year recognition as a Part I training school cannot be considered'. (The 1946 maternity admissions totalled 477.) Training of the Unit's own staff did continue, including a month's course for two Sisters at Sorrento Maternity Home, Birmingham, on the care of premature babies. And plans for the new Unit slowly moved on. Some optimists felt it was uneconomic to proceed with converting C Block – the increasing maternity work meant that the time had arrived to consider the erection of a new building! Eventually a scheme was prepared using part of the first and second floors of C Block, which meant reorganising accommodation for some of the nursing staff and involved alterations to the resident Medical Officer's quarters on the 3rd floor. The Ministry approved, but required extra expenditure on the Premature Baby Unit, the provision of two sterilising rooms, more heating for the Nursery and a call-bell system for the Medical Officer. The total cost had risen from an original £1,850 to £3,470. By now it was June 1948. All agreed that since the heating work must be done in the summer months the contract should go ahead at once even though take-over by the National Health Service was imminent.

While the maternity work advanced under Dr Harvey's enthusiastic superintendence, the shortage of general nurses was affecting more than just the acute services. In May 1947 the Public Assistance Committee asked for extra beds for aged and chronic sick persons, the number having been reduced because of lack of nursing staff. The Medical Superintendent could not offer much help. 'While we appreciate the efforts of the Relieving Officers to reduce to a minimum the number of applications for admission of such cases, there is little which can be done in the present day conditions.' He was authorised as an emergency measure to move certain types of cases from F to D Block[4] and thus provide beds in F Block for the treatment of aged and chronic sick. It was at this difficult time that the Ministry of Health Inspectors reported on Battle's care of the infirm and chronic sick with suggestions to improve arrangements in D, E, F and H Blocks. Some were done, the remainder were 'authorised when equipment and labour were available'.

In August 1947 the Ministry's advisory dietitian also inspected Battle. This visit was very different from the perfunctory wartime inspection; it took four days and was followed by a 20-page Report from which many improvements resulted. A fully qualified Cook was appointed, additions were made to the kitchen equipment and despite food rationing, the Hospital diet was expanded. Porridge was offered five times a week, fish and chips for supper on Mondays, fish and soup on two other nights. Fried fish for dinner on Wednesday allowed bacon rashers to be served for breakfast. Tea was made in the wards instead of the main kitchen and a gas stove and refrigerator were installed upstairs in H Block. The decision to appoint a Catering Officer was left to the forthcoming Regional Hospitals Board.

In February 1948 further improvements were made to the nurses' diet. A part-time Cook was employed in the nurses' canteen in the evenings; fishcakes or meat pasties were offered for supper; porridge, cereal and toast for breakfast and instead of vegetable soup for dinner a main mid-day meal was now provided. Slab cake would be purchased from Huntley and Palmers in such quantities 'as may be required by members of the nursing staff', and from local firms a supply of fancy cakes. Arrangements were to be made with Messrs T Walls and Sons to supply ice cream as a portion of a main meal once a week for patients and for staff. The Steward reported that ice cream could be obtained locally without surrender of margarine and butter from the hospital's allocation, but higher in price and lower in fat content. The Health Committee insisted on using Walls.

Financial inducements were probably more effective than foodstuffs in encouraging key staff to stay. Mr Watts, the Attendant who had been promoted 10 years previously, was put on the 1946 revised scale of salaries for male nurses and special application was made regarding Assistant Nurse Mr Janes, in charge of H Block male wards. The Minister agreed that as an assistant nurse acting in a higher capacity his salary could be a matter for discretion, and Mr Janes was placed at mid-scale on £5 4s a week.

To help with Reading's chronic shortage of nursing staff the County Organiser for the British Red Cross offered to appeal for more volunteers to render part-time assistance in the Hospitals, an offer accepted with alacrity. One of the volunteers was Jean Rose who at the end of the war came to Reading University from South Africa and then worked for a time in the Royal Berkshire Hospital pathology laboratory. Her volunteer duties were mainly in Nuffield 3 Ward at the Royal Berks but she recalls:

'We came down to feed the Battle patients at lunch time because they were so short of nurses. They didn't have the time to help get food into someone who was half conscious.'

Retaining staff and furthering progress in other departments depended on improved salaries and making additional appointments, which became an expensive business. A new set of minimum rates of pay and conditions of service for domestic and other workers had been introduced nationally from 1st April 1946. For those over 21 the minimum rates were £4 6s a week for males and £3 4s for females. A 48-hour week was adopted with revised rates for overtime and Sunday working and 12 days' annual leave in addition to Bank Holidays and all public holidays. By just applying these basic rates for current staff it was estimated that the increase in costs per year would be £2,720, but more was soon expended. The Head Porter's wages were raised to £5 a week. Mrs E Bennett, Dressmaker, having regard to her experience and long years of service, was given a wage increase of 5s a week. The Head Laundress was paid an additional sum for additional work due to shortage of labour, despite which Miss Paddick resigned. A whole-time Domestic Supervisor was appointed to release the Home Sister from this task and allow her to devote more time to nursing duties. Applications were invited for an Assistant Radiographer. Miss Dell, the Radiographer and Dispenser, had had some assistance during the war from Miss B Turnbull as a temporary Assistant Radiographer; now she was very hard pressed, particularly as all the radiographic work for the TB service was being done at Battle. When no suitable applicant could be found, an Assistant Pharmacist locum was employed. By 1947 the records show two Hospital Pharmacists, both attending a course in London on the preparation of sterile injections.

Battle's first fully trained physiotherapists appeared in 1946. Miss J Richards had been appointed to the post of Masseuse in June 1941 at a salary of £250 a year which was switched in 1944 to the rates of the Chartered Society of Massage and Medical Gymnastics. In May 1945 Mr Clancy, the Masseur, was given paid leave to attend a one-week course for physiotherapists at Botley's Place Hospital, Chertsey. A year later, in the round of salary increases, he was put on £5 a week as an Assistant (untrained) Physiotherapist. When Miss Richards left in 1946 applications were invited for the post of Physiotherapist at £320 to £380 per annum; if the appointee was a man, the Health Committee Chairman was empowered to appoint a woman part-time on a sessional basis. The successful candidate was Mr R Awbery, who had been acting in a temporary capacity since Miss Richards' resignation. Because the work was increasing, especially in maternity, surgery and children, it was decided instead of the sessional proposal to appoint an Assistant Physiotherapist and offer the post to Miss S Reece, the unsuccessful candidate at the interview.

Next, in 1947, came the start of Occupational Therapy, a very modest beginning for a service which was to assume such importance in rehabilitation. An Occupational Therapist was appointed 'for three sessions a week at 15s per session for long-stay medical and surgical patients in the first instance and subsequently to cover suitable chronic sick patients'.

Several other important appointments were made during the lead-in period to the National Health Service. In February 1946 Mr Gordon Annand, Attendant in charge of the Arthur Hill Memorial Baths, was appointed Engineer. The Clerical Department was expanded from its pre-war establishment, which by now was quite inadequate. A new position was created of Deputy Clerk and Steward. The Senior Clerk Mr J Kingsley was promoted to the post and his appointment was confirmed at a salary of £330–£375 per annum in January 1947. It was also agreed to appoint two additional clerks, a secretary for the Medical Superintendent and two shorthand typists. When a qualified Almoner was appointed, a shorthand typist would be employed in that department as well. A disabled ex-serviceman was sought as Telephonist but when no one of a suitable type was found an extra clerk was added to help with telephone duties.

A separate Records Office was set up, standardising the records for the Region and additional office and clerical accommodation was put into K Block for the increasing out-patient work. Miss Ivy Farmer, aged 28, was made Clerk and Shorthand Typist for the Almoner's Department, herself acting as Assistant Almoner until Miss P Shirley, four years her junior, took up the duties of Hospital Almoner in September 1947. Finally, only a month before the start of the National Health Service and linked to the arrival of a new 4-valve X-ray apparatus, Miss Dell at last got an Assistant Radiographer, Mrs Fraser (nee Turnbull). None of these is likely to have had a job description to compare with that of the additional Night Porter appointed in May 1948. His instructions covered any coming eventuality under the National Health Service, switching smoothly from the specific to the all-encompassing: 'Attend the main switchboard till midnight, relieve the Night Porter at the entrance lodge, patrol the grounds and carry out any necessary porter's duties.'

There were some changes, too, in medical staffing before the Council relinquished control to the National Health Service. September 1947 saw suspension of most rules on Hospital B2 and B1 posts, but this was of little significance since the positions at Battle were comfortably occupied. At specialist level in mid-1947 it was arranged for the Royal Berkshire Hospital physician Dr Horace Le Marquand to have fortnightly consulting sessions at Battle and to be available for special visits. He was paid at the recognised rates of £3 for a two-hour session and a minimum of £2 per visit. When the Battle ECG machine broke down Dr Le Marquand's personal apparatus was used temporarily, operated by Mr Forder, the Royal Berks Radiographer, 'subject to payment of an inclusive fee of £3 on each occasion'.

In February 1948 Mr Bone, now titled Deputy Medical Super-intendent, was allowed to go on a surgical course in London for two months, Mr Baxter being paid £150 for emergency operations while he was away. Many doctors were eyeing prized posts in the National Health Service and were jockeying to improve their chances of a consultant appointment. Dr Ratcliff, who had been Visiting Medical Officer to Park Hospital (in succession to Dr Cane) since October 1944, now wanted his title changed to 'Paediatrician to Battle Hospital (to include the care of infectious fevers at Park Hospital)', pointing out the voluntary service he was giving as Clinical Assistant in the children's ward. There would be no change of salary and perhaps it is surprising that the Health Committee did not make any official response.

Dr Hausmann, possibly thanks to advice from Dr Le Marquand, did get some recognition – in May 1948 the Medical Superintendent was 'empowered to inform the Registrar of the General Council of Medical Education and Registration of the United Kingdom that the services of Dr Walter Hausmann have been rendered in a satisfactory manner and to recommend that his service as a foreign practitioner in this country qualify him for registration in the Medical Register without limit of time'. This would have been one of the last major decisions approved by the Medical Officer of Health, Dr Wright before he put in his resignation. He was to take a similar post in the County Borough of Croydon in October. The Health Committee expressed to him fulsome thanks which were to be engrossed on vellum, sealed with the common seal of the Corporation, bound in book form with the Arms of the Borough on the cover and presented as a memento. This gesture, after just two years' service as Medical Officer of Health, contrasts jarringly with the off-hand treatment of Dr Thomas.

Neither did the Clerk and Steward hear many fanfares when he announced he would retire in February 1948, although the Battle Sub-committee did record high appreciation of Mr Farmer's '27 years' service, 18 with the Council'. The appointment of a successor was referred to the Oxford Regional Hospitals Board which was already in place with an embryonic Establishment Committee. They agreed that the post of Steward should be advertised now. 'In view of the probability that he would have to work in close co-operation with the Royal Berkshire Hospital it would be an act of considerable courtesy if the Corporation would invite a representative from Royal Berkshire Hospital as well as the Secretary of the Hospital Board to be present as observers at the appointment.' This was agreed; six candidates were interviewed and the post was offered to Mr L C Niles from Staffordshire. When Mr Niles started in February 1948, he was accommodated as a temporary measure in a room in H Block with nearby bathroom and with meals in the nurses' dining room. Not surprisingly, considering the shortage of housing, he was unable to find outside accommodation for himself and his wife so the arrangement continued into the era of the National Health Service. The new Steward was quick to stamp his mark, notably with improvements to records and stores control, and with the appointment of additional stores staff. It was he who tried to augment the hospital's food ration by changing the supplier of ice cream. Mr Niles attended a one-week summer school of the Institute of Hospital Administrators in June 1948. No doubt this was a well-subscribed course and his expenses were paid by the Oxford Regional Hospitals Board.

The Corporation and its Health Committee had done their best to hand over a fully staffed and properly equipped general hospital. They, however, like the Guardians before them, had to leave unfinished several matters which were for the most part outside their control. Some were relatively minor, such as moving the telephone switchboard from the general office; the Post Office was unable to start this work for 12 months. When the Austin ambulance was destroyed by fire, £1,000 insurance was recovered, the chassis purchased from the insurers and returned to Austins for rebuilding and fitting a new ambulance body. Their quote in February 1948 was for £1,050 with an estimated delay of six months! St John Ambulance Brigade may have come to regret a public-spirited offer of temporary use of their vehicle at no charge. Transporting staff to and from 42 Bath Road was another problem. The question was raised of purchasing a utility van but it was decided to continue hiring transport until the National Health Service take-over.

The major disappointment was that the Corporation's hospital was being passed on still handicapped by a severe shortage of nursing staff. In April 1948 scarcity of student nurses compelled Matron to reduce the number of acute female beds; admissions from the female waiting list were restricted to urgent cases only. This was scarcely a happy note on which Battle's 18 years as a municipal hospital would be ending, despite all the local authority's high hopes and tireless endeavours. How galling that the single most important cause was failure to provide sufficient high-quality accommodation for the nurses, the major deficiency inherited from the Guardians. Had the Health Committee taken this up just a year or two earlier, their new Nurses' Home might have been in place before building plans were scuppered by the Second World War. They did continue with the struggle for more accommodation right to the finish. In January 1948 alterations and additions were proposed at 42 Bath Road to house 11 more nursing staff, including four Night Sisters in the cottage and conversion of the laundry to quarters for the Assistant Matron. The plan went ahead, again approved by the new Oxford Regional Hospitals Board.

In truth, Reading Borough Council could be proud of their stewardship of Battle. The engineering facilities and estate had been maintained and modernised as well as possible in the most difficult of circumstances, recession followed by war. The farm and market garden had provided fresh foods for the Hospital and healthy employment for fit paupers, although their dwindling numbers meant that these activities would soon lapse. The Public Assistance Committee had kept a caring watch on the pauper inmates, the aged and infirm. The Council had tried repeatedly at the Board of Control's request to have the mental defectives transferred to certified institutions or approved homes, but there were simply no places available. Overcoming huge obstacles, the Hospital had advanced in many fields with staffing levels expanded to meet the new demands. In time of national crisis it had once again played its part. Without World War II, Battle would surely have become one of the finest of England's municipal hospitals.

It was not until April 1948 that the Emergency Hospital Service finally declared that it was no longer necessary to reserve any beds for emergency use. In that month the Regional Health Council was wound up and the Reading and District Hospital Management Committee came into being. Dr Wright, who was still in post as Medical Officer of Health, nominated Dr Harvey as a member, but without success.

Months before the Appointed Day the Health Committee had had to deal with the bureaucratic complications of transfer involving matters such as ambulances, mental health, maternity care, vaccination, voluntary associations, services for mothers and young children – all these in addition to the Hospital services. In June 1948, they met at Battle and observed for the minutes: 'As this is the last occasion on which we shall have the opportunity of visiting the Hospital before it is transferred and vested in the Minister of Health, we desire to place on record our appreciation of the valuable services rendered to the Corporation by the officers and staff of Battle, Park and Manor Smallpox Hospitals.'

NOTES

1. The first floor had a small nurses' dormitory and Sister's bedroom, sleeping a total of five.
2. Weil's Disease or leptospirosis is an infection contracted from rats.
3. The nitrous oxide and air apparatus permitted for use by midwives, invented by Dr Minnitt of Liverpool in 1933, was an effective means of pain relief, although later it was found to sometimes deliver dangerously low levels of oxygen.
4. D Block was still being used for female mental patients.

3

THE NATIONAL HEALTH HOSPITAL

The Changeover

The National Health Service held great promise for those local authority hospitals still bearing the stigma of the workhouse. Although their institutional accommodation was to be taken over by the Minister of Health, the County and County Borough Councils would retain responsibility for the welfare of the inmates. When new accommodation was found for these unfortunates the Hospital could expand, developing new clinical services while shedding along the way the mistrust and folklore fears of its local community. The NHS Area Management Committee would decide the Hospital's new role; Health Service funding would provide the staff and facilities for those functions to be proudly fulfilled. The second half of the twentieth century beckoned invitingly.

How glittering was this future for Battle Hospital? Even its most optimistic supporters must have realised that the main hospital for Reading was still to be the Royal Berkshire. In 1947 a Report by the Regional Hospitals on the planning of hospital services in the Berks., Bucks. and Oxon. region had dismissed the possibility of building the key hospital for Reading on the Battle site, despite the wide spacing and solid construction of its buildings and the large area of farm land available for development. Even if it were possible, the Report said, 'only a small section of the present buildings could be used'. The Regional Planning Committee were also dubious about expansion of the Royal Berkshire Hospital until the University of Reading suddenly offered to sell its adjacent properties. Space was now available; the Committee charged with running the area's hospitals, the Reading and District Hospital Management Committee, consisted mainly of Royal Berkshire Hospital stalwarts; despite recurrent financial crises the Voluntary Hospital had always retained status and respectability. Undoubtedly the Hospital Management Committee would plan for rapid advance of their county hospital.

If Dr Wright or other Committee members not aligned with the Royal Berks held any faint hopes for Battle supremacy, those hopes were soon quashed. The Chairman of the Oxford Regional Hospital Board attended the Committee's second meeting, with the Appointed Day only a month away. His main purpose was to deprecate the pre-National Health Service proposal for a new Nurses' Home at Battle Hospital to accommodate 100 nurses at a cost of £100,000. Dr Wells used the opportunity to make clear the attitude of the Regional Board and its Government masters. The Board felt this matter was closely linked with the development of the Royal Berkshire Hospital as 'the future key hospital in the area'. The Chief Medical Planning Officer to the Ministry of Health had now made his recommendation, and plans would be drawn up for the ultimate expansion of the Royal Berkshire Hospital to approximately 800 beds. In the interim period, the Board proposed that the plan for Battle be modified to provide temporary accommodation for 40 nurses!

The members of the Reading and District Committee were highly experienced and well aware of the difference between plans and reality. Much as they supported expansion of the Royal Berks, they could also judge the importance of a well-staffed Battle Hospital in coping with pressures soon to come. In January 1947 the Berks., Bucks., and Oxon. Regional Hospitals Council had estimated the requirement for specialist services in Reading to be 1,052 beds. The Royal Berkshire Hospital had 461 beds including Blagrave Annexe. Battle had 229 beds for acute sick and maternity cases plus accommodation for 155 chronic sick and Public Assistance cases. How long would it take before 800 beds were available on the Royal Berks site? How long before the Public Assistance patients were removed from Battle? Matron Brace was already warning that with poor staff accommodation and facilities, nurse recruitment to Battle remained disastrous and that not only beds but whole acute wards would have to be closed. The Hospital Management Committee protested vigorously to Oxford and managed to achieve a peculiar partial retraction. At their next meeting, the Oxford Regional Hospitals Board clarified its proposal for the Battle nurses: 'a unit of 40-50 beds of a semi-permanent nature, as the first part of a scheme for 100 beds, which could be completed in, say, a year or two's time when the situation as regards raw materials might be easier …' The woolly phrases and shifting of responsibility for a problem have a decidedly familiar ring although modern management jargon had yet to be acquired.

Early Problems

So the Royal Berkshire Hospital was definitely to be the key hospital where the major developments would occur. And Battle would certainly not be closed. It was badly needed, at least for the care of some chronic sick and to help provide acute beds. The long-term future was soon under consideration by a host of committees, all reporting finally to the Hospital Management Committee and thus to the Regional Board. These were pressure groups representing the specialities, a consultants' Medical Advisory Committee and a co-ordinating Battle Hospital Planning Sub-committee. Since nearly every proposed development was inter-related with the Royal Berkshire Hospital, by April 1949 this latter became simply the Hospital Planning Sub-committee which was to deliberate, frequently in vain, for years to come. Meanwhile there were many immediate problems, big and small, associated with the changeover of control at Battle from the local authority to the NHS, and in establishing the precise relationship between the two Hospitals.

The National Assistance Act 1948 terminated the existing Poor Law. Under Part III of the Act every local authority still had the duty to provide residential accommodation for persons who, by reason of age, infirmity and any other circumstances, were in need of care and attention which was otherwise not available to them. From July 5th 1948, these patients were administered by the local authority's Health Committee, maintaining the status quo although under a different administration. But many of them still lived in the hospitals taken over by the National Health Service. The common attitude to 'Part III patients' in the larger hospitals was a sympathetic hostility: they were bed occupiers and their removal was urgently requested. Provision of alternative accommodation for those at Battle was to be a long time coming.

Having nationalised the hospital services of local authorities, the National Health Service left them not only the Poor Law patients, but a range of healthcare responsibilities and part-responsibilities which included tuberculosis, infectious diseases, midwifery, mental patients, health education, health visiting and ambulances. The strangeness of the mixture is well illustrated by the arrangements for tuberculosis. Dr Edward Hughes DPH, MD, DPA who succeeded Dr Wright in October noted: 'It is unfortunate that the responsibility for aftercare of TB patients and prevention of the spread of TB should be the responsibility of one authority, whereas the treatment of the actual disease is the responsibility of two others, the Regional Hospital Board or the Local Executive Council.' (The latter controlled the local general practitioner and pharmaceutical service). Dr Harley Stevens, Superintendent at Peppard Sanatorium, wanted administration of the TB services to be concentrated in Reading. Negotiations were proceeding for a chest clinic in Gun Street, but he urged planning to start immediately for a chest clinic and ward unit in the grounds of Battle Hospital.

The Royal Berkshire Hospital physicians had much to say on the distinction between local authority responsibilities and their own. Some was trivial. Continuation of the scabies clinic at Battle was agreed as part of the Hospital specialist skin service, on the understanding that it would be for treatment as distinct from detection and cleaning. To address the more major and wider problems involving both Hospitals the Medicine Sub-committee prepared a comprehensive Report. Before considering this long-term Report and those from other medical specialities, it is worth noting some of the immediate difficulties on the administrative side and how they were resolved.

Mr Niles, formerly the Clerk and Steward, was sensibly appointed Administrative Officer at Battle Hospital and continued living in rooms in the administrative block adapted to provide married quarters. There was no such comfortable position in the committee structure of the NHS for Dr Harvey, who as Medical Superintendent had been head of a hierarchy in the municipal hospital. Dr Harvey seems not to have relinquished his post too readily. It was six months before 'on the suggestion of the Secretary of the Oxford Regional Hospitals Board' he informed the Special Advisory Committee on the Status of Senior Members of Hospital Staffs that it was with mutual agreement between the Hospital Management Committee and himself that he wished to be relieved of his administrative duties and to work full-time as an obstetrician and gynaecologist at Battle Hospital. He resigned in December 1949.

Other problems with the new bureaucracy came swiftly. In September 1948, Mrs Stride, Secretary and Administrative Officer to House Committee No.1 (Reading Area), drew attention to difficulties arising as a result of the appointment of an Administrative Officer at Battle Hospital and at the Royal Berks. This really only involved Mr Niles; the RBH post was not filled until Mr Les Parcell was appointed in January 1949. The Finance and General Purposes Sub-committee resolved that 'having regard to the views previously accepted that Battle Hospital and the Royal Berkshire Hospital should be administered as one unit, the post of Administrative Officer to House Committee No.1 shall carry with it the responsibility for the administration of all the hospitals in the Reading area, and that this officer shall be assisted in this respect by Assistant Administrative Officers at the Royal Berkshire Hospital and at Battle Hospital.' Not surprisingly, Mr Niles was immediately in correspondence concerning the redesignation of his post. He was invited to attend the next meeting, where Mr McIlroy, the Chairman, must have been at his most diplomatic and persuasive. At the end of discussions Mr Niles told the Committee that having regard to the suggestion now made by the Chairman concerning the question of full co-operation and goodwill from all members of the staff associated with the administration of the new health services, he was prepared to accept the decision of the Committee. He resigned four months later to take up another post.

There would not be similar problems with the administration of supplies. The Finance and General Purposes Committee approved a report from the Chief Administrative Officer that in each of the House Committee areas, one officer be designated to undertake responsibility for purchase of supplies. For House Committee No.1 (Reading area), this was Mr C E Buck, Purchasing Officer to the Royal Berkshire Hospital. Miss Glascock was appointed Catering Officer to House Committee No.1 while the purchase of all drugs, dressings and chemicals in every hospital managed by the Reading and District Hospital Management Committee was to be under the control of Mr Burton, Chief Pharmacist at the Royal Berks. On the engineering side, Battle was given more autonomy. Additional maintenance staff were appointed in 1948, a carpenter, bricklayer, builder's labourer, four painters, and electrician's apprentice. Against the staffing trend, Mr G Annand the Engineer at Battle was appointed to be Engineer in Charge of the Royal Berkshire Hospital, Blagrave, Dellwood Maternity Home, Grove Maternity Home, Park Isolation and Whitley Smallpox Hospitals while Mr J W V West from the Royal Berks took his place as Engineer in Charge at Battle.

The Physicians' Report

The Medicine Sub-committee's Report was presented in December 1948. It detailed serious problems and urged rapid action:

The population of the Division was 290,000 and accommodation for medical cases in particular was inadequate. The Royal Berkshire Hospital had 60 acute specialist medical beds available and 19 for children. Battle had 20 acute medical beds for women (half of B Top: later Ipsden Ward, later Stubbs), 39 for men (half of A Top: later Chiltern Ward, later Lowry), 15 for children (C Lower: the ground floor of Thames Block). The other half of B Top was occupied by chronic sick patients. Beds in Block F (the original Union infirmary, later female workhouse, later Shiplake and Eversley, later Gainsborough and Constable Wards), where these acute medical patients should be housed were occupied by patients for whom the Reading Borough Council and not the Regional Hospital Board was responsible. In this way beds for the acutely sick women were being blocked.

The Report noted that the chronic sick fell into three categories, the elderly sick (chronic and acute), the incurable of any age and the destitute. It went on to say: 'The elderly suffer from being grouped with the others and more can be done for them. They should be a separate responsibility and looked after in their own acute wards, chronic wards and long-stay annexes.' The physicians recommended that a geriatrician be appointed. Dr J G Bird, who had been in charge of the Electro-therapy and then the Cardiological Departments at the Royal Berks, was willing to undertake this work and they were prepared to give him every support should this recommendation be favourably received. As an immediate measure, Dr Bird had taken over the care of the aged sick at Battle Hospital.

The Report made five recommendations directly affecting Battle: appoint a Geriatrician; remove Section 3 cases from H and F Blocks (the male and female workhouses); use A Top and B Top for acute medical cases only, then a geriatric unit can be formed grouping the elderly sick into acute and chronic wards; appoint an Assistant Almoner and a part-time Occupational Officer mainly for use in the chronic wards to enable the proper care of the elderly to be carried out; provide convalescent beds for the Royal Berkshire and Battle Hospitals at Park Hospital and Wallingford Isolation Hospital. The physicians urged the great benefits which would follow. 'The acute beds at the key Hospital will only be occupied by those patients who require the full facilities of a modern hospital. The acute medical sick at Battle will be separated from the chronic sick with raising of standards in diagnosis, treatment and nursing. Better provision will be made in the existing buildings for the elderly patients. Nursing at Battle will be made more attractive.'

The physicians also documented the plight of the mentally defective patients at Battle. 'Although Battle Hospital is an Approved Institution for the purpose of housing mentally defective patients, there is no provision for such patients and the situation is as follows. Six mentally defective children go to school daily and on their return to hospital, four boys aged 8-16 have to go to bed because of restricted facilities. The two girls, ages 10 and 14, sit with about thirteen senile destitute women. Two defective small children live in the Nursery. During the school holidays the four boys do not leave the ward.'

With a few minor amendments the Medical Advisory Committee recommended the Hospital Management Committee to adopt this Report and forward it to the Regional Board with a request for guidance as to how far it should be implemented. The question of urgently needed accommodation for the mental defectives was referred to Dr Harvey and Dr Le Marquand for consideration and report. Their reply was prompt. Since patients of that particular type could not properly be looked after in any hospital in the area of the Hospital Management Committee, they were unable to make any recommendations and the only solution would be for the Board to provide additional accommodation for the purpose. The Board responded that the problem was under active consideration. It was unlikely however that any great extension of accommodation could be achieved in the immediate future; in the meantime the Board was reluctantly compelled to continue the use of all the accommodation currently holding defectives.

By 1951 all the Part III men in H Block and nearly all the female inmates of F Block had been removed. A few were accepted by Dr Bird as hospital cases and taken over as the responsibility of the Hospital Management Committee. The last Part III women left in 1953, while the deplorable situation of the mentally defective children was not completely resolved until April 1955, when the last child was transferred from F Block Nursery to Bradwell Grove Hospital. In May 1955 the Minister withdrew his direction that Battle Hospital should be used for the accommodation of mental defectives.

Changes in Medicine and the Use of Park Hospital
There was some progress on the medical staffing side although many decisions were being deferred. The Medicine Sub-committee confirmed the recommendation that Dr Bird be in charge of the elderly patients at Battle and agreed that Dr L M Jennings should do two sessions a week of ward rounds. They felt that all specialist out-patient services should be in one building, but until new accommodation was available at the Royal Berkshire Hospital they recommended as a temporary measure extra out-patient sessions at Battle Hospital. Dr Bird would run a geriatric clinic, Dr Jennings a diabetic clinic and Dr Le Marquand a neurological clinic in association with the Neurological Department at Oxford. Dr Ritchie Russell, the eminent Oxford neurologist, was prepared to co-operate. The physicians also succeeded in getting more junior staff. By September 1949

the Finance and General Purposes Committee had approved the appointment of a Resident Medical Officer with some duties at Battle, and a second House Physician specifically to Battle.

The pressure on medical beds at Battle was eased by the diminution of infectious disease cases at Park Hospital. In 1951, Park was adapted to receive acute medical cases and it was agreed that the House Officer for the Medical Department would rotate between the Royal Berkshire, Battle and Park Hospitals. The Oxford Regional Hospital Board suggested that since there were already two other Park Hospitals in the Oxford region and Park Isolation Hospital was situated in a suburb bearing a euphonious name, the Hospital Management Committee might consider a name change. The name Prospect Park Hospital was officially approved in May 1951. By 1952 Prospect Park had 40 acute medical beds transferred from Battle, still leaving 30 beds allocated for either infectious diseases or general medicine, eight fully reserved for infectious diseases and 25 for patients with tuberculosis.

Dr Walter Hausmann moved from Battle to Prospect Park to remain in charge of the medical beds. Dr Hausmann had obtained the specialist qualification of MRCP in 1949. He published several important and erudite papers and was probably a more knowledgeable and skilled physician than the consultants at the Royal Berkshire Hospital, but was held at the lesser rank of Senior Hospital Medical Officer. His particular interests included endocrinology and cardiology. Evelyn Aust, who was the technician for his primitive ECG machine housed in one of the old padded cells in Out-patients, still marvels at his expertise and his teaching. In a mean-minded decision of 1952, the Regional Board granted Dr Hausmann 'the personal rank of Consultant without change in status or salary'. He was to give sterling service at Prospect Park, particularly in the care of patients requiring artificial ventilation.

In 1955 a flying squad was formed for respiratory paralysis cases. The members were Dr Hausmann, an anaesthetist and the Porter Frank Rackham who had returned to Park Hospital in 1946 after serving as a medic in the RAF. Mr Rackham and his wife were granted residence in the Porter's lodge. He became an expert with the iron lung and cuirass respirators, making himself available 24 hours a day, seven days a week. Frank was one of the earliest respiratory technicians, but since there was then no such NHS position, he was promoted for pay purposes firstly to Foreman Porter, then Head Porter. Considering his skills and dedicated service he was still appallingly underpaid. Dr Hausmann also stayed unrewarded until in 1959 the Board and the Ministry approved his proper upgrading and the additional Consultant post on the Board's establishment. In later years Walter Hausmann would conclude his outstanding service to Reading as the greatly loved and respected Medical Officer to the nursing staff of Battle Hospital.

The Annual Report for 1952 showed Battle as having no acute medical beds following the transfers to Prospect Park. There were still

4,169 out-patient attendances in general medicine, but at the Royal Berks the figure was 8,437. A year later a further 2,000 medical out-patient attendances had shifted from Battle to the Royal Berkshire Hospital. Acute general medicine would not return to Battle for another 20 years.

Tuberculosis
Before the advent of streptomycin and the many more effective anti-tuberculous drugs, TB was a major problem for the brand new National Health Service, the difficulties made worse by its disjointed pattern of management. In Reading's district the Sanatorium at Peppard under Medical Superintendent Dr Harley Stevens had 242 patients; Dr Tattersall, Reading Borough Council's Chest Physician, had arranged for some TB convalescent beds at Park Isolation Hospital; Dr D Kemp and Dr G Shaw left the service of the Berkshire County Council to join the Regional Hospital Board as Chest Physicians, though a proportion of Dr Kemp's services were retained in connection with the prevention of tuberculosis; in central Reading Drs Kemp and Shaw ran the County's Chest Clinic in Abbots Walk, and Dr Tattersall the Borough's London Street Clinic, next to the Coroner's Court.

In 1950 the Hospital Planning Committee finally agreed with Dr Harley Stevens' early vision of a central, hospital-based chest clinic, but they wanted it on the Royal Berks site. For once, Battle Hospital prevailed. Following an abortive plan to convert the nursery part of F Block, the new site chosen was K Block at No. 330 Oxford Road, originally the Tramp Wards with the padded cells on the ground floor and stone-breaking punishment yard. Changing decisions, debates over building works and the provision of necessary equipment particularly X-ray facilities all took their time so that transfer of the Reading and the Berkshire Chest Clinics to the Battle Central Chest Clinic did not occur until July 1954. In the meantime Dr Tattersall had resigned and been replaced in 1951 by Dr A J Karlish, who was appointed to be Assistant Chest Physician to the hospitals and clinics in the Reading area. Arthur Karlish, Polish-born with an MD from Rome, had been Registrar to the Paddington and Kensington Chest Clinics and St Charles Hospital, London. The very British ex-Army Medical Officer Dr R D Foskett was appointed as Consultant Chest Physician in January 1952. The mutual dislike of these opposite personalities would become legendary within the future Department of Chest Medicine at Battle Hospital.

Surgery, Accident Surgery and Hospital 'Fusion'
The first surgical bid for additional junior staff had come in September 1948 from Mr J W Bone, who like Dr Hausmann had been granted only Senior Hospital Medical Officer status. Now described as Senior Surgeon at Battle, he asked for a Medical Officer for surgical duties there and a locum Resident Surgical Officer to cover holiday periods 'until the question of a permanent employment had been settled'. The Medical

Advisory Committee ponderously recommended that the surgical staff of the Royal Berkshire Hospital be asked to assume responsibility for the surgical work at Battle in the absence of the Senior Surgeon and that the question of the appointment of an additional Medical Officer for surgical duties be deferred pending the decision of the Regional Board regarding the amalgamation of the Royal Berks and Battle.

The exact relationship of the two Hospitals was still not settled months after the NHS take-over but there was steady progress towards fusion at least in the clinical fields. The Surgery and Accident Surgery Sub-committee reported in November 1948. They were adamant that the surgical service at Battle and Royal Berkshire Hospital should be fused. They also wanted transfer of the Accident Service to Battle as soon as possible. The Medical Advisory Committee unanimously agreed and Mr Aitken Walker, the Senior Surgeon, was appointed to act as Supervisor of the Accident Service. The same meeting received a memorandum from Mr Aitken Walker on Co-ordination of Medical Services in Reading. He spelt out the problems:

'Some executive committee or person is essential for co-ordinating and running the medical services in Reading. This has been apparent during the last few months in our efforts to organise the surgical service, and to fuse the work of the two Hospitals. There is no one with the authority to direct what minor changes of organisation are to be done, even though these have been agreed upon in medical committee. All that happens is that recommendations are passed on from one committee to another up to regional level, by which time three months or more may have passed. The Visiting Medical Staff Committee is large and unwieldy and passes on all recommendations to the Area House Committee. This Committee meets fortnightly and passes on recommendations concerning medical staff matters to the Hospital Management Committee. At this point the Hospital Management Committee may prefer to consult the Medical Advisory Committee or refer to the Regional Board with corresponding delay.'

One man's plea was not enough to cut through the burgeoning bureaucracy of the National Health Service. No streamlining occurred and the roundabout of committees continued. Mostly the Hospital Management Committee managed to agree with all the important suggestions of its Medical Advisory Committee, but significant decisions had to be approved by Oxford. In fact the fusion of the clinical services was such an obvious step that it appears to have happened without any official pronouncement from the Regional Board. During 1950 the Board simply approved proposals for Area Departments in surgery, medicine, paediatrics, ophthalmology, followed shortly by anaesthetics, pathology, physical medicine, radiology, radiotherapy, dermatology and orthopaedic surgery.

By March 1952 the Management Committee was able to state in its Report: 'The fusion of the medical and nursing staffs of the Reading Hospitals have rendered possible the putting into effect previously prepared plans for the co-ordination and development of the medical services.' The essentials of this plan were to have general surgery, general medicine, paediatrics, ENT, gynaecology and ophthalmic services at the Royal Berks, acute medicine and infectious diseases at Prospect Park, and to concentrate obstetrics, geriatrics, accident and orthopaedics at Battle. The junior staff appointments were already being advertised to cover rotational duties at the different sites: for example, 'House Physician, Area Dept of Medicine' or 'Resident Anaesthetist, Area Dept of Anaesthetics'. With cessation of general surgery at Battle, Mr Bone, having earlier asked for increased surgical staff, now found himself with no work. After a period 'on loan' to Banbury, in 1952 he was officially released for duty with the Banbury Hospital Management Committee.

There was general agreement with the 1948 plan for moving the accident service to Battle, but intriguing sub-plots developed in regard to staffing of trauma and orthopaedics. This was a time when responsibility for orthopaedics was shifting from the general surgeons to a new breed of specialists and the transition was not always straightforward. In early 1949, the renowned Oxford orthopaedic surgeon Mr J R Girdlestone, who had been Consultant Adviser to the Royal Berkshire Hospital Orthopaedic Department, intimated through the Regional Board that the time had arrived when he should resign his appointment. He noted that Mr J C Scott had been working in the Royal Berks but had not had any formal appointment on the Hospital staff. The Board wanted to regularise his position as Orthopaedic Surgeon to the Reading Group of Hospitals. The Surgery and Accident Surgery Sub-committee chaired by Mr Aitken Walker supported the appointment of a Consulting Orthopaedic Surgeon, but not of a Senior Orthopaedic Surgeon because it would permanently lower the status of the Accident and Orthopaedic Surgeon in Reading; it might lead to control rather than supervision. They also recommended the appointment of a Registrar as soon as possible after the appointment of the Accident and Orthopaedic Surgeon. Was Mr Scott being groomed by the surgeons as the Accident and Orthopaedic Surgeon, who would still be under their control? The available minutes do not record any of the background discussion.

In June 1949 the Regional Board appointed Mr C M Squire to the post of Accident and Orthopaedic Surgeon at the Reading and District Group of Hospitals, in association with the Wingfield-Morris Orthopaedic Hospital in Oxford. This move kept the new Department under the aegis of the Region's specialist orthopaedic services and helped to separate Mr Squire from the Reading surgeons. In September Mr Scott 'of Harlow Wood Orthopaedic Hospital', was appointed Senior Registrar. The following year Mr Scott was upgraded to Consultant and Mr P Benham was appointed Junior Registrar.

Mike Squire, energetic and ambitious for his new Department, was certainly not under the thumb of general surgeons. By January 1950 he had submitted detailed plans for the alterations necessary at Battle for the complete transfer of the Accident and Orthopaedic Service. He demanded more beds plus an extension and improvements to the operating theatre in Centre Block. The present theatre was most unsatisfactory due to its small size, inadequate storage space and sterilising facilities and the necessity for sharing the theatre with other departments involving septic cases. For his out-patient service, a more complete take-over was required of the ground floor of H Block (the original workhouse building). All this, however, was to be only an interim arrangement. The Hospital Planning Committee agreed that the long-term future of the Accident and Orthopaedic Service would be in purpose-built accommodation at the expanding Royal Berks. Doubtless the Battle diehards hoped this distant plan would never be fulfilled.

The Hospital Planning Committee supported all of Mr Squire's interim proposals, which would also depend on adequate nursing facilities. Approximately 20 male and 15-20 female beds would be used for the casualty cases; the balance of the beds might be utilised for orthopaedics or selected cases from the general waiting list. The male patients could go to Back Ward A Block Lower (later Kennet Ward, later Reynolds), and females to Back Ward B Block Lower (later Mortimer Ward, later Turner). A Block Front could be used for resuscitation and observation for both sexes, B Front Lower for gynaecological cases and occasional overflow surgical cases.

For accident out-patients (Casualty Department and orthopaedic out-patients) the Planning Committee agreed to the replanning of H Block. Mr Niles' flat was a temporary arrangement; the general office, almoners and records need not be on the ground floor; the Dispensary and stores could be moved to the Part III accommodation at the north-east corner of the ground floor; the padded cells were no longer required. The 39 male chronic sick and the four mentally defective children on the first floor would be accommodated elsewhere; the nurses' lecture and demonstration rooms, Sister Tutor's office and male nurses' rest room would not be needed when the Preliminary Training School in the Bath Road was established and the 'block' or 'study day' system introduced to permit all lectures and theoretical nurse training at the Royal Berkshire Hospital. This major reorganisation of H Block would allow the new Casualty Department to be housed with both the physiotherapy and rehabilitation services.

As early as March 1950 the new Accident and Orthopaedic Surgeon was invited to serve on the prestigious Medical Advisory Committee. There he learned that the Regional Board offered no hope of the Battle Hospital modifications being included in the capital expenditure programme for 1950–51. Transfer was to be a piecemeal business, depending not only on the required building alterations, but on bed availability, X-ray and

Bell tower above Casualty

laboratory services and particularly on adequate nurse staffing. However, enlargement of the Battle theatre in Centre Block could start immediately into the next financial year. The tender of Messrs McCarthy E Fitt was accepted and total expenses of £3,075 approved. By March 1952 the work was complete and Mr Squire had fought and won a funding battle on equipment for his new theatre, raising this expenditure from £500 to £1,257. At this stage he also had won 91 trauma and orthopaedic beds, while during the year his Service had dealt with 5,162 out-patient attendances at Battle. The Casualty Department still remained at the Royal Berkshire Hospital however, totalling 16,165 'out-patient attendances'. Gradually the revamping of H Block progressed and once the Part III patients and the mentally defective children were gone only the bell tower was left as a reminder that this building was the original 1867 Workhouse.

Work started on the ground floor Casualty Department in November 1952, while Physiotherapy and a Rehabilitation unit were established on the first floor. Installation of new equipment for the Casualty X-ray Department was supervised by the Consultant Radiologist just appointed to 'the hospitals in the Reading area'. This was Dr George Burfield who during the next 25 years was destined to play a major role in developing the X-ray service at Battle. The Finance and General Purposes Committee approved the appointment of an additional Radiographer and two dark room Technicians for the Casualty Department. At the same time they authorised a porter for duty in H Block and three full-time cleaners, strong evidence of the high importance given to hospital cleanliness half a century ago. Today's NHS hospitals are relearning the need for full control of adequate staff to ensure the necessary standards of hygiene.

The Regional Area of Orthopaedics reiterated in 1953 that the Wingfield-Morris Hospital in Oxford should continue to have overall responsibility for the orthopaedic organisation in the Reading area and that a member of staff should visit Reading weekly to conduct clinics with the local surgeons. Mr Squire and Mr Scott accepted this, but made the point that when the new Out-patient Department was open they would be able to 'deal adequately in all respects with the orthopaedic out-patient numbers, as they are at present, so long as one of the two senior residents we are allowed is available'.

Battle Casualty finally opened in March 1954. Adaptations to a building nearly 90 years old meant the new Department was scarcely inviting. It was long and narrow, with a stone-floored corridor and box-like side rooms. However, its situation only a few yards from the main entrance on the Oxford Road was very convenient for walk-in patients and for the emergency ambulances. Nobody realised how quickly and how dramatically the numbers of both would increase.

Obstetrics and Gynaecology

The 1948 Report by the obstetricians and gynaecologists was a demanding one. Consultant Obstetrician Peter Wheeler planned to transfer all the obstetric work from the Royal Berks to Battle, and use the freed beds for gynaecology. He was emphatic that the obstetrics and gynaecological services could not be run with less than the whole of their existing accommodation at the Royal Berkshire Hospital, the whole of the existing accommodation at Battle, together with the ground floor of C Block. This meant they wanted the whole of Thames Block, the whole of the Front Ward on Lower B and the isolation accommodation in Centre Block. They also needed Dellwood Hospital, and the Chiltern Maternity Home in Peppard Road to replace the Grove Maternity Home, which was soon to become part of Highdown School. Control of the obstetric services of the region, at that time divided between the Regional Hospital Board, the local authorities and the local executive councils, should pass solely to the Regional Hospital Board.

For the Reading Area, they offered a comprehensive plan: fusion of the Battle and Royal Berkshire Hospital beds, both gynaecological and obstetric, into one unit, which would be the centre of those services in the Reading area; fusion of the medical and nursing staff; a training school for midwives; development of ante-natal services in both Reading and the area; extension of the present scheme of out-patient and operating sessions at the peripheral Hospitals, Newbury, Henley and Wallingford by visiting specialist staff; inclusion of all the newborn babies in the area into the paediatric service and the development of the nurseries for premature babies; formation of a flying squad for the area; standardisation of clinical

Opening of Maternity Unit, September 1952

records; extension and improvement of the hospital accommodation and facilities for obstetrics throughout the area, with the formation of a 20-bed obstetric unit in each town. There was originally suspicion from the general practitioners and anger about the loss of GP maternity beds when Grove Maternity Home closed and purchase of the Chiltern Maternity Home fell through. The Oxford Regional Hospital Board and the Hospital Management Committee agreed that in addition to the existing unit at Dellwood, those at Wokingham, Henley (Townlands), Newbury (Sandleford) and Wallingford (St Georges), should all be GP maternity units.

The way obstetric practice was changing was well illustrated in the 1948 Report by the County Borough Medical Officer of Health. In 1938 there had been 1,552 confinements in Reading, of which 1,000 were domiciliary. A decade later the figures were a total of 2,100, but only 645 were domiciliary. Home deliveries had thus dropped from 64% to 30%. At Battle during 1948 midwives conducted 453 deliveries and doctors 37. These figures would of course change dramatically if Battle took on all the complicated obstetric cases from the Royal Berks. The Medical Advisory Committee agreed with all of the obstetrics and gynaecological recommendations, subject to it being understood that the accommodation in the Front Ward of Block B Lower could be utilised according to day-to-

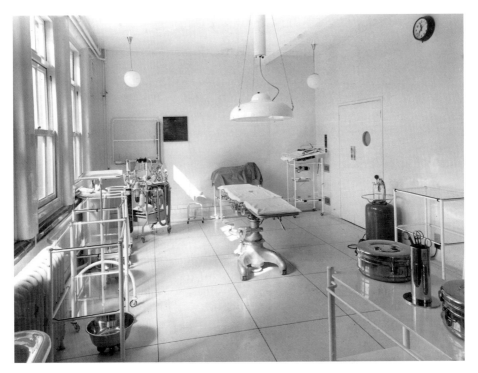

Maternity Unit Operating Theatre

Premature Babies' Nursery

day demands between surgical and gynaecological patients! Was this naivety or diplomacy?

The obstetric developments at Battle required adaptation of the ground, first, second and third floors, a bed lift, new steam main and sterilising equipment, complete re-wiring and redecoration. They were recalled by Dr Wheeler in an article for the December 1962 issue of a short-lived publication, the *Reading Hospitals Journal*. He said that the reconstruction provided ante-natal and lying-in wards, a labour ward suite with operating theatre. An ante-natal clinic was built and premature baby and neonatal unit were added. It all took two years and cost £75,000. Certainly the path was not smooth. The minutes record a serious problem in the proposal for a lift which would 'encroach on the Board's allocation of steel, two tons of which were already involved'. Thames Block was being converted to a major obstetric unit on three floors. How members of the Regional Board thought the patients and staff would cope using only stairs is not recorded. Their reluctant, delayed provision of the lift is unlikely to have been mentioned by Sir George Schuster, Chairman of the Oxford Regional Hospital Board, when he officially opened the new Battle Maternity Unit on 13th September 1952.

This conversion of the 'Block for the Aged and Infirm' to a modern Maternity Unit was a major triumph for the staff at Battle. Here was the first solid evidence that they were moving towards parity with the former Voluntary Hospital. For Mr Wheeler, however, it was merely a holding operation. He was already planning a multi-storey obstetric unit in the expanded Royal Berkshire Hospital.

Radiology, Pathology and Anaesthetics

Among the claims by other specialties during 1948 was a comprehensive Report by the Radiology and Radiotherapy Sub-committee, submitted by Dr E H P Cave. The Report noted that the Royal Berkshire Hospital was the main diagnostic centre and urgently in need of expansion of facilities and accommodation. Developments at Battle would ease the pressure, but the effect was counterbalanced by an increasing number of patients taking advantage of the facilities afforded by the NHS. An Area Superintendent Radiographer was needed and they recommended Mr O Forder, the Superintendent Radiographer at the Royal Berks, with Mr Todd strongly recommended to fill the vacated post. An area pool of radiographers was also needed. At Battle, the radiological services must expand simultaneously with those of medicine and surgery. The planned concentration of obstetric and of accident services at Battle would demand increased radiology and accommodation must be extended. Two half-day sessions by Radiologists had been instituted but additional sessions would be needed. The Radiography staff consisted of one whole-time and two part-time Radiographers. It was essential to have two whole-time. Miss Dell, one of the part-time Radiographers, wished to devote the whole of her time to the Dispensary and to sever her connection with the X-ray

Department. (Miss Dell became Chief Pharmacist, resigning in June 1957 to take up another post).

Dr Cave's Report noted that major equipment needed included a thermostatically controlled film processing unit, a portable X-ray unit for theatre use and a tomograph. His measured and well-reasoned arguments were difficult to refute. An Area Department of Radiology was created and staff and facilities were provided at Battle in reasonably close step with the developing clinical services. In those euphoric early days of the National Health Service, Dr Cave was one of the few to sound the warning that expenditure for new developments would lead inevitably to the need for further expenditure.

The new Area Anaesthetics Department took on the extra work at Battle in the Maternity Block, the Orthopaedic Theatre and the Casualty Department, with repeated warnings about the dangers of providing general anaesthesia in so many scattered sites. Close supervision, or even swift back-up in emergency, was impossible for some sessions staffed with inexperienced anaesthetists. This was a serious problem in both Hospitals, and not adequately resolved for another 50 years. A fourth Consultant was only appointed in 1958 to share the work load of Drs Basil Hill, Martin Bristow and Bryn Thomas. This was Dr Tom Boulton who recalls that the service was necessarily very consultant-based. There were just two Senior House Officers, plus one Registrar whose sole duties were looking after the Obstetrics Department at Battle. The Consultants did about eight lists a week between the two Hospitals. 'Anything at all major, either in surgery or anaesthesia, was consultant-based,' he said, a concept coming back in the modern NHS.

Until 1952, the small laboratory behind F Block was manned only in the afternoons on Monday to Friday with Mr Ernest Ingarfill as the sole technician. Dr John Mills centralised the Area Department of Pathology by closing this laboratory and having all the Battle clinical lab work done in expanded premises at the Royal Berks. Concurrently, E Block, the single-storey detached building nearby (later used by Speech Therapy and Chiropody) was taken over by the Public Health Laboratory Service, with an adjacent small animal house. The work of this Laboratory Service was public health only, such things as testing milk and water samples, investigating outbreaks of food poisoning and so on. According to Mr Ingarfill, the Public Health Laboratory Service moved from the Royal Berkshire Hospital because Dr Mills fell out with Dr Woods, the Director. This Service did not return to the Royal Berks till Dr Frank Hampson had replaced Dr Mills in charge of Pathology. Meanwhile for 20 years, until Abbey Block opened in 1972, all Battle's pathology specimens were transported to the Royal Berks.

Nursing and Nurse Training
The early decision to remove both general medicine and general surgery from Battle Hospital meant there was no long-term future for the nurses'

tiny training school, squashed in H Block with the Part III old men and mentally handicapped boys still upstairs. Some remember their Battle training with great affection. Mrs Joyce Benham did her general nurse training from 1947 to 1950. She recalls it as a very happy time under Matron Brace, who was 'efficient yet motherly'. They worked hard but with a good social life, tennis and badminton on site and some scrumping of apples at night in the orchard. Others were less enamoured. Denis Petty, one of the early male nurses, thought the training facilities were quite inadequate and he recalled students struggling at midnight to decipher notes from lectures by one of the foreign doctors.

Now Battle's student nurses would have to become part of a centralised training programme. In 1952 Paxton House and later Pendragon in the Bath Road became the Group Preliminary Training School. The more senior student nurses went to the newly designated Reading Combined Hospitals Training School for Nurses at the Royal Berkshire Hospital. Approval of Battle Hospital as a complete training school for general nurses was withdrawn by the General Nursing Council as from the end of June 1952 and the Principal Tutor at Battle transferred to the expanded Training School. Mrs Doreen Thomas had come to Battle in May 1949 following the death of her husband and she eventually retired in 1970. When I interviewed her in 1987 she was proud of two particular achievements in her brief time at Battle: they had male student nurses 'long before the Royal Berks' and she developed a State Registered Mental Nurse training programme in association with the Hospitals of Broadmoor, Fairmile and Borocourt.

As Matron Brace had forecast, recruiting adequate nursing staff continued to be a nightmare. There was still a nation-wide shortage anyway. Battle with its old buildings, its elderly chronic sick, its mental patients and diminishing opportunities for experience in general medicine and surgery, hardly offered an attractive prospect. And accommodation remained a fundamental problem as the start of the much-discussed new Nurses' Home was constantly delayed.

Some indication of the size of the problem is given by the monthly statement of numbers of nursing and midwifery staff at the Reading hospitals. The figures include trained and student nurses, state certified midwives and pupil midwives, enrolled assistant nurses, pupil assistant nurses and nursing orderlies. For October 1948, the Royal Berkshire Hospital including Blagrave and Greenlands, had in actual numbers 241 full-time and 28 part-time nurses. To make up the establishment on the basis of a 96-hour fortnight, the requirement in terms of full-time staff was another 38. For Battle the figures were: actual 81 full-time, nine part-time; required 157! The great deficiency was in student nurses. For the whole of the Area, the total shortage of students was 336. With the limited nursing numbers at Battle, whole wards did sometimes have to be closed, but the figures slowly improved. By October 1952 the Battle requirement was down to 85 while at this time the Royal Berks was still 39 short of establishment.

Thames Block

Work on the Nurses' Home project at last started in January 1952. The site chosen was close to the eastern boundary corner where Valentia Road meets Audley Street. The general layout was to be two substantial semi-detached houses on two floors with a corridor through, the first to house 26 student nurses. They could however be adapted for trained nurses' bedrooms and sitting rooms or small flats. Unsurprisingly, it was soon decided that the new building would be used for trained staff while students would be accommodated in the old Nurses' Home behind the Centre Block. The new Home for trained staff, having been built in Coronation year, was called Elizabeth House.

Administrative Changes

Following a major reshuffle in 1952 a new and stable administration was put in place. To meet the Ministry Auditors' requirements, Mr H E Ryan, the Chief Administrative Officer (now called Group Secretary), proposed 'the whole of the House Committee No.1's units form too big a command for a single administrative officer'. Mr Geoffrey Weston, his Deputy, was given direct responsibility for Battle and Prospect Park Hospitals. Mrs Stride was to continue to administer the Royal Berkshire Hospital, Blagrave, Whitley Smallpox, Dellwood Maternity Home and Greenlands Nursing Home. She became ill and shortly resigned in strained circumstances, impugning the integrity of both Mr G Cashell, Chairman of

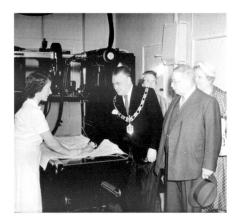

Opening of Elizabeth House, July 1954   New X-ray equipment

the Medical Advisory Committee and Mr W McIlroy, Chairman of the Management Committee. The Hospital Management Committee expressed complete confidence in them both.

Mr A D C Williams was now appointed Hospital Secretary to the Royal Berks; Mr R E Penney was made Deputy to Mr Williams and Hospital Assistant Secretary to Prospect Park. Mr J P Kingsley, the Assistant Administrative Officer for Battle, became Assistant Hospital Secretary at Sandleford. He in turn was replaced by Mr L H Parcell who became Hospital Assistant Secretary at Battle under the nominal supervision of Mr Weston. Les Parcell was to guide Battle Hospital through perhaps its very best years.

From a messy and confused entry into the National Health Service, Battle Hospital had now developed its basic structure and function for the next decade and a half. Of the large estate, 20 acres of farm had been leased since 1950, leaving three acres for a market garden around the poultry sheds and piggeries. The Part III residents who had worked the farm and the laundry were all gone, together with those less fit and the mentally handicapped. Instead of the Public Assistance chronic sick, there was now the beginnings of a modern geriatric service. Acute medicine was restricted to out-patients, including a specialist Neurological Clinic. The original Workhouse was transformed into Reading's Accident and Orthopaedic Service. Alongside it the vagrants' reception block now housed the Central Chest Clinic, while the 1911 Hospital for the Aged and Infirm had become the central Maternity Unit. Its building was called Thames Block, one of the pleasant-sounding local names chosen in 1951 to replace the soulless designations of Blocks A to F. The new names were taken up at once and were now in universal use. A Upper had become Chiltern Ward, A Lower, Kennet; B Upper, Ipsden; B Lower, Mortimer; F Upper, Eversley; F Lower, Shiplake; D Block, Purley; C Block, Thames. Only the centre of Centre Block lacked a new name. It was to have been

Casualty staff group 1954. Nurse Eileen Heading on right

Dingley Children's Ward, but became instead the sick bay for nurses from Battle and Prospect Park Hospitals.

Modern technology had also arrived, most notably with the latest X-ray equipment installed in Casualty, the Chest Clinic, Maternity, and in the expanded Centre Block operating theatre. Official recognition of Battle's growing status came when the 'new' Nurses' Home, the Casualty Department and the Central Chest Clinic were all ceremoniously opened by Mr H A Benyon, the Lord Lieutenant for Berkshire on 12th July 1954.

4

NEW ENDEAVOURS: RHEUMATOLOGY, GERIATRICS, PAEDIATRICS

Rheumatology

Reading's first Consultant in Physical Medicine was not appointed until 1954. He had much to do since services for patients in this field had been very sketchy, poorly organised and poorly financed. In 1949 as part of a regional scheme for the treatment of chronic rheumatism, The Oxford Regional Hospital Board had recommended that a clinic be started under the control of Dr L M Jennings as physician, associated with Dr Price as the Medical Officer in charge of physiotherapy. In the first instance this was to be a closed clinic, only accepting consultant referrals to prevent it being overwhelmed by patient numbers. Dr Jennings, like Dr Bird, was a GP with no formal specialist training. He had started at the Royal Berkshire Hospital in 1924 as a Registrar, working his way up to be made a Consultant in the NHS. The Rheumatology Clinic was at the Royal Berks, although Dr Jennings was now doing two physician sessions (rounds of the wards) at Battle. Dr A H Price had been in charge of the Electro-therapy and Massage Department at the Royal Berkshire Hospital since 1942 (in succession to Dr Bird) and had introduced some physical training and occupational therapy. It was at his suggestion that in 1951 the physiotherapists were allowed to circulate between the Royal Berkshire Hospital and Battle. Miss Olive Clark, the Superintendent at the Royal Berks was redesignated Group Superintendent, which did not greatly please Mr Awbery at Battle. Her salary was increased 'by the sum of £75 per annum in excess of the scale laid down for Superintendent Physiotherapists'. This obviously was against the rules and the allowance was discontinued. It was not until 1965 (by which time the establishment at Battle was one Superintendent, two seniors and five basic grade physiotherapists) that the Ministry of Health authorised an extra sum for Group responsibilities. The ministerial generosity amounted to £50 a year.

In 1953, Dr Price went on sick leave. The Medical Advisory Committee, gracing the still fledgling organisation with the title of Area Department of Physical Medicine, decided that responsibility for supervision of treatment should be Mr Squire for the accident and orthopaedic cases, and the consultants concerned in the remaining cases. When Dr Price retired soon afterwards, they recommended 'appointment of a maximum part-time Consultant for the area hospitals, the Department be a closed one, to work in conjunction with the Chairman of the Area Department of Accident and Orthopaedic Surgery insofar as his rehabilitation unit is concerned'. The appointee was Dr R I (Ian) Meanock.

Dr Meanock was another go-getter, destined in less than a decade to become Reading's first Postgraduate Clinical Tutor. I interviewed him in 2004 to ask about his early years at the Royal Berks and Battle. What he found on arrival was 'a shambles'. Dr Price had been ageing, with Drs Bird and Jennings trying to fill the gap. It was Mr Squire who most realised the rehabilitation needs, while Alastair Anderson was the most supportive of the physicians, giving up five of his beds at the Royal Berkshire Hospital to the new Consultant. With the diminution of acute poliomyelitis a ward soon became available at Prospect Park and this was really the basis of the Rheumatology Department. But Dr Meanock's patients were scattered. As well as covering the Royal Berks and Battle, he did monthly visits to Henley, Wallingford, Hungerford, Newbury, and Wokingham. The orthopaedic patients he was most involved with were those whose limbs had been affected by polio. His chief interest then was the younger severely handicapped patient. He was concerned that those for example with hemiplegia were just being 'written off'. Coming from London, he had been inspired by the physiotherapist/remedial gymnast at Arsenal Football Club who convinced him of the value of active remedial therapy rather than the more passive physiotherapy massage techniques of the time. He was also convinced of the value of water support for lower limb injuries, and began immediately what was to be a long fight for a hydrotherapy pool.

The struggle for all facilities, especially in rehabilitation, was long and difficult. Following discussions with Dr Lionel Cosin, Clinical Director of the Cowley Road Hospital at Oxford, Dr Meanock took the powerful triumvirate of Geoffrey Weston, Aitken Walker and Matron Brace to visit Dr Cosin's rehabilitation unit. As a result it was agreed in 1955 that Upper Floor of F Block (later Eversley) be upgraded and used as a rehabilitation ward mainly for arthritis and stroke cases 'to provide the final stage in the patient's journey back to home or to a local authority institution'. Dr Cosin's unit dealt only with true rehabilitation cases, but the new Battle unit would have to admit some patients requiring nursing care. The staff authorised seems scarcely adequate – one Staff Nurse (also to assist in F Lower), two Nursing Orderlies, two Physiotherapy Orderlies and one and a quarter domestics.

With orthopaedics, rheumatology and geriatrics all pushing for improved rehabilitation, Battle was gradually developing a reasonable service, albeit a fragmented one. As well as the trauma and orthopaedic set-up – the physiotherapists, remedial gymnasts and occupational therapists in H Block – there was now Eversley Ward and below it Shiplake, offering some rehabilitation training aimed at getting female geriatric patients back to their family or residential home. The Annual Report for 1956 quantified some small early success of the rehabilitation programme. Fifty-three in-patients were discharged to their homes, 11 to chronic sick wards, two to other hospitals, two to convalescent homes, one to an old people's home and one to Part III accommodation. The Accident and Orthopaedics Report noted that the out-patient rehabilitation unit had worked to capacity, its activities closely integrated with the Physical Medicine Department.

Dr Meanock recalled that his 'name became mud' from trying to raise funds for causes with little popular appeal. Neither rheumatology, rehabilitation nor later the Medical Postgraduate Centre at the Royal Berkshire Hospital captured the public imagination and purses were not readily opened. At Battle he had tremendous help from Les Parcell who coaxed celebrities into giving support. Mr Parcell remembers that Dr Meanock, Miss Ross the Occupational Therapist and himself as Hospital Secretary organised a fete at Battle in 1956. The celebrity guest was a popular singer with the Edmundo Ros orchestra. The Meanocks took her to lunch, then brought her to the Hospital, where Mr Parcell gave Mrs Meanock an effusive welcome, mistaking her for the guest.

The Start of the Reading Hospitals' League of Friends
It is not generally known that this fete was directly responsible for the start of the League of Friends of the Reading Hospitals. Lady (Eric) Palmer who was a member of the Hospital Management Committee talked to Les Parcell after the fete. It was such a success that she felt the Reading hospitals should have their own specific League of Friends, with an annual fete as the main fund raiser. Formation of a local League of Friends was brought up at the Financial and General Purposes Committee in July 1956. Discussions followed with the Mid-Southern Hospitals Contributory Association and it was agreed that the Association's Welfare Sub-committee would continue its modest work always in consultation with the new League. An ad hoc Committee was formed in March 1957 and Lady Palmer became Chairman. The new League had a small stand at Battle's second summer fete, then in 1958 the organisation of the fete was taken over by the League for the benefit of all the Reading hospitals.

This Friends' first fete, held at Battle in the summer of 1958, was opened by Rosemary Miller, star of the television programme *Emergency Ward 10*. For many years thereafter a succession of famous TV, radio and film performers were recruited: Raymond Glendenning, Hattie Jacques, Gerald Flood, George Baker, Robert Dougall, Sam Kydd, Ed Stewart, Robert Hardy, Michael Barrett, Johnny Morris, Robert Morley and Dinsdale Landen all played their part. When reconstruction work on the site began in 1963 the fete moved to Brock Barracks, further down the Oxford Road, returning to Battle in 1978. In the early 80s the League of Friends' fete was organised by Reading Rotary Club, with much help from the *Reading Evening Post* and Radio 210. They managed in successive years to attract hugely popular entertainers such as Roy Castle, Paul Daniels and Ernie Wise.

Opening of Hydrotherapy Pool, 1977. L to R Mrs Kathleen Sage, Dr Ian Meanock, Mr Claude Fenton, Sir John Hedges (Chairman Berkshire Area Health Authority)

The League was a great success and had the pleasant task each year of distributing funds to improve the welfare of patients and staff. Early benefits for Battle were new equipment for the nurses' tennis court and wiring to the wards from the new chapel. (In 1956 Matron Brace had found funds for a pillow phone for every bed, helped by £250 from J Arthur Rank for her assistance in the filming of the Douglas Bader story *Reach for the Sky*. The chapel had been created in 1958 from the disused hospital laboratory behind Shiplake Ward. Its worldly origins were disguised by gifts such as stained glass windows, one from the staff and patients of Dingley Ward, and a prayer desk in memory of Sister T Morris, who had been in charge of Shiplake.)

The first really major project for the League of Friends was not undertaken till 1967, when £2,000 was raised for improvements to Dingley, the children's accident and orthopaedic ward. The Friends were active in support of Dr Meanock's much wanted hydrotherapy pool but raising the full £44,000 took many years. Rotarians, Round Tablers and many other organisations and individuals all made contributions. Ian Meanock recalls that it was Claude Fenton, head of the machinery hire firm, who finally achieved the target. The pool, next to Thames Block, was at last opened by Mrs Kathleen Sage the Mayor of Reading in 1977, only to be closed immediately for correction of a problem due to evaporation of the heated water.

Ian Meanock remembered that some donated funds were used to set up a lathe workshop behind Casualty. Tom Harris was a most dedicated man who gave up a career in engineering to run this enterprise in occupational therapy. The patients were mainly young men with rheumatoid disease or limb trauma from the Accident and Orthopaedic Department. The workshop made hospital items such as bed-side lamps and a specially designed foot-rest for bed cradles. It also produced income for the Hospital by contracts with Great Western Railway's signalling department and with local firms like Pulsometer. Many of Mr Harris's handicapped but well-trained workers went on to useful outside employment.

The Rheumatology Department slowly grew. Originally Dr Meanock had to share a Houseman before one was allocated full-time to his unit. The first Registrar in Physical Medicine/Rheumatism was appointed in 1962, followed in 1964 by two clinical assistants for the clinic at the Royal Berkshire Hospital. Rheumatology at Battle went from strength to strength with the arrival in 1965 of orthopaedic surgeon Patrick Chesterman, highly skilled in the surgical treatment of rheumatoid joints. In 1966 Dr F M Andrews was appointed as the second Consultant in Rheumatology/Physical Medicine for the Reading Area. What the team most needed now were more beds, a cry to be answered in a few years' time.

Geriatrics

From the very first years of the National Health Service optimistic plans have usually met with some disappointment. Neither removal of the 'Part III accommodation' inmates to local authority homes, nor transfer of the acute medical beds to Prospect Park and general surgery to the Royal Berks, solved bed shortage difficulties at Battle. The last of the dependent old folk left in 1953 just at the time when the problem of medical care for the elderly was beginning to be taken seriously. Certainly more hospital beds were now available and the majority were reserved for geriatric patients. But trauma, orthopaedics and maternity had together taken nearly 150 beds while in the wards for the elderly many beds remained empty due to nurse shortages, and the waiting list remained long.

Nor was there much hope of early improvement in nurse recruitment. The glamour acute specialities of medicine and surgery were gone. Although the old buildings may have been adapted and modified for their new departments they still looked their age. Only Elizabeth House was completely new and that was an undistinguished brick box, too small for the accommodation needs. The long-term staff might stay fiercely loyal; for the public and for potential nursing applicants Battle retained too much of the old Workhouse, a gloomy place occupied mainly by the old and chronic sick.

To help cope with the geriatric waiting list, the Hospital Management Committee asked Oxford to approve 'contractural arrangements with certain nursing homes for temporary accommodation of chronic sick patients in urgent need of care and attention, pending their admission to hospital'. The Regional Board responded that no funds were available. Instead they expressed a hope that the new geriatric techniques would increase the turnover of chronic sick beds. This new approach was being promulgated by the few Consultant Geriatricians appointed in the early years of the NHS. The call was for the treatment of patients to be based on medical need rather than age. People were living longer because they were healthier. An episode in hospital for an 80-year old need be no more burdensome to the health service than the same in a 60-year old. Unfortunately a large percentage of the population tended not to see things in the same way. Their longer-living elderly relatives had become a nuisance and any illness was an excuse to pack them off. General practitioners were constantly being pressured to find the necessary beds in already overstretched hospitals.

Dr Bird, who had volunteered to take on the care of Battle's elderly, was himself a well-loved and respected GP turned Consultant. He did his best despite having no specific training in geriatrics and completely inadequate resources. In 1955 Eversley Ward, as we have noted, was upgraded and staffed for rehabilitation. Other revenue funding was obtained for developments in the services for the chronic sick including three physiotherapists, three occupational therapists, two senior almoners and a clerk. In 1956 Dr Bird became ill and some assistance was provided from Dr Bedford, a geriatrician with the United Oxford Hospitals. When Dr Bird died in January 1957 there was no doubt that his successor would be one of the new breed of doctors trained in the speciality. Dr Sam Vine was appointed that August. Thirty-five years later he tape-recorded memories of his early days as Consultant in Geriatrics to the Reading Group of Hospitals.

He was appointed at a time when hospitals were being bombarded with advice on the care of the elderly. He expected to be welcomed with open arms, but found that to begin with he had few friends. Dr Bird had left no accurate records. Dr Vine had no office, no secretary and no ancillary staff. His office was his old Austin A 40 as he moved around trying to sort out 500 in-patients. At Battle Hospital, Shiplake and Chiltern Wards each had 43 female beds, Ipsden had 43 male beds and Purley had 33 chronic sick females. The others, nearly three-quarters of the total, were hospitalised at Henley, Wallingford, Newbury and Wokingham. Particularly at Sandleford and St Mary's, Wallingford, there was a blurring between which beds were part of the Hospital and which were Part III accommodation. Dr Vine was treated with great suspicion. His two allies were Walter Hausmann at Prospect Park Hospital and Ian Meanock, who was pushing the concept of rehabilitation. Five hundred was far too many beds for the needs of the time. But the stipend of some of the Hospital administrators depended on how many beds they looked after, so talk of reduction in numbers fell on deaf ears. Turnover of patients was by death alone. Once admitted to a geriatric bed the patient was never expected to appear again in the community.

Dr Vine said: 'When I started discharging patients all hell broke loose, mainly from the general practitioners who had sent them in in the first place. Then there were the consultants who used the geriatric beds as a dumping ground for anybody of any age not expected to recover.' On his first day, he was called urgently to Shiplake Ward where he found a 42-year old woman with chronic ulcerative colitis bleeding to death. Facilities for any sort of treatment scarcely existed in geriatric wards at that time and he had to threaten to report the imminent death to the Coroner before the physician at the Royal Berks would take her back.

Another unexpected problem was the 'young chronic sick' in geriatric beds. Dr Vine had not envisaged such patients in his care, but had found himself with a small number, mainly at Townlands Hospital in Henley. These patients were in one of two groups. If they came from local hospitals, he could see the medical staff and relatives before admission to explain the nature of the care available in Townlands. Some, however, were transferred from specialist hospitals such as the spinal injuries centre at Stoke Mandeville. The extremely high standard of skilled care there could not possibly be continued with the existing staff and equipment at Townlands and it was usually not possible to prepare the ground in advance. The Oxford Regional Medicine Sub-committee held the view that every speciality should have its own beds for young chronic sick, but this was simply not possible owing to the pressure on acute beds. Dr Vine agreed to accept medical administrative responsibility, but reserved the right to refuse patients who had received specialist care which could not be continued in the Reading area.

Oxford was planning a pilot scheme for the treatment of young chronic sick. The essentials would be to set aside specific accommodation in three or four hospitals in the region and to provide additional staff and facilities to meet the needs of these patients. Little progress was made and Reading could not expect any unit in Oxford to give them material help. Dr Vine eventually gave up all his geriatric beds at Townlands Hospital, where he was at his most unpopular, and transferred into them all the young patients alleged to be irremediable. His unpopularity increased, especially among the families of transferred patients, but Townlands did become recognised as providing a more enlightened management for the seriously handicapped patient.

At his first very sticky meeting of the Area Department of Medicine, Dr Vine asked his fellow physicians in what way they felt he could best help them. He was delighted to be told: 'Please take on the treatment of stroke.' This was an area where he had had much experience as Senior Registrar in Geriatrics in the Brighton and Lewes hospitals. Unfortunately there was little support in obtaining the necessary staff and equipment and it was several years before he had what he felt were the basics of a rehabilitation programme. There were problems with geriatrics being separated from general medicine. He believed strongly that his patients needed exactly similar facilities to medicine in other age groups. They needed more in the way of rehabilitation resources like physiotherapy, speech therapy and occupational therapy, but the principles in the practice of medicine were identical. Thanks largely to the support of pathologist Dr Frank Hampson, appointed at the same time as Dr Vine and who was rising to become influential in hospital politics, this was eventually achieved, but many battles had to be fought.

Mr Les Parcell, the Hospital Secretary, was very helpful on the administrative side. He found an office for the new consultant, and a part-time secretary, later to become full-time. At first the agreed establishment was an Area Department of Geriatrics comprising Dr Vine as Chairman and the GPs in charge of the peripheral chronic sick units, 'as a separate entity to the Area Department of Medicine but with liaison with that Department by virtue of Dr Vine's membership'. Over the next few years he got a resident Senior House Officer and Registrar and a GP Clinical Assistant (Dr Tom Stewart of Sonning Common was the first). The wards were upgraded and a day centre started, originally on Shiplake Ward. A Rehabilitation Unit of 18 beds was created at Wokingham and a scheme for providing care in hospital for aged invalids while relatives were on holiday.

Dr Vine was also forward-thinking on another major problem: 'The confused elderly patient in the 1960s tended to be labelled senile. If they were in any way not socially acceptable they had to be admitted to the geriatric service or to Fairmile Mental Hospital. Dr Ogden, Physician Superintendent at Fairmile, was concerned that many elderly patients dying at the psychiatric Hospital had remedial physical conditions such as diabetic coma or a brain tumour. Psychiatrist Dr Bill Davis and I set up a team trying to differentiate these patients and those suffering from metabolic disturbances and drug side effects from those with true dementia. The sub-speciality of psychogeriatrics has now become an integral part of geriatric medicine.

'By the mid-sixties, the number of recognised acute geriatric beds was down to about 100, all in Battle, with up to 30 chronic sick in Purley Ward (a small but very caring ward for patients who were truly long-stay) and a number of rehabilitation and long-stay beds split between the outlying hospitals. The need was now for more acute beds, mainly because of the old problem of bed-blocking.' In 1964 Dr Vine was complaining to the County Welfare Services officers that he had 36 cases awaiting transfer to Part III accommodation.

In 1964 the Hospital Management Committee appointed an ad hoc Committee chaired by Dr Hampson to advise on the whole scope of the geriatric service. That it had to meet seven times is an indication of the problems and differences of opinion. The first difficulty noted was lack of any satisfactory definition of 'geriatric'. On a random day the Committee noted that 30% of patients in the medical wards were over 64 and 16% over 70. In his evidence to this Committee, Dr Vine was against integration of the Geriatric Department and the Department of Medicine although in his 1992 recording he said he 'was one of the few geriatric physicians who was opposed to geriatric departments being separated from general medicine'.

The Committee reported firstly on the acute geriatric service. They felt the departments should be integrated, that about half the acute geriatric beds at Battle should be reserved for transfer of cases from other acute departments and that the integrated department should discuss the type of patient suitable for direct admission to a geriatric bed. They noted the Ministry of Health Document (HM(57)86) on Geriatric Services and the Care of the Chronic Sick which suggested that patients admitted to geriatric beds should be those who do not require the special services available only in the other hospital departments, and that geriatricians should be enabled to develop a line of special interest. The Committee suggested that acute situations such as stroke rather than acute investigative problems were the most suitable; a second consultant was not needed at the present time, but a second Senior House Officer should be appointed to the geriatric team. The Committee supported setting up out-patient clinics and planning for a Day Hospital. Finally, they agreed that the geriatrician should not be responsible for the young chronic sick and that a committee concerned with their care should be set up immediately.

This Report was discussed at a meeting between representatives of the Regional Board and the Hospital Management Committee. The Board view was that an Area Department was intended only to be a free association of senior medical practitioners in the same speciality. The Board had no objection to the Hospital Management Committee requesting the two Departments to combine specifically for the purpose of ensuring more effective management of available beds. They approved an additional Senior House Officer, but not a consultant at the present time and welcomed an ad hoc committee to look further into the care of the young chronic sick. Appointed to this committee would be Dr J D Kidd, Neurologist, Dr R I Meanock, Consultant in Physical Medicine, Dr A Gatherer from Oxford, and one each from trauma and orthopaedics, paediatrics and psychiatry. A good idea, but it appears never to have been put into effect. Two years later the Medical Advisory Committee was still seeking clarification on the question of clinical responsibility for the young patients at Townlands. Dr Vine, not expecting this delay in the lifting of his unwelcome burden, was more receptive to the other proposals. He would regard the two Departments as one and 50% of acute geriatric beds would be reserved for transfers from other departments.

The Arrival of Paediatrics

Specialist medical care at the opposite end of the age scale came to Battle almost by stealth. Until 1948 there was very little in the nature of a paediatric service. The healthy offspring of unmarried 'fallen women' were

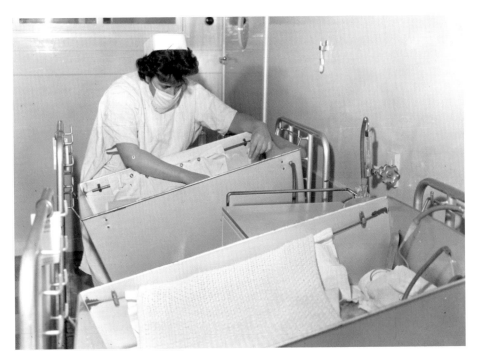

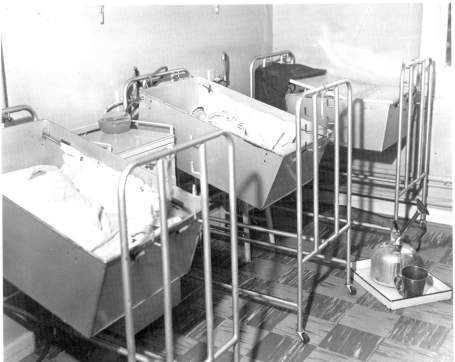

Premature Baby Unit, 1950s. Note the steam kettle for humidification

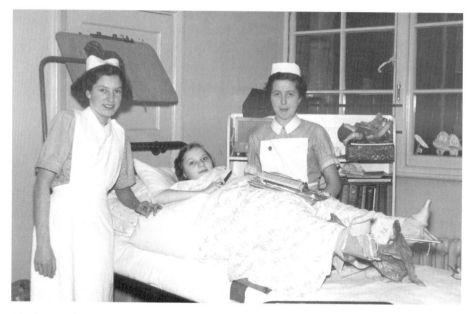

Dingley Ward interior, 1954. Pre-Student Nurse Ruth Hewett (Ruth Clark) on left

cared for in the Nursery adjacent to F Block female workhouse, while their mothers drudged in the laundry. Above was a small children's ward, under the care of the hospital medical staff and the experienced but unqualified Clinical Assistant Dr Ratcliff. There were also the few young 'mental defectives' resident in the Nursery to be later miserably incarcerated with the adult chronic sick. In happier circumstances there were the newborn babies of Battle's burgeoning Maternity Unit.

With the advent of the NHS, Dr Jack Kempton was appointed as the first Consultant Paediatrician in Reading. His base, and therefore the centre for paediatrics, was in the Nuffield Block for Women and Children at the Royal Berkshire Hospital. Transfer from the Royal Berks in 1952 of the service for difficult obstetric deliveries naturally meant increased work for the premature and sick neonate unit being established on the third floor of Thames Block. Although the equipment was minimal by modern standards, this Battle neonatal unit of some 24 cots in four nurseries produced excellent results based on meticulous nursing care and hygiene, but also on regular visits by experienced paediatricians. Moira Tarnoky recalls attending several times a week as Paediatric Registrar, Dr Ratcliff (now a Senior Hospital Medical Officer) often came in and Dr Kempton made a weekly consultant round.

It was Mike Squire who brought many older paediatric patients to Battle when he transferred the complete work load of trauma and orthopaedics from the Royal Berkshire Hospital. The original plan had been to use part of Centre Block for the children's ward, limited in space

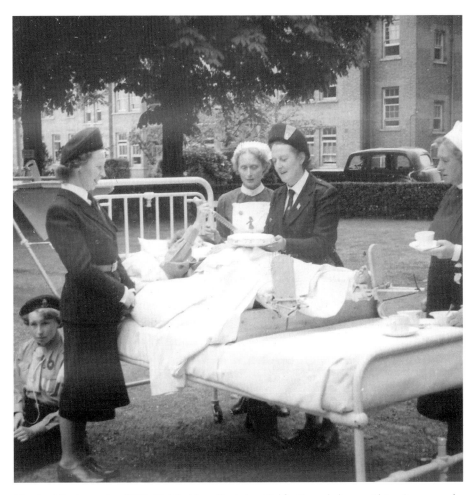

Dingley Ward exterior, 1954. Girl Guide patient, two Guide Commissioners, Sister Cooper and Matron Brace

but handy to the operating theatre. The name Dingley was chosen by Mr Squire who lived not far from the pretty village of Stamford Dingley. In July 1951 the Nursing Sub-committee had asked for more consideration on the accommodation for orthopaedic children, most respectfully suggesting a re-think on the proposal that the Nursery become the Central Chest Clinic. The Chest Clinic went to the Oxford Road site and the Nursery, previously sometimes called Z Block, became Dingley Ward for children.

Many of the Dingley children came for treatment of spastic limbs associated with cerebral palsy and Mike Squire showed great concern and compassion for these young patients. He was determined they should receive the very best treatment and improvements were constantly sought to make Dingley a happy place. Much special equipment was purchased for the 'spastic unit'. In 1954 the unfurnished accommodation in F Top nursery was rented to the Local Education Authority for spastic children attending the Hospital. The Reading and District Spastic Welfare Society sent a letter of appreciation for the better arrangements made in the teaching and treatment of spastic children. By 1957 alternative school accommodation had been found and the Society now began paying the cost of a part-time physiotherapist. In 1960 Dingley Ward was redecorated and the door widened to allow children's beds to be wheeled on to the lawn to enjoy the sunshine. The following year the Welfare Society agreed to fund an additional physiotherapist for the Dingley Unit. Then in 1967 the £2,000 provided by the League of Friends' first really big fund-raising project, together with major help from Mr C F Taylor, created a two-cubicle ward, mainly for burns cases, and a two-bed mothers' overnight room and bathroom. The benefit for small children following severe injury and for their stressed families can scarcely be overstated,

Dr Kempton was tragically lost at sea in 1961. He was replaced by Dr David Stone and in 1963 a second Consultant Paediatrician was appointed, Dr Joyce Burke. These two quiet, dedicated doctors were still based in Nuffield Block, with a watching brief on the care of the neonates and the Dingley children. Although Battle had specialist paediatric cover, if there were a real problem in Dingley, the sick child was always transferred to the Royal Berkshire Hospital. Full paediatric services would not come until 1972.

NURSING, MATERNITY, CASUALTY

The Last Matrons

In 1960 Matron Brace was granted permission to become non-resident – from 14th November until her retirement at the end of the year! As had become the custom for distinguished members of staff, in addition to a leaving present she received a sealed and bound copy of a resolution by the Hospital Management Committee: 'In recognition of the long and devoted service given by her for a period of upwards of thirty-two years at the Royal Berkshire and Battle Hospitals.'

Miss Gladys Morgan from Gravesend Hospital was appointed to the Matron's post at a salary of £1,035 rising to £1,236 over five years, less £285 per annum for board, residence and other services provided. Her residence was Miss Brace's vacated flat at No. 344 Oxford Road. Matron's flat, at one time the Head Porter's and originally the Union Board Room, was most strategically situated. On her right was the New Inn, not altogether unknown by the hospital staff. To her left were the comings and goings of the main Hospital entrance; on the other side of the archway the terraced row of staff cottages led up to the Chest Clinic. Just within the entrance stood the Board Room building, behind it the accident and orthopaedic in-patient facilities and the old Nurses' Home; opposite lay the Casualty Department and its adjacent administrative block. Like all good matrons, Miss Morgan knew most of what was going on.

Fifteen years after the idea was first mooted, the new Matron was quick to propose forming an Enrolled Nurses Training School at Battle. A meeting in 1961 involving the Group Secretary, the Matrons of both Hospitals and the Education Officer of the General Nursing Council advanced the discussions and the following year the Matrons of Battle, Peppard and Newbury were sent to a three-day Royal College of Nursing Conference on 'The Changing Scene: The Enrolled Nurse'. A scheme for training was prepared by Miss Morgan in consultation with the matrons and tutors at the Royal Berkshire Hospital and Peppard Hospital and in March 1964 Miss K F B Jeffery was appointed Teacher to the Enrolled Nurse Training School. The Preliminary Training School for the new school was set up at Paxton/Pendragon in 1965. At Battle the lectures and tutorials were mostly held upstairs in Purley Block, with some in the Nurses' Home basement. With an intake of about 20 pupils twice a year, hundreds of Enrolled Nurses received excellent training at Battle. But the sad truth was that these first-class practical pupil nurses were always perceived as inferior to the students doing their State Registered Nurse training; again Battle was made to feel the poor relation.

Few could have guessed that Battle's State Enrolled Nurse Training School would last only 25 years. As the demand within the nursing profession grew world-wide for higher qualifications and status, the advantages of a cadre of non-academic, 'hands-on' nurses who by inclination and training were ideally suited to deliver traditional, loving care were swept aside. The 1966 Salmon Report resulted in a nursing structure which rewarded those most ambitious for administrative and academic power and reduced the influence of the traditional matron and ward sisters for whom cleanliness, comforting and feeding the sick were important priorities. Many of the finest nurses chose early retirement. Nursing moved on towards Project 2000 and the requirement for a university diploma or degree qualification. The State Enrolled Nurse Certificate became unacceptable and Enrolled Nurses were urged to convert to State Registered Nurse. The enrolled nurses were gradually replaced by nursing auxiliaries and care assistants, equally dedicated but inadequately trained and of course inadequately paid.

In 1968 under the Salmon scheme, Miss Morgan became a No.9, Principal Nursing Officer with responsibility also for Newbury, Henley and Peppard Hospitals. She retained her Battle duties and was still called the Matron of Battle. Assistant Matron Miss E W Garrett took over when Miss Morgan was asked to fill the gap created by Chief Nursing Officer Rosemary Bromley's marriage and retirement. Until Margaret Brain was appointed, Gladys Morgan remained Acting Chief Nursing Officer to all the hospitals within the Hospital Management Committee. She retired herself in 1974 and was doubtless pleased to escape the upheavals and the confusing nomenclature of that year's ill-conceived reorganisation.

Now there was to be a Divisional Nursing Officer covering both the Royal Berkshire Hospital and Battle. This post was held first by Miss Margaret Revell. When she became District Nursing Officer in 1978, responsible for nursing in the community, her replacement was Miss Jennifer Ingram. The Divisional Nursing Officer was based at Battle, with an office downstairs in the Committee Room building. Miss Ingram, though, was soon spending more time at the Royal Berks getting South Wing commissioned and the Accident and Emergency Department transferred. The Senior Nursing Officers (No. 8s) Ella Garrett and Frank Cox took the day-to-day responsibility at Battle until the next reorganisation in 1982. This time Jennie Ingram became Director of Nursing Services at the Royal Berks. Battle, Prospect Park and Blagrave became one unit with Mrs Margaret Jones from Newbury Hospital appointed as Director of Nursing. Margaret Jones, spending most of her time at Battle, was still 'Matron'. When she retired in 1991 the title of Battle Hospital Matron, with so distinguished a history, to all intents and purposes disappeared.

Maternity Crisis
By the 1960s the transferred Maternity and Casualty Units had become increasingly busy. Although both were scheduled for return to the Royal Berkshire Hospital in a few years' time, these two Departments needed and received major capital monies to upgrade and enlarge. Revenue funding, however, always lagged well behind the ever-growing demands and nurse staffing remained the most difficult and protracted problem.

The Maternity Unit in 1954 had an establishment of one Super-intendent, one Sister Tutor, seven Midwifery Sisters, 14 Staff Midwives, 12 trained Nursery Nurses and 14 Pupil Midwives (including seven on the district). The flying squad was formed this year to deal with obstetric emergencies outside the main Hospital unit. By 1956 Battle was dealing with 1,000 births a year compared with 450 at Dellwood and about 250 each in Sandleford, St George's, Townlands and Wokingham Hospitals. To free accommodation in the top floor of Maternity, the Superintendent was moved to a flat converted from half of first floor Centre Block. The vacated area in Maternity was used to create side-ward accommodation for an additional four beds. The Ministry of Health approved three of these as Section V beds (for private patients) and one single room for general use, including patients requiring privacy on medical grounds. Additionally three beds in a small ward of the main Obstetric Unit were designated for use as Section IV beds. National Health Service patients could pay a part-fee to have the extra privacy of these so-called amenity beds. (Very few private or amenity beds were provided for or used by Battle in-patients. Maternity was the exception and these facilities of course went with the Unit when it returned to the Royal Berks.)

The Annual Report for 1959 noted that since 1953 the number of ante-natal patients was 80% greater, the emergency admission rate was up 65% and deliveries had doubled. With a complement of 51 beds the Unit had undertaken 1,404 deliveries in the labour wards, treated 314 in the operating theatre, dealt with 1,671 patients through the admission room, sent out the flying squad on 66 occasions, trained 33 pupil midwives and maintained normal out-patient clinics. The Premature Baby Unit had treated 197 babies during the year. Such an increased turnover was possible only by reducing the length of stay in hospital. The Nursing Sub-committee rather hopefully recommended that staffing should be increased by 20.

On the medical staffing side a most significant advance came in 1961 when a Senior Registrar joined the obstetric team. The Senior Registrar was to be resident on the Battle site and Dr Begg moved into 338 Oxford Road. That year the births went up to 1,578 and crisis point had been reached: beds in Nuffield III Ward at the Royal Berkshire Hospital had to be used for obstetrics patients. The multi-storey new unit at the Royal Berks was still years away. It was obvious that Battle Maternity, though due to be closed, must be expanded. The planning, to include more beds and a new labour and theatre suite, began its slow journey through the NHS committees.

In June 1964 the Central Midwives Board expressed concern at 'the unsuitability of Battle Hospital to provide the intern part of the second period midwifery training', citing the lack of classroom accommodation, inadequate premises, shortage of bath and lavatory facilities and the increasing pressure of work. The Midwives Board were aware of the new unit to be built, but threatened withdrawal of approval or alternatively suggested that Part II training might be temporarily moved to Dellwood. Pressure like this from a training authority was to become a frequently employed weapon in the fight for improvements to National Health services. It has usually proved an effective stimulant to positive action and was so in this case. For Superintendent Miss A John, already relying on 12 agency staff, loss of the pupil midwives would be disastrous. Rapid provision of the required accommodation was essential to prevent a breakdown in the service. The plans were altered to provide extra bathroom, lavatory and classroom facilities; work started quickly on a temporary single-storeyed 12-bed ward adjacent to the Maternity Block and linked to the new labour suite of progress rooms, delivery rooms and operating theatre.

This was commissioned in November and the old suite converted to a 14-bedded ante-natal ward. The Ante-natal Clinic was transferred to the Royal Berkshire Hospital and its old site adapted for a further nine beds. By mid-1965 the bed complement was 79 and an additional 10 nursing staff had been approved. Only the Premature Baby Unit remained seriously congested. David Stone asked for the official complement of premature baby cots to be raised from 18 to 24 to reflect what was actually happening. Despite this unresolved problem, the Central Midwives Board was satisfied.

Following a return visit in July, the Board declared that 'the new accommodation had effected considerable improvement'. Six months later, a further advance came with the appointment of a third Consultant in obstetrics and gynaecology to join Bill Frewen and Peter Wheeler. Mr Peter Stallabrass would have less than two years to serve in the revamped premises. In December 1968, the Maternity Unit was back at the Royal Berks, now in a purpose-built block with brand new furnishings and equipment. Thames Block and its adjacent 'temporary' ward and theatre were available for new occupants.

Casualty Expansion

Mike Squire's confidence that the new Casualty Department would cope with its work load was sadly misplaced. Even in 1954 the Standing Committee of Departmental Chairmen noted in their Report that Mr Squire was overworked and urged the appointment of a Registrar or Senior Hospital Medical Officer to his Department. Early in 1955 the Rotary Club of Reading sent a letter, obviously a seriously considered response to problems reported by its members, with 'suggestions for improving the relations between the Hospital and community'. What a difference between this dignified offer of co-operation and the barrage of angry and litigious complaints hurled at today's hospital managers! The Hospital Management Committee responded most appropriately by appointing a special sub-committee to visit the Out-patient and Casualty Departments. They noted problems with the large-scale reorganisation, increased numbers of patients and staffing difficulties which were being solved by new appointments. Urgent representations were being made for an additional anaesthetics appointment. A Sister in overall charge was soon to be appointed, senior to the Sisters in charge of Casualty and Out-patients. They commended Mr Squire's frequent staff conferences emphasising the 'human approach' and his continued endeavours to ensure efficient working arrangements. They were impressed with the smoothness with which 80 patients attending the afternoon clinic were dealt with. They suggested improved signs and improved information for the patients, but felt that everything possible was being done within the limits of available manpower.

The Department's effectiveness in a major emergency was tested by a railway accident at Didcot on Sunday 20th November 1955. Battle received 20 casualties and four were admitted. The General Manager, Western Region, British Transport Commission, wrote a letter expressing their great appreciation of the excellent services by those concerned at Battle Hospital and enclosed a cheque for £10.00 'to be used in some way to benefit the staff'. The money was made available to the casualty staff for their Christmas festivities. This welcome fillip came at the start of a period when things were seriously deteriorating. On the wards, staff shortages during 1956 meant that 35 trauma and orthopaedic beds in Kennet Ward had to be closed. The Reports for the next two years showed new patients in Casualty up from 14,900 to 17,700 and total attendance up by 6,000 to 41,250. Emergency admissions were so great that extra beds were in almost constant use. In 1958 further complaints about the trauma and orthopaedic service led to a meeting of the medical members of the Management Committee. They came to a conclusion which could have surprised nobody: 'Taking into account the work load there appeared to be a shortage of medical staff.'

The long-awaited Registrar appointment, rotating to the Nuffield Orthopaedic Centre in the second year, finally came in 1959 with Mr James as the first appointee. To combat the shortage of junior staff the Oxford Regional Hospital Board approved in 1961 the establishment of six clinical assistant sessions per week to enable general practitioners to undertake work in the Casualty Department. This was 'for an experimental period of two years in the first instance'. Some well-known local GP names appear on the list: Dr M J A Davies of Southcote Lane, Dr J C Garnham of Oxford Rd, Dr R H Oldfield of Western Elms Avenue, Dr P Dure-Smith of Bath Rd, Dr E M Sproston of Crazies Hill and Dr P Wiesendanger of Bradfield were the first appointed, soon followed by Dr J B Williams of Tilehurst. The 'experimental period' was repeatedly extended and to this day experienced clinical assistants continue to give sterling service in Reading's Accident and Emergency Department.

The worsening problems in Casualty were not only due to insufficient staff. Accommodation and facilities were becoming completely inadequate. Casualty X-rays, for instance, were rising by thousands a year. In the wards there were not sufficient staffed beds to deal with the trauma cases and keep abreast with the orthopaedic waiting list. On one night in November 1960 the three depleted wards of Mortimer, Kennet and Dingley between them had to accommodate 94 patients against an approved bed complement of 75. By 1962 a bed allocation committee recommended and got Oxford approval for the transfer of 11 geriatric beds in Shiplake and 16 chronic sick beds in Purley Ward to Accident and Orthopaedics. Dr Vine dissented strongly: 'The real need,' he said, ' was urgent provision at Battle of additional beds either for accident and orthopaedics or geriatrics, since Battle was the only Hospital with the full facilities that both required.'

In 1961, after seven winters of patient transfers in the rain, a canopy for the ambulance entrance was provided at a cost of £350. Over £7,000 was then spent on a new gymnasium for the Casualty Block, while planning began for the desperately required major extension. Mr Squire pleaded repeatedly for the appointment of a third Consultant and another Registrar when the new facilities were ready. The tenders for the Casualty and X-ray Departments totalled over £150,000, with George Burfield championing the modern cluster system for the new central X-ray unit. The work would have to be done while normal services continued and would take 18 months. Delay in starting meant that the deficiencies of the Department were graphically described in the Report of February 1963 by a Working Party of the Oxford Regional Hospital Board on Accident Services and their Setting in the Oxford Region:

'Description of Facilities in Reading.
The Accident and Orthopaedic Departments share a single entrance and it is impossible to separate the different streams of patients. Patients queue at a reception desk in a narrow passage through which other patients, some with walking appliances or in wheelchairs, are continuously threading their way. There is a separate entry for ambulance patients to which a resuscitation room for the seriously injured is immediately adjacent. Should these patients need transfer to the operating theatre they have to be wheeled across the open part of the Department. The building is far too small for the volume of work. The waiting area is bleak, cramped and lacking in amenities. There are no special facilities for children. It is rarely possible to ensure privacy.'

The Report noted a good relationship with GPs, who do not refer in minor injuries, good cover by the two consultants and two registrars in addition to junior staff and adequate nursing staff. It also observed that the Department had a physiotherapy department and rehabilitation unit but the latter was above and only accessible by an awkward staircase. The Report concluded: 'It is a tribute to the staff that so much work can be done despite the problems. A large extension is planned linked to a new Central X-ray Department and a third consultant is due when this is completed. A new Accident Department is being provided at the Royal Berkshire Hospital as part of phase III, due to open in 1971.'

In October 1964 Mr Squire took his plight to the Visiting Medical Staff Committee, requesting 'consideration of the extreme inadequacy of the present accommodation at Battle of the Area Accident and Orthopaedic Unit'. Opinion differed on the feasibility of establishing forthwith a separate unit on the Royal Berks site. After much discussion the Committee resolved unanimously: 'The medical staff consider that the Area Accident and Orthopaedic Unit in its present site and accommodation is... quite unable to provide an adequate, or even safe, service. The greatest hazards arise from: 1. Wide separation from necessary advice and collaboration of all other acute specialties and urgent ancillary help, particularly pathological. 2. Gross overcrowding in archaic ward and theatre accommodation ... The Staff Committee fully support the demand of the Accident and Orthopaedic Unit that plans for ... new premises for this service as part of the new acute hospital on the RBH site ... should be proceeded with immediately.' Fine words, but almost meaningless since the Committee, consisting simply of all the consultant medical staff, lacked any real power. Soon afterwards, following Ministry

Extended Casualty Department

cutbacks, Phase III at the Royal Berkshire Hospital was dramatically scaled down and Accident and Emergency allocated to a future Phase VI.

The 18-month time scale for the huge Battle Casualty development proved wildly inaccurate and it was not completed until February 1966. Among many adaptations and changes needed, Pharmacy had to be moved to a new site adjacent to Purley Ward. To provide a roadway alongside Casualty, past the large new X-ray building and leading to the out-patient entrance beside the gymnasium, staff cottages 332 to 342 Oxford Rd had to lose up to 8 ft from the rear of their gardens. Not all the occupants were happy about this. Mr K Eggleton at No.332, the driver/porter who had been Battle's ambulance driver since the 1920s, extracted an ex gratia payment of £1 for the loss of chrysanthemums from the shortening of his garden.

Meanwhile there were other advances elsewhere on the Battle site. A proposal for a temporary single-storey Accident and Emergency[1] ward was abandoned because Maternity had got there first with their temporary ward and theatre development. However, the new Royal Berks Maternity Unit was being hurried and soon vacated maternity accommodation would become available. The ward staffing was improved to the extent of one Sister and six State Registered Nurses. These were specifically to staff the 'intensive care cubicles of the Accident and Orthopaedic Department', a move with wider ramifications than might be supposed. The so-called Kennet Cubicles were four single-bed cubicles in Kennet Ward which had been provided in 1960 for the specialised treatment and nursing of serious head injuries. Five trained nurses had been sent 'to attend discussions' with Mr Pennybacker, the neurosurgeon at Oxford, presumably to absorb some information and disseminate it to their colleagues and juniors. This was hardly adequate training for the progress being made at that time in the management of head injuries. It was small wonder that few nurses liked being rostered to care for the concussed, the comatose and the noisily confused patients. Increasing the establishment to provide a permanent staff for 'Kennet Cubicles' not only advanced patient care, it relieved some of the staff shortage in the Accident and Orthopaedic wards and improved nursing morale.

Battle's third Accident and Orthopaedic Consultant was appointed in December 1965, just before the new Casualty Department was finally completed. This was Mr P Chesterman, the hand specialist so urgently needed by rheumatology. Pat Chesterman was another thrusting orthopaedic surgeon, big in physique and personality and due to play a dominant role in Reading's hospital politics. In 1974 he would become the first Consultant Representative on the West Berkshire District Management Team. He arrived in time to assist in setting up another temporary venture. This was a pre-fabricated Honeywell Operating Theatre which cost £47,000, including £28,000 to Honeywell Controls Ltd (Theatre). Oxford suggested this brand new facility should replace the existing 1911 theatre, but Mr Squire got agreement that the old theatre should be retained for emergency work. The first crates arriving in March 1966 included a high vacuum autoclave and a 'package-deal' diathermy apparatus. A new orthopaedic operating table had been pre-ordered. The

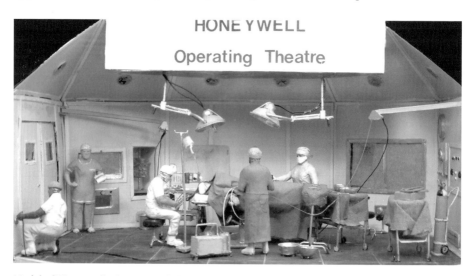

Model of Honeywell Theatre made by Theatre Technician Frank Cooper

building envelope of the new theatre, a pre-fabricated shell erected by Vic Hallam Ltd for £2,558, was connected to the back of Centre Block to create a two-theatre suite. Adaptations to the existing building included an anaesthetic room, a recovery room, 'a small area for the application of plasters' and changing accommodation.

The modern generation of clinicians and administrators would not be able to comprehend the volume of work which was undertaken in this hybrid set-up, nor the preparedness of staff to cut corners to get the work done. It was common practice for a single anaesthetist, with skilled help from operating theatre technicians such as Reg Carter, Frank Cooper, Pat Sheehy and Bob King, to be caring for a patient in each theatre. The 'small area' plaster room soon got an anaesthetic machine as well, so it was not unknown to have three anaesthetised patients on the go at the one time, with the orthopaedic consultant rushing between cases in support of his junior staff. Charge Nurse Denis Petty, Sisters Millichamp and Bradby and their willing nurses organised amazingly swift cleaning and sterilising to speed the changeovers. Mr Squire allowed Charge Nurse Petty a small engineering corner, where he repaired, modified and improved on standard surgical instruments. Mr Adams, Charge Nurse in Accident and Emergency and David Chitty in charge of the main plaster room were a constant source of support. The whole ethos of the orthopaedic service was to get the maximum amount of work done. Despite all this, the waiting list kept growing, 785 in 1965, 979 in 1966, 1083 in 1967 ... Still more beds and more theatre time were needed. Both were soon to come; when Maternity departed in 1968 the Orthopaedic Department would spread further, to occupy its fourth site in Battle Hospital.

NOTES

1. The terminology of this period is confusing. Accident Surgery, Accident and Orthopaedics, Trauma and Orthopaedics were used interchangeably because the orthopaedic surgeons ran the accident service. Accident and Emergency was starting to be used to describe what would become a separate speciality.

5

THE SAGA OF THE 'EXPORT' HOSPITAL

In terms of staffed beds, during the mid-1960s Battle and the Royal Berkshire Hospital were to all intents equal with 350 beds each. Battle was providing an accident and orthopaedic service for a catchment population of about 400,000, the 'abnormal midwifery' unit for the same Reading Group, a geriatric service increasingly concerned with acute assessment, and rheumatology and rehabilitation. The bed allocations for these were 112 trauma and orthopaedic, 97 geriatric, 17 chronic sick, 18 physical medicine, 76 obstetric and 24 special care babies. However, in 1968 the Maternity Unit, after 16 years in Thames Block, would be taking its 100 beds back to the Royal Berks. It was now also certain that Accident and Orthopaedics, strongly backed by the full consultant staff, would similarly be returning. Just when morale among Battle staff might have been expected to plummet, it was boosted by the rumour, then the likelihood and eventually the confirmation, that they would be getting a large new facility, a return of acute medicine and surgery and modern specialities within these fields. How the underdog Hospital regained its acute services and attained much more is a remarkable story, worth recounting in some detail.

At least as early as 1961, the Oxford Regional Hospital Board had decided that Reading must have two District General Hospitals. In that year the Minister of Health asked Regional Boards to prepare proposals on capital development for schemes starting up to 1971. The Board responded immediately, having already prepared a paper, *Proposals for the Long-Term Development of the Hospital Services in the Oxford Region*. Its policy was unequivocal:

'It is felt that the total needs for Reading itself, approximately 1,400 beds, would create too large a unit if concentrated on one site and the continued use of Battle must be regarded as an essential part of the Reading plan. It is likely that the development of the Reading area will not stop at the figure estimated for 1971[1] and a single hospital centre for a population of this size cannot continue to expand indefinitely. It is proposed, therefore, that the maximum size of the Royal Berkshire Hospital should be fixed at about 850 beds and subsequent development should take place at Battle. If this policy is accepted then it is important that in the early stages of development Battle must not be regarded as merely the long stay hospital and *the nucleus of future acute departments must be established.* (Author's italics). During the next 10 years, however, the provision of a modern hospital on the Royal Berkshire site will remain the top priority for the area. When this has been achieved it should be possible to close some of the outlying units and the abandonment of Prospect Park, Blagrave and Peppard would contribute most to the economy and ease of staffing in the group.'

These proposals went to the various Hospital Management Committees for consultation in early 1961 and swiftly drew a unanimous resolution from the Reading Area Hospitals Visiting Medical Staff Committee: 'This meeting is strongly in favour of a new hospital building on the Royal Berkshire Hospital site to include all departments. It opposes strongly the suggestion for two hospitals on widely separated sites.' The representations made by the Reading doctors and their Management Committee are evident in the revised final wording approved at the Oxford Regional Hospital Board meeting in June. The document sent to the Minister now had several changes of emphasis and a significant increase in the proposed future size of the Royal Berks:

'The most urgent need in the area is the development and modernisation of the Royal Berkshire Hospital as the main central hospital for the group ... With all the known disadvantages of splitting clinical departments between two hospitals in one town it is the natural wish of the Hospital Management Committee and medical staff to provide the local needs on one site. If sufficient land could be obtained in one area[2] this policy would be pursued although it might be desirable to establish two separate administrative units to avoid the creation of an excessively large single hospital ... The total island site of nineteen acres[3] could accommodate a comprehensive District General Hospital of up to 1,000 beds. The remaining 400 beds in Reading would be provided at Battle Hospital which would be planned as a complementary unit, sharing clinical staff and providing jointly with the Royal Berkshire Hospital the total service needs and training facilities of the area.'

How delicately this last sentence skated around the Board's own predilection for acute services at Battle.

Enoch Powell's Command Paper *A Hospital Plan for England and Wales* was published in 1962. It broadly conformed with the Board's proposals, but spread the developments over 15 years instead of 10 as a way of reducing the immediate pressure on NHS finances. The Oxford Regional Hospital Board produced a *Narrative on the Command Paper* describing its likely effects in the Oxford Region. The section on Reading and District aimed at placating the near-mutinous local consultants by continuation of the conciliatory message: 'The final distribution of services between the two Hospitals will be a subject for further detailed consultation.' Jumping any consultative gun, the Visiting Medical Staff Committee passed another unanimous resolution: 'The Staff re-affirmed their opinion that there must be complete centralisation of all acute departments and services in Reading in a single district general hospital of 1,200 – 1,400 beds on the present Royal Berkshire Hospital site.' An attached memorandum reiterated all the arguments such as duplication of facilities and time wasted in staff travel. Its final paragraph began: 'Finally, it is conceded that there will be a use for Battle Hospital in the future. Whilst the provision of an acute geriatric unit at the main Hospital is necessary, the care of the chronic sick would be a suitable continuing use for Battle Hospital. In addition, isolation beds could well be provided there.' Nurse staffing difficulties, they suggested, might be overcome by seconding nurses from the Royal Berkshire Hospital in short-period rotations.

Sir George Schuster, Chairman of the Oxford Regional Hospital Board, now brought his most senior officers to Reading for a Special Meeting of the Visiting Medical Staff Committee. After a discussion on the local elements of the Command Paper, the Board's representatives made several observations. The Board accepted and agreed with the principle that there should be only one district general hospital in Reading, on the Royal Berks site, but it would be necessary to retain Battle as a second hospital. It was not advisable at the present time finally to determine the number of beds to be provided on the Royal Berks site, as the needs of the Group would undoubtedly change with the passing of time. With the growing importance of out-patient and diagnostic facilities, emphasis would be placed on the provision of adequate accommodation for such facilities on the site. The resolution and memorandum by the Visiting Medical Staff Committee would be considered by the Board in due course. Other general promises were made including hoped-for start dates for the first two new buildings at the Royal Berkshire Hospital and the plans for temporary provision of additional beds and operating theatre facilities for the Accident and Orthopaedic Department at Battle.

Soon came a follow-up letter from the Board which again managed to avoid the main point. Its key passages read:

a) The Royal Berkshire Hospital should be developed to provide a comprehensive acute and emergency hospital for Reading. The total beds would probably be limited to 1,000 within the present phase, that is until 1975, but the site development plan would be drafted to allow further development beyond 1,000 in subsequent years.

b) During the present phase of development, the remaining 400 beds in Reading would be on the Battle site, with provision for subsequent development to 500 beds.

The Committee reluctantly accepted this ambiguous message. Officers of the Regional Board and in particular Deputy Senior Medical Officer Dr J A Oddie continued the offensive in discussions away from official meetings; the Reading Group officers and consultants fought equally vigorously for all the acute services to be provided at the Royal Berkshire Hospital. In 1965 the Royal Berks development plans were ruthlessly slashed by new financial restrictions. The Hospital Planning Committee were furious to be told that the Regional Board still considered there should be a parallel development at Battle Hospital to make it a District General Hospital complementary to the District General Hospital at the Royal Berks. 'It is not the Committee's policy to split departments between hospitals if it can be avoided and the Committee could not support any parallel development at Battle until all the acute development at the Royal Berkshire Hospital is completed.' The local planners may have been defiant, but their pronouncements were of little consequence against inflexible determination at Oxford.

The row was still seething when there came startling news, brought officially to Reading in the spring of 1966 by the Chairman of the Oxford Regional Hospital Board. This new Chairman was Mrs Isabel Graham Bryce. She came with her team to address another Special Meeting on the concept of an 'Export' hospital to be sited in Reading. Her audience were the Hospital Management Committee together with selected members of the Medical Advisory Committee and we can be sure that she had their undivided attention. The Minister of Health, she explained, following representations by the British Hospitals Export Council, had decided that a hospital building project designed to help the export drive should be built in the Oxford Region. The Council existed to promote the export of British expertise in hospital design, construction and equipment by helping British firms to enter this field. After consultation with the Oxford Regional Hospital Board it had been agreed that a site at Battle Hospital, being convenient to London, should be chosen for the project. A number of consortia of architects, consulting engineers, builders, engineering contractors and equipment suppliers were to be invited to submit proposals to meet the requirements of the Board. The completed building would serve to demonstrate their joint capabilities and be a 'shop window' for the export trade. There was no comparable demonstration building anywhere in the country and the need was widely recognised. The necessary finance for this hospital would be quite separate from, and additional to, funds already promised for development in the Oxford Region and would in no way delay or affect the development of the Royal Berkshire Hospital as planned. It would represent an unexpected and valuable contribution of hospital facilities for the population served by the Reading and District Hospital Management Committee and would bring much-needed relief to the hard-pressed services in the area, which would otherwise have been subjected to greater demands for a longer period of time. The content of the project was yet to be determined but it was hoped that about 200 beds could be provided. Planning would start without delay, as it was the intention that every step would be taken to bring the project to completion as soon as possible.

The response was recorded in carefully worded minutes. 'The several members of the Management Committee and the senior medical staff who spoke were unanimous in their enthusiastic support for the project.' The Chairman of the Hospital Management Committee, Aitken Walker, in closing the meeting assured the Board's representatives that the Committee would assist to the utmost in the speedy realisation of the new hospital.

Although true enthusiasm for this oddly conceived project probably came only from the long-serving members of Battle's administrative, nursing and supporting services, Reading was in no position to reject a free 200-bedded hospital. What it now meant was undoubted duplication of acute services – as a show-piece, the Export Hospital would obviously have to demonstrate the latest and best in the glamour specialities. The proposal having been accepted, how should the new hospital be run? The Financial and General Purposes Committee, which made most of the important decisions, resolved that it should have a separate administration. The medical staff rightly expressed anxiety at this unnecessary split. The response at Battle, perhaps fortunately, went unrecorded while a more rational approach gradually developed. At its next meeting the Financial and General Purposes Committee decided that the administration would be complementary to rather than rival the existing Battle administration. After another month's consideration there came at last a sensible resolution: 'As the Export Hospital scheme is now seen to be the first stage in the major development of Battle Hospital, its administration be integrated within the existing framework.'

An ad hoc sub-committee of five consultants and four administrators was formed to discuss the re-naming of Battle Hospital and of 'the proposed extension on the Battle site'. Another astonishing decision was made. The Visiting Medical Staff Committee agreed with their idea that Battle should become the Royal Berkshire Hospital, Oxford Road Branch and that the Royal Berkshire Hospital should be entitled Royal Berkshire Hospital, London Road Branch. Again wiser counsel eventually prevailed, as the Hospital Management Committee rejected the suggestion. They observed that whatever new title was chosen, Battle would continue to be known by its old name by the general public and that any re-naming might well cause resentment.

With administration and naming issues at least partially resolved, major questions remained about the enforced division of Reading's acute services. In May 1966 the Hospital Planning Committee finally accepted that the Royal Berkshire Hospital and Battle would be 'developed eventually as more or less independent acute general hospitals of equal status, although certain departments need not be duplicated'. The re-allocation of beds was agreed in principle. General surgery would be divided between the Royal Berks and Battle. The general surgery, chest surgery and medicine from Peppard and acute medicine from Prospect Park would all transfer in to the new hospital. Twenty-four children's beds at the Export Hospital would be used as flexibly as possible with periodic ENT allocations to eliminate the tonsil and adenoids waiting list. The vacated Maternity Block would be given over to neurology, rheumatology, physical medicine, trauma and orthopaedics. This latter raised a pertinent question: was it still the correct policy to transfer the Accident Service back to the Royal Berks, since the Battle site would soon have the other acute specialties whose advice and collaboration the Visiting Medical Staff Committee had deemed so important? Mr Squire, having for years put up with ancient accommodation and make-do facilities, was adamant that the move must go ahead. In the scramble for space following abandonment of the proposed Phase III tower block at the Royal Berkshire Hospital, he intended to get both Accident and Emergency and his orthopaedic beds into the brand new block of Phase VI.

While the jockeying was going on among the clinical services, preparations for the Export Hospital moved swiftly. In May 1966 a letter from the Oxford Regional Hospital Board announced that a tender of £1,000 had been accepted from Site Survey Co. and another of £1,916 from Terresearch Ltd for ground exploration on the site. In November the main brief was issued to the five contracting consortia with a closing date of 17th May 1967 for initial tender bids. The programme was timed to start on site in April 1968 and completion was expected in 21 months.

The optimism of this schedule was soon rudely shattered. In February 1967 the Oxford Regional Hospital Board reported that the design consortia had declined to accept the high risk of incurring considerable losses in the form of fees, and that neither the Ministry of Health nor the Board of Trade were able to meet this liability. So much for promoting the export of British expertise in hospital design by helping British firms to enter this field! The Board had now been asked themselves to bring the scheme to sketch-plan stage and were recruiting a design team. In May 1967 Messrs Felix J Samuely and Partners were appointed Structural Engineers, R W Gregory and Partners Consulting Engineers and Messrs Yorke, Rosenberg and Mardall Consulting Architects.

This fundamental change, and disquiet at the grievously curtailed plans for the Royal Berkshire Hospital, resulted in yet another Special Meeting of the Hospital Management Committee in September 1967. Present were the officers of the Committee including the Matron and Secretary of Battle, senior medical staff and representatives of the Oxford Regional Hospital Board including the Regional Architect, the Senior Administrative Medical Officer and his Deputy, Dr Oddie. The Chairman summarised the recent events in respect of the Export Hospital and reported the views of the Visiting Medical Staff Committee. The consultants were gravely concerned about the proposals for Phase VI at the Royal Berkshire Hospital and the major modifications in the Export

Hospital proposals. The Visiting Medical Staff Committee 'was convinced that its original strong recommendation had been and was still correct. The funds to be devoted to the building of the Export Hospital should be used for further development on the Royal Berkshire Hospital site. (The Medical Advisory Committee had made the point that transfer to the Royal Berks should not be a problem for a hospital designed to be built quickly and in any part of the world). The stimulation of the Export Hospital buildings and equipment could be equally effective, valuable economies could be achieved, doubts about the adequacy of Phase VI for its purpose would be resolved and the development of a unified and effective hospital service for the area would be hastened.'

The Chairman assured the members of the medical staff that the Hospital Management Committee would give full consideration to their resolution, then introduced the Regional Architect. He explained the proposed plans. The main issue was that the contracted architects had advised that a multi-storey building would prove uneconomic to construct in view of the site difficulties (at another meeting the wording used was 'ground conditions', presumably referring to the low-lying land, the 19th century excavations and subsequent building up by labourers' toil). Various questions were asked and it was resolved that the Oxford Regional Hospitals Board be requested to supply relevant comparisons between the running costs of single and multi-storey layouts, with details of the staff walking distances involved, before a firm decision was taken on whether or not to approve the plans.

At the next Hospital Management Committee meeting, the Chairman had some different phraseology in explaining 'the current position in respect of the Battle Hospital development which had originated as the "export" hospital'. The concept of competing consortia which had been abandoned for the design aspect now applied also to the equipping of the unit. Correspondence from the Secretary of the British Hospitals Export Council had announced that the consortia were of the opinion that the project was no longer suitable for a consortium operation and that they therefore did not wish to submit competitive tenders for equipment on a consortium basis, which was now to be undertaken under normal procedures. Another letter from Oxford gave brief comparisons on staff walking times and blandly favoured the single-storey layout. This obviously did not answer the questions which had been asked and on the proposal of Mr J C H Butcher, further information was sought on the advantages and disadvantages of multi- and single-storey developments.

A further Special Meeting was held in October, with invited members of the medical staff and some officers, though none this time from Battle. There had been another report from the Visiting Medical Staff Committee and the controversy had become public with an article appearing in a local newspaper to the effect that the British Hospitals Export Council were no longer participating in the development. The medical staff's view, presented by Dr F Hampson, was that in the changed circumstances there was no justification for developing the Battle site at present for acute cases. They would, however, support the development at Battle if the Ministry were unable to divert the allocated funds to the Royal Berks site. The Hospital Management Committee agreed and now recommended to the Regional Board that the funds for the project be utilised for a separate development on the Royal Berks site.

The Board responded promptly and firmly with a letter from George Watts, the Board Secretary to Frank Naylor, the Group Secretary, saying that the present policy would not be changed. Three main reasons were given by the Oxford Regional Hospital Board and their presentation seems to have been in reverse order of importance:

'Firstly, the hospital needs of the people of Reading and the surrounding area. The area served by your Committee is expanding rapidly and with this growth in population, the demand for hospital services. The development of the Export Hospital will provide an early alleviation of the pressures on the existing services.'

How breathtakingly patronising! The Hospital Management Committee knew all about pressures on their service. This was simply Oxford again deciding without evidence that two acute hospitals are better than one. The only justifiable phrase is 'early alleviation' which belongs to the Board's next point:

'Secondly, a change in policy will lead to considerable delay in augmenting the services available to Reading. Even if it were possible to use the special allocation ... as your Committee recommend, this could not be done without a serious delay in the commissioning of the additional facilities.'

The final reason is the most significant and the least satisfactory:

'Thirdly, informal soundings at the Ministry indicate that a suggestion from the Board that the special allocation be used other than as originally proposed would lead to a close examination as to whether the allocation should not be withdrawn. Your Committee will appreciate that the Board could not communicate the terms of the resolution to the Minister without comment.'

Certainly the risk of withdrawal of the funds is a legitimate concern, but one wonders about the nature of those informal discussions between a Board wanting development at Battle and a Ministry embarrassed by an over-optimistic scheme which had foundered.

So that was that. Mr Butcher, knowledgeable from his rapidly progressing James Butcher Housing Association, again pushed for information on whether the advantages of a multi-storeyed layout were to be put forward. The Group Secretary reported that the Building Research Station had shown that the running costs of single and double storey buildings were comparable, but that above two storeys the costs became progressively higher. The Hospital Management Committee, although agreeing with its hospital planning sub-committee that the single-storey layout was a waste of space, in the circumstances accepted the sketch plans as previously submitted. The Visiting Medical Staff Committee thanked the Hospital Management Committee for supporting the views of the medical staff; as the Board intended to proceed despite these views, they would now seek to provide the best possible service.

Under the new Cogwheel structure in 1969 the Medical Advisory Committee was replaced by the Medical Services Committee. The consultants on this Committee met many times to prepare a policy on the planning of hospital services. They considered in detail the ideal use of the beds, theatres and out-patient facilities in the new Battle Hospital and the effect on every other hospital in the Group. It is important to recognise that despite the split site, every effort was being made to centralise the acute facilities. Their detailed scheme followed the general principles outlined three years previously and was accepted as policy by the Hospital Management Committee.

The new hospital would provide 217 beds, four operating theatres with a Theatre Services Sterilising Unit, an intensive care unit, six day beds, an Out-patient Department, Physiotherapy Department, pharmacy, X-ray, pathology and supporting services such as catering and administration. The Medical Services Committee recommended that the beds be used for children (25), general surgery (53), thoracic surgery (14) and general medicine, including chest medicine (111). Thus the acute medical patients of Dr Pay and Dr Hausmann would come in from Prospect Park, which would then be used for geriatrics. Chest medicine, chest surgery and general surgery would transfer from Peppard, and general surgery also from the Henley War Memorial Hospital. In the light of the closure of the War Memorial Hospital in 1983 and the more recent furore over the suggested down-grading of Townlands, the Medical Service Committee's plan for Henley is of some interest. They suggested closing the War Memorial in 1971 when the surgical cases went to Battle, but this would be dependent on improvements at Townlands, notably in GP unit, out-patient and ward facilities.

With over 200 new beds coming to Battle, re-allocation of the vacated space in Maternity had produced little controversy. The new 'temporary' ward with 12 beds went to Neurology. Physical Medicine took over the delivery suite of six single-bedded progress rooms and four delivery rooms together with Ward 1 on Thames Block's ground floor. These were used for the rehabilitation patients previously housed in Eversley Ward. Drs Meanock and Andrews were also allotted the second floor for Rheumatology, giving them a total of 48 beds. Orthopaedics, with a waiting list now numbering over 1,400, got main use of the operating theatre and

38 beds on the first floor. Ian Meanock recalled that there were many discussions on co-ordinated names for the wards in Thames Block. Patrick Chesterman wanted to commemorate pioneers in orthopaedics, Drs Meanock and Andrews championed early names in rheumatology. The stalemate was overcome by Mr Parcell. He had already named Thames Block; now he suggested the names of Thames-side villages where the consultants lived, hence respectively Caversham, Whitchurch and Cookham for the ground floor, first and second floor wards. In 1971 the neurology ward followed the pattern to become Streatley Ward.

The new occupation of Thames Block and its recent extensions thus released beds at Prospect Park and Peppard Hospitals and created a centralised unit for Neurology, Orthopaedics, Physical Medicine and Rheumatology. Ian Meanock and Francis Andrews were delighted. They now had sumptuous offices in the previous duty obstetrician's suite. They had close contact with Pat Chesterman's specialist surgery and access themselves to a first-class theatre, where they did minor operations, manipulations and more modern techniques including radio isotope injection treatment for single joint disease. There was space for a gym staffed by remedial gymnasts. Thanks to the midwifery training facilities

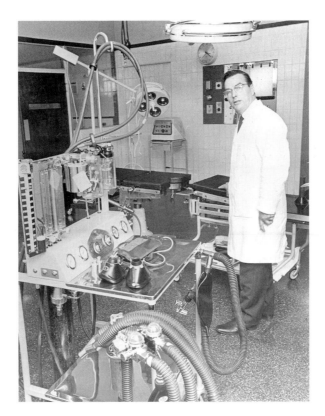

'Streatley' Theatre behind Thames Block, 1970. Nursing Officer Frank Cox

they had a library and seminar room. Francis Andrews developed a small laboratory, partly financed by a private showing of the popular film *A Man Called Horse*. The Department produced numerous academic papers, and ran a Section Meeting of the Royal Society of Medicine. With Doreen Thomas, the Prinicipal Tutor of the Group School of Nursing they ran a post-registration course on musculo-skeletal disorders. The original Block for the Aged and Infirm was a hive of clinical activity in this its third and almost final phase.

The Medical Service Committee's concept at this stage was well short of equality between the two major Hospitals. The Royal Berkshire Hospital should become the Hospital for all accident, emergency and major acute work, with Battle caring for planned admissions and rehabilitation. They foresaw that this would mean consultants having charge of beds on both sites (although one surgical firm would undertake all its work at Battle until Phase VII). Many other staff would have to work in more than one place and some pathology services would need to be provided at Battle. The movement of patients, staff, stores, specimens and records all required special consideration. Other features they wanted at Battle were Day Hospital facilities for geriatric, psychiatric, young chronic sick and others, with an expanded Department of Rehabilitation. Regarding staff accommodation, since the two blocks of flats for married medical staff built in 1962 had proved to be very satisfactory, the Medical Committee did not concern themselves with the residential development of 61 dwellings to be built on the far side of Elizabeth House. Neither did they comment on the proposed kitchen and dining areas between the new hospital building and Thames Block, nor the Industrial Zone incorporating boiler house, external engineering services, new group laundry, central stores, workshops and transport. They did however note the need for a Group Central Sterilising Supplies Department to free space at the Royal Berks.

During April 1970 an official request was made to Oxford for increases in establishment to cover the staffing requirements for 'Phase I Battle'. The additional staff asked for included Anaesthesia: one consultant, one registrar, two senior house officers; Surgery: one consultant, one registrar, three pre-registration house surgeons; Medicine: one senior house officer (shared by Drs Kidd and Andrews); Paediatrics: one registrar, one senior house officer, one pre-registration house officer; Pathology: one consultant; Radiology: one consultant; Nursing: seven nursing officers, 53 trained staff (SRN and SEN) and 117 untrained nurses. There was of course a long list of supporting staff – administrative and clerical, professional and technical, ancillary, catering, engineering and laundry. The Oxford Regional Hospital Board quibbled, particularly on the new consultant posts, although with expansion most of the demands were eventually met.

In May 1971, having taken advice, the Financial and General Purposes Committee recommended names for the new block and its wards. According to Les Parcell, it was anaesthetist Martin Bristow who suggested Abbey Building, based on the historical connection with Reading Abbey. As Hospital Secretary, Mr Parcell 'offered everybody the chance to come up with names for the new wards but none would really do'. He therefore chose (possibly in a punning mood) names of political Wards in Reading – Redlands and Tilehurst for the surgical wards, Castle, Minster and Whitley for the physicians, and the paediatric ward would be Norcot.

The Regional Board suggested that if the Hospital Management Committee were considering a special guest to open the Abbey Building, the President of the Royal Institute of British Architects be invited as this development was the largest incorporating the Oxford Method of building in the Oxford region. The Committee did not take up the suggestion. The Oxford system had been used in the Out-patients Department and the Nurses' Education Centre at the Royal Berkshire Hospital and there were many complaints about the bleak appearance and leaking flat roofs; the Committee members had disliked the wasteful single-storey layout of the new Hospital. Most of all they resented being forced to accept its siting at Battle. Instead of any official ceremony, an Open Day was held on 8th April 1972 which was attended by nearly 500 members of the public.

Politically this must have been a tricky time, not least since in January 1972 Mr D Woodrow, the Chairman of the Reading and District Hospital Management Committee had been invited by the Secretary of State to succeed Dame Isabel Graham Bryce as Chairman of the Oxford Regional Hospital Board. Years later when the Health Authority had ceased to exist an informal history was written of the Board and its successor organisation. The authorship of *Diary of a Regional Health Authority 1947/1994* was anonymous. Perhaps we are not too surprised that it contained no mention at all of the long confrontation between Oxford and Reading, nor the genesis of the 'Export Hospital' and its uncomfortable transition to Abbey Block at Battle Hospital.

NOTES

1. The estimated population of the Reading area in 1971 was 360,000.
2. No mention was made from Reading or from Oxford of Battle's 26 acres of farm land in addition to the hospital site.
3. This refers to the Royal Berkshire Hospital site after purchase of the University's Wessex Hall site.

6

1972: START OF THE GOLDEN YEARS

Clinical work in the Abbey Block developed in rather a slow and piecemeal fashion. The medical wards began taking patients on 24th April 1972. Norcot Ward saw its first children in July, but lack of nursing staff meant that only 15 of its 25 beds could be used. The operating theatres had to wait many weeks to become fully functional, again due to lack of staff. Gordon Bohn had thrown his considerable prestige and influence into making this venture a success and had moved his unit completely from the Royal Berkshire Hospital, while Colin Kirkham had come in from Peppard as the second consultant general surgeon. The original concept had long been abandoned of having only planned surgery at Battle. These full surgical teams obviously had to take their share of emergency duties, so it was particularly galling that the Abbey theatres were at first unable to do night and weekend work. A £3,500 advertising campaign to recruit staff for the new acute block had achieved only limited success. To attract married nurses back to work a well-furnished creche had been established in the hut previously used as a changing room for non-resident nurses. The creche could care for 12 children, but the demand was so small that the wooden hut again became redundant.

Many doctors, especially those married to nurses, felt that a major problem was the old-fashioned system of split shifts and late notification of rotas. Women with infants and school-age children could make themselves available for work, but only if they knew well in advance when they would be required. Provided those times were agreed, there could have been some flexibility in where the nurses worked. Mr Bohn wanted staff to be easily transferable so that gaps could be covered; it was essential, he said, to regard the two major Hospitals in Reading as one. Some lip-service was paid towards this wishful concept but the Hospital Management Committee would not reconsider its decision to appoint nursing staff to one Hospital only. The Royal Berks and Battle were always to remain separated by more than simply distance. Interestingly, there was a general belief that the Abbey Block would be a very temporary venture. Sue Mears, for instance, when starting as a Staff Nurse in Abbey theatres, was told by Frank Cox, her Senior Nursing Officer, that it was only a temporary building and that surgery

Abbey Block. Elderly Care Day Hospital under construction

Abbey Block entrance

would be going to Phase VII at the Royal Berkshire Hospital in a few years' time.

The early and continuing staffing problems were sufficiently overcome so that within a few months Battle's new acute block was in full swing. The Abbey Building could never be described as attractive; viewed from the elevated position of Thames Block, its interlocking grey boxes extended in a singularly dreary pattern on the flat acres of previous pastureland. However, despite its drab external appearance and the local doubts about prefabricated construction and single-storey layout, this proved to be a very comfortable and functional building. All were soon agreed that Abbey was efficient both as a work place and in providing a pleasant environment for patients and staff. Most of the engineering services were located in an 'undercroft' and in the hollow partition units, where they were hidden yet easily accessible. The entrance foyer was spacious and well furnished, with a convenient reception area and strategically sited WRVS tea bar. The corridors were sufficiently wide to allow simple passage for wheelchairs, patient trolleys and bulky equipment (although the cardboard-like walls suffered when moving metal did make occasional contact). The walking time for staff was rarely wasted: as well as providing exercise, much needed in some cases, many of the routes passed through ward areas which meant there was useful contact between workers from different parts of the Hospital. The wards themselves, six-bedded bays and single rooms plus comfortable day rooms, were bright and airy, surrounding large courtyards with well-tended gardens or looking out on to open grassy spaces. In the centre of the building were administrative offices, a staff library and pathology laboratory. There was also a small multi-denominational chapel of pleasing simplicity, brightened by the two stained glass windows transferred from the previous chapel behind Shiplake Ward.

Abbey Block Chapel

An outstanding feature of the Abbey Block was the section occupying the north-west corner of the complex, consisting of theatre suite, recovery room, Intensive Care Unit and Day Bed Unit. Here the author's biased views, seldom difficult to discern, can be stated directly. Having previously worked in some dozen large hospitals, from 1973 to1996 the major proportion of my clinical life was spent in this area, and the Abbey set-up was better and more convenient than in any of the others. The theatre system, commissioned by Nursing Officer May Cook, included an adjacent Theatre Services Sterilising Unit which was got up and running by Mrs Gill Powell. This was then a relatively new concept and it made for the very efficient and smooth handling of large numbers of operations. Immediately on the other side of the theatres and anaesthetic rooms, were Recovery, the Intensive Care Unit and the Day Bed Unit. This meant that anaesthetists and surgeons were easily able to keep an eye on pre- and post-operative patients, to communicate with the nurses caring for them and to help deal with the inevitable emergencies associated with intensive care. The functional layout of Abbey's theatre complex provided greater patient safety and reduced stress for the medical and nursing staff.

Intensive care is perhaps the best example of the expensive duplication which Reading had tried so hard to avoid. This makes it all the more ironic that when the Hospital Management Committee first began demanding that all acute services should be on one site the very concept of intensive care was unknown. Only at Prospect Park were there the beginnings of a respiratory unit. The final polio epidemic of the late1950s had been succeeded by a fashion for attempted suicide using barbiturates and in 1963 Prospect Park Hospital was designated as the District Centre for Poisoning. A medical registrar was appointed; an emergency on-call team was organised consisting of an anaesthetist and an ENT surgeon (for tracheostomy!). Dr Hausmann gave instruction to the casualty officers at Battle on emergency treatment before transfer to the specialist facilities.

A Sub-committee chaired by Consultant Anaesthetist Bryn Thomas reported in July 1964 on the recent idea of Progressive Patient Care, with different wards providing a range of facilities from the simplest to the most technical and intensively staffed; patients could be moved according to the facilities required. Anaesthetists were by now regularly using muscle relaxant drugs like curare and had become skilled in controlling the respiration of paralysed patients. They were logical leaders of the new field. The Committee's advice was that 'when appointing a new consultant anaesthetist, someone should be looked for with a special interest in intensive care and allocated one or two sessions per week accordingly'. An Intensive Care Ward was included in the Board's Royal Berkshire Hospital Interim Development Schemes in December 1964, but then deleted. Within a few years the Hon. Alastair Anderson, by now Viscount Waverley, was also pressing for a four-bed Coronary Care Unit on Sidmouth Ward. Meanwhile the surgeons had been fully converted to the advantages of post-operative intensive care. They and David Price, the duly appointed Anaesthetist/Intensivist, harried the Hospital Management Committee until the Cyril Taylor Unit was opened in the autumn of 1970.

Less than two years later, thoracic surgery and major general surgery were coming to Battle and a second Intensive Care Unit was deemed essential. Here again it was assumed that the acute services in Abbey Block would be a temporary measure: the Reading anaesthetists in their bid for more staff told the Regional Anaesthetics Committee that 'it would be necessary to run two Intensive Care Units for several years'. Running a second unit was never going to be easy. David Price worked unceasingly to obtain skilled nursing staff and more resident anaesthetists to provide 24-hour cover at both sites. With acute medicine and the Poisoning Centre closed at Prospect Park, Frank Rackham[1] became supervisor of the newer positive pressure breathing machines in both units. In Abbey, one iron lung and a few negative-pressure chest cuirass units were retained for occasional use by patients whose breathing had previously been affected by poliomyelitis.

The new Abbey Intensive Care Unit suffered particularly from a fluctuating work load. There was rarely enough intensive care work from the 200 patients in Abbey Block and the clinicians in the older part of Battle were reluctant to transfer their very ill patients. The four-bedded 'Kennet Cubicles' for severe head injuries were a particularly contentious issue. They were cramped, dingy and inadequately staffed, but the orthopaedic surgeons wanted to retain control of their patients in their own ward area. A Working Party on Neurosurgical Services chaired by Mr Chesterman had concluded that the demand did not justify a new neurosurgical unit for the Reading Area, but that the provision locally for neuroradiological investigations was urgent (a weekly carotid angiography session was established at the Royal Berkshire Hospital). The Oxford Neurosurgery Unit offered to provide an out-patient clinic in Reading, giving the opportunity for consultation on problems not pressing enough to warrant a patient travelling to Oxford. But the specialist unit at the Radcliffe Infirmary were very wary of what they offered on patient transfer, accepting cases on a 'courtesy basis only'. They did not want to block their beds with long-term unconscious patients. As a result, Kennet Cubicles were usually full and the intensive care anaesthetists were frequently called to deal with problems better suited for management in the Abbey Intensive Care Unit. The situation was not adequately resolved until 1980 when Phase VI at last opened as South Wing of the Royal Berks, housing both the Accident and Orthopaedic services and Intensive Care.

The paediatricians, too, were concerned about splitting their acute services. In 1970 they had asked for consideration of a paediatric centre on the site of the Craven Road Nurses' Home. The Medical Services Committee discussed a memorandum from the Department of Health recommending centralisation of all paediatric departments. Nothing came of it, and with child in-patient numbers growing from 2,079 to 2,463 in the previous three years, Drs Stone and Burke were pleased to accept the extra beds at Battle. The duplicated facilities were at least equal to those at the Royal Berkshire Hospital and David Stone recalled two bonuses: firstly the appointment of Sister Pam Simpkins, previously second Sister on Kempton Ward, to be in charge of Norcot; secondly, having on site Gordon Bohn's paediatric surgical expertise.

The area next to Out-patients which had been allocated for pharmacy had insufficient storage space for the hugely increased volumes of fluids and medical gases now required. It was used only for a Quality Control Laboratory and the pharmacists had to make do with the 'temporary' building of breeze-block and wood opposite Thames Block, freezing in winter, hot in summer, which would remain as Battle's Pharmacy to the very end.

Radiology posed another problem. With the high usage demanded by all the acute services the Abbey facilities proved to be inadequate, as had been forecast by George Burfield. Early in the planning he had stressed the proposed facilities would not be able to provide an immediate X-ray service for out-patients. Two more radiology rooms had to be created. In only one area were grumbles to be heard because a service was not duplicated. Greenlands Private Ward at the Royal Berks had been relocated to the top floor of the new Eye Block and was very busy. Abbey Block could only treat private patients as day cases since the expanded and modernised Battle Hospital still did not have a designated private ward. It was a significant factor in the continuing perception that Battle's status was the more lowly.

Nevertheless the 'Export Hospital' had carried Battle into an era of advancement which staff at the Royal Berkshire Hospital might well envy. With Walter Hausmann leading the return of general medicine, Gordon Bohn pushing forward the surgical service and thoracic surgeon Clem Grimshaw's unit now in immediate support of chest medicine, there was a distinct air of enthusiasm and optimism in the new Block. The geriatricians too received a boost soon after Abbey opened with the establishment of a 40-place Day Hospital. There were now two consultants, Sam Vine having been joined by Glenn Foubister, one of the growing number of young physicians trained in the speciality. The Day Centre, open five days a week with a mid-day meal provided, was sited almost alongside Abbey Building, thus helping to bridge the divide between 'Old Battle' and the new. The closely adjacent acute facilities meant that investigational and therapeutic services were more readily available for the elderly patients. Annual attendances climbed steeply to nearly 5,000 by 1975. The new Day Hospital was representative of two key trends in geriatrics. The speciality was being accepted as an increasingly important part of medicine and significant steps were being taken towards the ideal of management at home rather than as a resident in hospital.

Some completely new developments were inevitable under the Abbey impetus for progress and the first of these came in cardiology.

Dr Walter Hausmann and Sister Llewellyn (Allen)

Cardiology

Dr John Bell was appointed in 1976, replacing Lord Waverley as physician with a major interest in cardiology. However instead of Dr Bell going automatically to the Royal Berkshire Hospital there was a medical reshuffle. Ken North, who had taken on the endocrinology work when Dr Hausmann retired in 1974, moved his unit to the Royal Berks and Cardiology came to Abbey. This was an odd decision, considering that Accident and Emergency was also due to go back to the Royal Berkshire Hospital, splitting away the medical speciality with probably the highest incidence of acute emergencies. It created a problem unresolved until 2005.

So Dr Bell, sharing with Brian Pay, had Whitley and Minster Ward, where there was just a four-bedded bay with primitive cardiac monitoring. He had an office, a secretary, one registrar, a shared senior house officer, a pre-registration houseman but no technician. His autocratic predecessor had been feared or disliked by many GPs and in his first month Dr Bell saw only 36 new out-patients. Within a year, though, the fledgling Department needed an extra senior house officer and had an echocardiography machine plus technician. It was the start of a spectacular expansion.

Non-clinical Matters

The old question of re-naming Battle had come up again in 1973 because 'there had been several instances when the old and the new parts had been treated as two quite separate units'. The Hospital Management Committee noted that members of the staff seemed to wish to retain the present title but instead of leaving it there, they referred the matter to the Financial and General Purposes Committee. That body convened yet another Sub-committee, choosing a layman, a medical administrator and a clinician to consider the implications and make recommendations. Mr W Pettit, Dr A Gatherer and Dr D Stone harked back to the 1966 idea of hospital branches. They suggested that the newly created Berkshire Area Health Authority be asked to consider re-naming the District General Hospital in line with the new West Berkshire District and that participating hospitals should become wings of that hospital. More sensibly, they also took the opportunity to recommend that every effort be made to expand facilities at Battle in line with those at the Royal Berks, to include such matters as library, social club and occupational health service.

Of course the name was unchanged. And Battle Hospital, confident now of at least equality if not superiority in much of its clinical activity, was beginning to progress in other areas. During these years Battle was a proud and happy place. The 1974 reorganisation had given genial Geoff Part the post of Sector Administrator, with responsibility for all the Reading hospitals. His was a popular appointment in a most unpopular upheaval. Les Parcell still presided benevolently from his office on the first floor of Casualty, the quiet pacifist unifying the old and the new, amicably resolving potential conflicts, making himself available to all hospital staff and constantly striving to promote their interests. His attitudes were mirrored in Glyn Tattum, the Clerical Officer who had shouldered much of the work load in commissioning Abbey building and who had been promoted to the administrative grade. Modest Mr Tattum was a conscientious and friendly administrator who did much for the new consultants and resident staff. His early death was the Hospital's great loss.

The massive influx of junior medical staff had brought a few complaints about inadequate accommodation and lack of separate dining facilities. However, it was by now Departmental policy to encourage all staff to share the same dining area, so the new dining room remained ostensibly egalitarian while the users still kept to their own small groups. In the old administrative block, now mainly resident doctors' quarters, things could be done. The previous dining area was converted into a large games room together with a doctors' mess. Large parties and shows were now more feasible, but this facility was basically given over to the resident doctors. Social activities for the hospital staff up to this time had usually depended on the New Inn, which offered the benefit of convenience and on noisy nights the satisfying advantage of being adjacent to Matron's flat. Now the question was being asked, why not a social club like the doctors'?

Mrs Pam Miller, Sister in charge of Abbey Theatres and a local Royal College of Nursing steward, was asked at a nursing meeting why Battle had no club similar to that at the Royal Berks. In 1975 she identified a possible site when the old laundry and workshops to the rear of H Block were taken over for central group stores. Mr Parcell and Matron Morgan gave permission for part of the building to be saved for conversion to a club. Pam Miller received great support from Engineer Tom Willis, who organised the refurbishment work. She recalls that the key volunteer workers from the Works Department were John Beech and Andy Layley from the Engineering Department, Charlie Simpson, bricklayer and Bob Wicksen, carpenter. As work progressed a new Social Committee was formed with Pam Miller as Chairman. More willing people came forward or were co-opted to the Committee. Maureen Willis from the pharmacy became Secretary, Mike Edinborough from finance the Treasurer. Brenda Wellstead and Dolly Pendleton, domestic supervisers, took charge of entertainments with the switchboard operator Bill Moss organising bingo.

The Committee raised money with events such as raffles, jumble sales and discos at Brock Barracks. 'Every available hour was spent on the project, always working on a shoestring,' says Pam. A lounge and bar were opened in time for Christmas festivities. A darts team and table-tennis squad soon formed, while outdoors the activities of the Battle cricket team increased; practice nets were installed near the tennis court and in 1976 the cricketers won the Reading Mid-Week League for the first of several times. The successful captain was Deputy Head Porter Chris Bradby, soon to become Head Porter of Battle. Netball matches and five-a-side football were also started on the Abbey sports field. There was a revival of interest in tennis and the unkempt court beside the Nurses' Home was restored using amenity funds. In 1976 the Tennis Championships of Battle Hospital were held but as enthusiasts left for other posts sporting interests gradually waned.

Bat Bee (the name from a combination of Battle and Abbey), a monthly magazine for Battle staff, began in 1974, to be succeeded in later years by *News & Views*, *Battle Dispatch* and *Into Battle*. The Hospital Secretary was officially editor of *Bat Bee*, but in reality Les Parcell did all the writing, keeping everyone informed in a light-hearted way. His influence on morale at Battle can scarcely be exaggerated. It was commonly said that just three people kept the Hospital running smoothly – Mr Parcell, Matron Morgan and Chief Engineer Derek Winslow. He retired in 1977, succeeded by his deputy Norman Parker, and recalled with satisfaction that during 25 years of service to the Hospital no request by him to his House Committee had ever been refused.

Mr Parcell had overseen the huge growth of accident and emergency, of geriatrics and rheumatology. He had supervised the transfer in, build-up and departure of Reading's principal Maternity Unit. Under his charge Battle had achieved undreamed of heights with the triumph of Abbey Building. Would Battle's growth continue? In 1975 a report on the organisation of in-patient services in West Berkshire had been conducted by the Operational Research (Health and Social Services) Unit of the University of Reading. They concluded it was most improbable that there was room either at the Royal Berkshire Hospital or Battle for all the District General Hospital beds needed in Reading in the next few years and that both should continue to develop. The District Management Team agreed. Its 1978 Report on the Future Pattern of Hospital Services in West Berkshire considered that the cost of providing all facilities on one site rendered this impracticable. The present size of each Hospital (the Royal Berks 563 beds, Battle 497 beds) was moderate and the intention was to retain and develop both. Although Battle was soon to lose the accident and orthopaedic service, there were certain to be compensatory developments.

PROGRESS INTO THE EIGHTIES

During the late 1970s Battle was probably at its peak of activity in the acute specialties. The accident and orthopaedic work in the old Hospital was still expanding. In Abbey Block the medical and surgical teams were flourishing, with the exception of thoracic surgery and medicine. A severe reversal had come when the Regional Health Authority decided that following Clem Grimshaw's retirement in 1974 there would be no Reading replacement: 'It was no longer possible to have a single-handed thoracic surgeon in the Region; the need was for centralisation at Oxford.' This edict caused dismay in the theatres. Pat Saker had come from Peppard specifically to continue as thoracic 'scrub nurse'. Everyone appreciated the opportunities for teaching when the chest was opened and enjoyed the fascination of operating on the lungs.

From the wider viewpoint, the Medical Services Committee voiced vehement and unanimous opposition; the Reading consultants urged the need for an expert to deal with thoracic trauma and the importance of training junior surgical and anaesthetic staff in oesophageal and lung surgery. A deputation consisting of Orthopaedic Surgeon Pat Chesterman, Anaesthetist Tom Boulton and Chest Physician Arthur Karlish had a personal interview with the Regional Medical Officer, but to no avail. The only concession for Reading was agreement to appoint a general surgeon with thoracic interests. The appointee was David Goodwin and he was based at the Royal Berkshire Hospital.

With the decline in importance of tuberculosis respiratory medicine was also downgraded. When the feuding older chest physicians both retired, the replacement appointment in 1978 was for one general physician with respiratory interests. James Lyall's initial main concern was asthma, but his biggest contribution would be the creation in 1991 of Reading's first Sleep Laboratory.

The loss of chest surgery of course meant more beds, more out-patient slots and theatre time for other consultants. Richard Faber was appointed in 1977 when Newbury surgeon John Joyce retired and some of his work transferred to Battle. Mr Faber was told he would be moving to the Royal Berkshire Hospital when Phase VI was built. It would be 18 years before the move actually took place. In the meantime he snapped up extra theatre sessions at Battle and Newbury and began pushing for new services, particularly in gastroenterology. Gordon Bohn, who had operated on almost every day of the week since Abbey Block opened, finally retired on his 65th birthday in February 1978. Even then he stayed on to do two years' research work and in 1979, when Mr Faber was laid low by an infected leg, he returned as locum surgeon with operating skills undiminished. One of the last of the old-style general surgeons, Mr Bohn was keeping up to date and he fully recognised that a new era had arrived. The explosion of knowledge and new techniques were demanding more specialisation, even sub-specialisation.

Urology

Until the 1980s most urological operations such as cystoscopies and prostatectomies were done by general surgeons. In Reading, Conrad Latto at the Royal Berkshire Hospital had made urology his major interest and had built up a urological service with modern endoscopic instruments, thanks to his close association with Professor Harold Hopkins FRS. It should be much better known that Professor Hopkins, Professor of Optical Physics at the University of Reading, was the principal inventor of the camera zoom lens, the rod lens and fibreoptic systems, all used so widely in modern investigations and treatment, and that some of their applications to medicine were pioneered in Reading's hospitals.

On Mr Latto's retirement the first advertisement had been for another general surgeon with an interest in urology. It was because there was no satisfactory applicant that Reading moved ahead of the field with the appointment of a specialist urologist. Andrew Pengelly was told at his interview that the new department would be in Phase VI at the Royal Berks. Between his acceptance and starting work however, the orthopaedic surgeons achieved their goal of occupation of South Wing. So specialist urology began on April 1st 1980 in Abbey Block. As Sam Vine had experienced 20 years earlier, the consultant commencing a new specialty found himself without back-up – no specific ward, no office, just one senior house officer and one houseman. Mr Pengelly, a dynamic personality in the mould of Meanock and Chesterman, was more than equal to the challenge, relishing the task of building a new department. He got the out-patient sessions he needed and picked up 'spare' operating slots to have four massive urology lists in Abbey and another at Newbury. He obtained state-of-the-art equipment, and began a urodynamics service in a room hi-jacked from David Price's secretary. A new ward, Christchurch, was created by using one bay and the day rooms of Castle and Minster Wards. (When Mr Kirkham retired in 1984, Urology took over Tilehurst Ward.)

Dr Vine's early progress had been achieved thanks mainly to the

Hospital Secretary. In the 1980s a new speciality required wider sources of help. This came particularly from Consultant Surgeon Norman Rothnie who had clout as Chairman of the national Surgical Accreditation Committee, from Joe Smith, Consultant Urologist at Oxford, from Geoff Part in gaining the facilities in Abbey Block and from District Treasurer David Smith who managed to find the finances. After a year Mr Pengelly had built up his ward staff and had achieved a Registrar; the first was David Badenoch, son of one of Britain's earliest specialist urologists. It was soon demonstrated that the task in Reading was impossible for one consultant and Derek Fawcett was appointed, but the work load simply kept growing. The two urologists submitted a report in 1985 noting that they were trying to serve a population of 430,000 when the British Association of Urological Surgeons suggested a minimum requirement of one consultant per 150,000 people. Their waiting list for routine prostatectomy was two years. Already Reading urgently needed another consultant, a urology senior registrar, more beds and more operating sessions.

Urology endoscopies, originally only in Abbey theatres, were expanded by having three sessions a week in the Endoscopy Unit being modernised by physician Tony Mee. Peter Malone was appointed as the third consultant in June 1990, doubly welcome because he came as one of the 100 new consultants provided by Kenneth Clark with finance for secretarial staff and capital for equipment. This money was used to purchase one of the latest developments, a trans-rectal ultrasound machine for examination of the prostate.

Gastroenterology

Dr Tony Mee was appointed in 1984, replacing Brian Pay. His task was to bring modern medical gastroenterology to Battle. Richard Faber, at that time Secretary of the British Society of Gastroenterology, had been urging the need for a physician fully trained in fibreoptic endoscopies and the associated technical investigations. At first Dr Mee's endoscopy lists, using very basic equipment, were done in theatre and the adjacent X-ray Department. However, space was available in the 'pharmacy' area adjacent to Abbey out-patients and here an endoscopy unit was created. Gastroenterology built up a full complement of the most modern equipment funded from sources as diverse as central waiting list funds, drug trial monies and the League of Friends. Sister Margaret Bower was recruited from the X-ray Department to run the fully furnished and equipped Endoscopy Unit which was opened in October 1987 by Lord Hunt of Everest fame. Following this coup, Battle had the satisfaction of witnessing an odd twist in its rivalry with the Royal Berkshire Hospital. There Dr Margaret Myszor was appointed in 1990. Her job was to establish another modern gastroenterology unit with similar facilities to Battle's – duplication in the opposite direction.

A unique gastroenterology team at Battle was created with the arrival in 1985 of Howard Reece-Smith, another surgeon destined for high

ABBEY IN THE 1980s

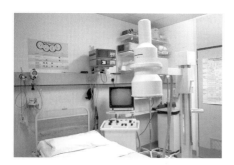 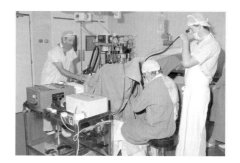

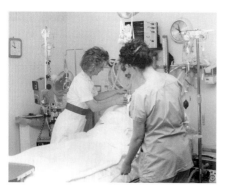 

Top left: Reception foyer; *Top right*: Minster Ward Nurses' station; *Centre left*: Cardiac unit; *Centre right*: Urology operating list; *Bottom left*: Intensive Care Unit; *Bottom right*: Kitchen

administrative responsibility. He joined the close surgeon/physician collaboration established by Mr Faber and Dr Mee. In replacing the conservative Mr Kirkham he brought new ideas and techniques, notably laparoscopic cholecystectomy (keyhole surgery for removal of the gall bladder), making maximum use of the Day Bed Unit for these patients and for many other procedures.

Cardiac Monitoring Unit

John Bell, always struggling to obtain finance for new developments, began a cardiac fund in the late1980s. His cause was greatly benefited from the high incidence of coronary artery disease among wealthy businessmen, whose donations matched their gratitude. With £230,000 from the cardiac fund and other benefactions, a 10-bedded cardiac monitoring unit with its own X-ray facility was opened in 1989 by Regional Chairman Sir Gordon Roberts.

Abbey Block was now a hugely busy clinical centre, coping with a punishing schedule of ward rounds, out-patient clinics, X-ray and pathology investigations and crowded operating lists. As the surgeons struggled to reduce waiting lists, routine operating sessions often did not finish until 7 or 8 pm. Morale was boosted by such long-serving 'characters' as the irrepressible Sue Mears and prankster Reg Carter who defied recurrent ill health to see out his long career as an Operating Department Assistant in Abbey theatres. Despite the constant pressure and recurrent problems from over-running lists, Pam Miller and her staff managed to keep a friendly atmosphere going. The Day Bed Unit, run by Sister Lesley Rosier since 1983 and now incorporating a busy Pain Clinic, had become a regional leader in the volume and type of work undertaken. The in-patient wards, constantly struggling to find beds, achieved remarkable turnover rates through the sheer hard work of the nursing and auxiliary staff.

Battle's nurses were devastated by the death of Sister Godfrey, Night Sister on Minster Ward, who was the first victim in the 1987 Hungerford massacre. Sue Godfrey had taken her family on a picnic to Savernake Forest, where she was shot and killed in front of her two children. An Appeal Fund was begun in her memory, the first disbursements being used to help three senior nurses, Christine Nelson and Julie Moore to attend advanced courses in cancer care and Chrissy Dunn to set up a complementary therapy group.

Another tragedy was narrowly averted when a fire was deliberately started adjacent to Abbey theatres and the X-ray Department in the summer of 1988. Margaret Jones, Director of Nursing Services, takes up the story: 'Having attended the annual Hospital Ball I arrived home about 2am on Saturday 20th August. At 7.30 I was awakened by the telephone and told that there was a fire in the service area of Abbey Building. The initial main problem was smoke. It became necessary to evacuate the Intensive Care Unit and Redlands Ward. The staff managed the move in a calm, reassuring way which avoided unnecessary anxiety for the patients. The press, Radio 210 and Southern TV were quickly on the scene and Radio 210 were able to reassure relatives by 9am. It took some considerable time to get the fire under control but there was only one casualty, the on-call duty Radiographer who was in the Department. Good always comes out of a disaster and the team spirit at Battle was quickly to the fore. A massive cleaning programme had to take place in theatres, the

Intensive Care Unit, Theatre Services Sterilising Department, the Out-patient Department, Endoscopy, Physiotherapy, Social Work Departments and the WRVS tea bar. Our aim was to get services back to normal as quickly as possible and no out-patient clinics had to be cancelled. The X-ray Department took the brunt of the damage. Heather Wyatt and her staff faced the mammoth task of sorting out their Department in very hazardous conditions.'

The immense effort to get a rapid re-opening was convincing evidence of the high morale throughout Abbey Block, from the cleaning staff to administrators and clinical workers. A double benefit followed this episode. Rebuilding of the damaged area included improvements to the X-ray Department; at the same time the two front rooms were redesigned to accommodate the Chest Clinic which had become somewhat isolated on the Oxford Road. A new situation right next to the revamped Radiology Department and close to the acute medical wards was ideal for what was now the Department of Respiratory Medicine.

Paediatrics
A third consultant paediatrician was appointed in 1977. Although Chris Newman's main concern was the neonatal unit at the Royal Berkshire Hospital, he took his share of the increasingly busy duties of Norcot Ward and children's out-patients in Abbey Block. Battle's other paediatric element was transformed by the departure of orthopaedics, to be more fully described shortly. When in 1980 the young in-patients of Dingley Ward transferred to Gauvain Orthopaedic Ward at the Royal Berks, upstairs Dingley continued as an out-patient cerebral palsy and assessment unit, run by David Stone in co-operation with Mike Squire and later Steve Copeland. The area was upgraded to accommodate a full assessment unit with consultants, physiotherapists, occupational therapists, speech therapists, a social worker and other appropriately qualified staff. The Dingley Family and Play Therapy Group was established so that the children with special needs could benefit from interaction with other children. Referrals came from the whole of Berkshire. In 1983 Dingley was opened officially as a 'temporary' Paediatric Assessment Unit (temporary because the hope was still for a 'mini childrens' hospital' in Craven Road). Two years later Sheila Wallis was appointed as the fourth paediatric consultant, with important responsibilities for the day-care assessment activities in Dingley and for the care of handicapped children in the community.

Departure of Orthopaedics
During the 1970s the Orthopaedic Department was joined by two new members known internationally for talents outside their clinical careers. Jazz saxophonist Art Themen was appointed Consultant in 1976, while Wales' rugby star J P R Williams became a Senior House Officer in Accident and Orthopaedics with special dispensations for match

Dingley Play Therapy

commitments. Despite these boosts to morale the staff, widely scattered among the buildings of 'old Battle', were becoming increasingly exasperated. As always, Casualty kept getting busier and the cold orthopaedic waiting list longer. The casualty theatre, the re-vamped 1911 suite in Centre Block and its Honeywell extension were all working to near capacity despite inadequate maintenance. Without extra staff, the single 'temporary' theatre behind Thames Block could not be efficiently used. The orthopaedic consultants, having won their fight for Phase VI, were spending hours each week planning and advising the architects on the layout of what was now called the Royal Berkshire Hospital South Wing.

Deteriorating conditions at Battle were tolerated on the assumption that transfer was imminent. Instead, although construction was completed in 1978, financial stringency forced delay after delay in commissioning the new block. Mike Squire retired without seeing his dream fulfilled. Pat Chesterman finally lost patience. He had medical photographer Lionel Williams take numerous photographs of the crumbling orthopaedic facilities (it was rumoured that Mr Chesterman surreptitiously planted some cockroaches) and obtained a determination on Health and Safety grounds that the Battle theatres were unsafe. This was decisive. If the operating theatres were a hazard they could not be used. With no operating there could be no accident and orthopaedic service. It was unthinkable that the purpose-built facilities in South Wing should continue to lie idle. In 1980, after 26 years of heroic endeavour in the face of multiple trials and difficulties, the entire Casualty and Orthopaedic Department returned to the Royal Berkshire Hospital.

Mr C M (Mike) Squire

Advances for Geriatrics and Rehabilitation

The departure of this vast clinical contingent left capacity in Battle's older buildings comparable to the spaciousness of their grounds. This was the opportunity and the stimulus for much-needed advances in the 'cinderella' specialities of geriatrics and rehabilitation. Although most of the buildings were in a poor state, some improvements had already been achieved. After years of waiting for funds a programme had begun in 1973 to upgrade Chiltern and Ipsden Wards, culminating with the installation of lifts to these upstairs wards. It was hardly before time – the patients and staff of Thames Block

Orthopaedic surgical team, early 1980s
Seated L to R, J P R Williams, Steve Copeland, Pat Chesterman, Arthur Theman

had gained their lift 25 years earlier thanks to the requirements of a full maternity unit. Now, following the orthopaedic exodus, the 19th century infirmary building was to benefit from a sweeping change of use. The entire block would become the centre piece in a major plan of reshuffling and refurbishments.

At this time there were 93 geriatric beds, Ipsden Ward for the male patients, both Shiplake and Chiltern still needed for the females. The preponderance of females was succinctly explained by Sam Vine: 'Women last longer, there are more of them and they do not give up as easily as the men.' His main problem remained blockage of acute geriatric beds for weeks and months, worsened by closure of local Social Service hostels. In 1976 a report to the West Berkshire District Management Team on Services for the Elderly noted district-wide deficiencies, particularly in residential homes, sheltered accommodation, home help and in the provision of hospital beds, facilities and staffing for support services such as physiotherapy, occupational therapy, chiropody, speech therapy, dietetics and social work.

The NHS planners had been doing their best. The 1978 District Plan included recommissioning Whitchurch in Thames Block as a geriatric ward and upgrading Shiplake. This latter completed the curiously inverse chronology of Battle's lifts – one of the two original Workhouse buildings was at last having an elevator installed. With this facility the Shiplake patients could be moved upstairs to Eversley Ward which would later become a psychogeriatric assessment unit. The plan was also for a day unit and improved rehabilitation services to be provided when the Casualty Department was vacated. Progressive care was the aim – patients admitted to Battle for assessment, care, early mobilisation and rehabilitation, then a speedy return to peripheral hospitals, residential accommodation or to home. At that stage no finance was available for further redevelopment of the ex-orthopaedic wards in Centre Block.

In 1982 the newly created West Berkshire Health Authority devised a much more ambitious programme. This scheme, entitled *Development of Services for the Elderly at Battle Hospital*, involved major upgrading and expansion of all the wards including Kennet and Mortimer in Centre Block, with conversion of Shiplake to an Assessment Unit. This would permit the closure of Prospect Park Hospital, since Battle's free wards could take back the Park geriatric patients. At the same time the facilities for care of the elderly would be vastly improved. The estimated cost of the building works was £850,000 for which Regional monies were found. The revenue implications of extra staff could be mainly met using funds released if Henley War Memorial Hospital were closed.

As we have seen, closure of the Henley War Memorial Hospital had been mooted by the medical staff in 1971 and it had long been an administrative goal. In 1983 the concept was 'sold' to the people of Henley in a campaign masterminded by community physician Peter Dixon. The intense publicity emphasised firstly that the Authority intended to improve

Oxford Road entrance closed to traffic

and develop Townlands as the local community hospital, possibly incorporating the name Henley War Memorial Hospital. Secondly, the proceeds from the sale would be used to provide improved accommodation on the Townlands site. Thirdly, revenue savings would be used as a contribution to the running costs of the Geriatric Assessment Unit at Battle Hospital. For a town with an ageing population, loss of its locally endowed and much-loved hospital could be accepted in return for improvements to Townlands and clear advances to the district geriatric service. Opposition was surprisingly muted and 'The Memorial' closed in February 1984.

The Health Authority made another controversial early decision which affected Battle, not in its clinical work but in the important sense of altering the character of the Hospital and its public image. In 1983, without consulting the Battle clinical staff, the Health Authority closed the main Oxford Road entrance to vehicles. There were good reasons for this. Traffic was massively increasing in Oxford Road; with no casualty department the emergency ambulances were now mainly involved at Abbey Block and members of the public were using the Hospital roadway as a short cut. Nevertheless the closure infuriated those staff who travelled daily between the Hospitals. They now had to choose between using narrow local roads or a long deviation to reach Battle and enter via the uninspiring rear access from Portman Road. For Battle's supporters, restricting the historic front archway to pedestrian traffic was an indignity,

New Elderly Care Unit

demeaning the Hospital in the eyes of its community just at a time when significant developments and important clinical advances were taking place. Closure of the front entrance, by converting the Hospital through road to a cul de sac, also exacerbated the divide between the 'new' and the 'old.' Staff working in Abbey Block no longer drove twice daily through the Hospital and many were almost unaware of the major new projects going on in the older buildings.

These developments were very impressive, aimed at providing a mixture of short, medium and long-term care for the elderly, using facilities flexibly according to need. The new style wards would have two-bedded bays, space for photographs and ornaments and cupboards for personal possessions. New buildings would link the wards to day rooms, activity rooms, therapy areas, a hairdressing salon and an assessment flat for use prior to discharge. The final cost of the radical upgrading was over £2 million. A programme on this scale took considerable time and it was not until June 1988 that Sir Gordon Palmer, the Lord Lieutenant for Berkshire, opened the new Elderly Care Unit in Centre Block. In the 'four wards scheme' the old ward names had been discarded along with their outmoded furnishings. Artists' names were chosen as likely to be familiar to the elderly age group. On the ground floor Reynolds and Turner Wards dealt with acute admissions and rehabilitation; on the first floor, Lowry and Stubbs were for longer term patients. Across the Hospital roadway the famous artist theme was continued; the revamped Shiplake had became Gainsborough Acute/Assessment Unit. Above,

Eversley was now Constable Ward for elderly patients requiring longer term rehabilitation.

Sam Vine had retired in 1984 and so missed benefiting from these considerable achievements. But he had already seen the essential change in the practice of geriatrics; with increased numbers of acute elderly care beds in Abbey Block the geriatricians were no longer acting mainly as back up to the acute specialties. Dr Vine was replaced by Mike Pearson and a third consultant post was created in 1987, which was filled originally by Dr Ros Allen-Narker. In September 1989 an age-related admissions policy was introduced for emergency medical patients aged 75 or over. All elderly patients with acute medical problems would be seen by a consultant geriatrician. With the improved staffing and facilities in the 'Painters' Block' they should also be able to return sooner and with more self-confidence to their own home or community accommodation. Unfortunately bed blocking remained a problem due to unsatisfactory home conditions and too few residential and nursing homes.

Support in the community was however slowly improving. Battle at the end of the 1980s had 169 geriatric beds. As well as the elderly from Prospect Park, they had received some 50 very reluctant patients and staff when Blagrave Hospital was closed in 1988 as part of District General Manager Michael Taylor's swingeing cuts. The originally convalescent beds at Blagrave had gradually been taken over by geriatrics and terminal cancer patients. Kate Ignatowski who was a Staff Nurse there remembers the pleasant conditions and happy atmosphere and how angry they all were to be told their 'temporary' move to Battle was in fact to be permanent. The Blagrave patients went to Caversham and Streatley, sharing with the oncology and younger rehabilitation patients, and to Lowry Ward in the refurbished Centre Block. Staff Nurse Ignatowski hated the expensive new block which she felt was unsuited to the patients. The two-bedded bays were too small for the equipment required, and too crowded at visiting time, the high windows could not be opened, the day rooms were too far from the wards and unlike Blagrave there was nowhere convenient to push long-term patients out into the sunshine. She left the NHS but returned 10 years later to Reynolds Ward, much happier with the greatly improved facilities.

Ian Meanock retired in 1985. His replacement Dr Tony Bradlow was appointed purely as Consultant Rheumatologist; the physical medicine function had been hived off two years earlier with the appointment of Claire Whitehead as Consultant in Rehabilitation. She had a few beds in Whitchurch, the ex-orthopaedic ward which was now mainly for the elderly. Until Francis Andrews astonished his colleagues by leaving the medical profession to become a priest, Dr Bradlow shared with him 25 beds in Cookham and seven in Caversham Ward. In the late 1980s there were huge concerns that junior posts in medicine would be lost under new training regulations. It was mainly to protect these positions that Dr

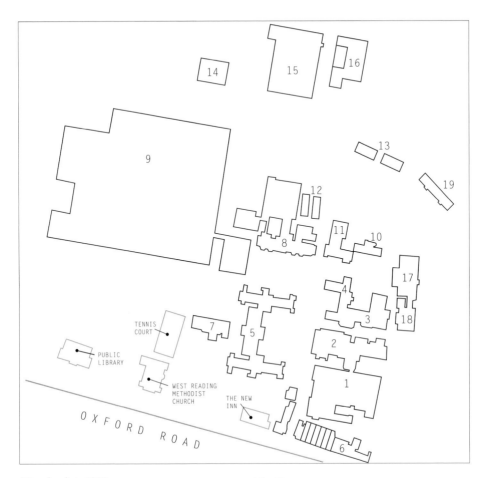

Site plan late 1980s
1. Old Casualty and Out-patients
2. Doctors' residence
3. Gainsborough and Constable Wards
4. Dingley Paediatric Assessment Unit
5. Centre Block
6. Chest Clinic
7. Nurses' Home
8. Thames Block
9. Abbey Block
10. Purley
11. Pharmacy
12. Wartime huts. Dietitians and Hospital Radio
13. Doctors' flats
14. Elderly Day Centre
15. Group Laundry
16. Boiler House
17. Old Laundry
18. Social Club
19. Elizabeth House

Bradlow agreed in 1989 to rheumatology joining general medicine. With some misgivings, he and his new colleague Joel David became part of the consultant medical emergency rota. The move was a complete success. Rheumatology has since become Reading's largest Department in general medicine and Dr Bradlow became Director of Education and Training and Clinical Tutor.

Christine Collin replaced Claire Whitehead in 1991 as Consultant in Neurological Rehabilitation. She was given an office in the near-deserted old casualty building, where in the loft space she found a lot of orthopaedic equipment which was sent to Cambodia. At first she had just four beds on Castle Ward, but she made a survey of all patients in the acute medical beds and documented 92 who would benefit from neuro-rehabilitation. With this leverage, she obtained 12 beds in Thames Block where the main physiotherapy and occupational therapy services were, sharing Caversham Ward with Rheumatology and setting up a close support network with Nigel Hyman's neurology service.

More than 30 years after Sam Vine's struggles to deal with the young chronic sick, the district at last had a consultant with both a specific mandate and the enthusiasm to take on their care. At Townlands Dr Collin reviewed all the long-stay patients, helped by the Government decision that continuing health care was no longer an NHS responsibility. Most could be moved on, leaving 12 beds for slow rehabilitation cases and for respite care of patients with neurological disease such as multiple sclerosis and those with head injury. The local branch of Headway, the charity for head injury patients, had begun in 1987, also temporarily based in Battle's old casualty building. Headway too moved to Townlands, developing their day centre services separate from but in close co-operation with the Neuro-rehabilitation Department.

Although it had lost casualty and orthopaedics Battle Hospital was at this time still a very big concern. With the build-up of geriatrics, rheumatology and rehabilitation and continuing developments in Abbey Block, the Hospital was caring for 429 patients in 15 wards. All were reasonably up to date and in several areas the most modern of facilities were in operation. The services included the four Abbey operating theatres, Day Bed Unit, Intensive Care Unit, Endoscopy Unit, Coronary Care Unit, Elderly Care Day Unit, Out-patient Department and supporting services – pharmacy, X-ray, pathology, physiotherapy including the hydrotherapy pool, occupational therapy, speech therapy, chiropody and dietetics. The industrial zone alongside Portman Road boasted centralised facilities serving much of West Berkshire and beyond: the huge laundry, the District Central Sterilising and Disinfecting Unit, Pharmacy Production Unit and warehousing of Southern Supplies Division, a Regional resource.

Successful centralisation of the industrial services served as a striking contrast to problems on the clinical side due to the two Hospital sites. These difficulties were growing, and were being better documented by the changing administration. Peter Holbrook for instance was asked in 1986 to report on inter-Hospital transport: Staff buses and courier vans carrying mail, records, specimens and X-rays were on a timetable totalling 20 daily journeys in each direction, yet still requiring taxis as a back up; the ambulance service was needed many times a day for transferring patients; much valuable time of consultants and other senior staff was being wasted as they crossed to and fro. All this was in addition to the increasingly expensive duplication of equipment, skills and facilities. Already the planners had some far-reaching proposals. Battle might still be a thriving establishment, but by the early 1990s its possible end was in sight.

NOTE

1. Following his retirement in 1976, Frank Rackham was awarded the British Empire Medal.

7

TRUST STATUS AND
SINGLE-SITE APPROVAL

Despite the revitalised geriatric service and spectacular developments in Abbey Block, most of Reading's consultants held firmly, and with growing impatience, to the requirement for a single acute hospital on the Royal Berkshire Hospital site. The local health administrators and planners also wanted progress towards a single site but were unable to make the key decisions with the urgency being demanded of them by the clinicians. Throughout the 1980s and into the 1990s their energies were repeatedly channelled into dealing with financial crises and a bewildering series of changes in the organisation of the National Health Service.

In 1982 the Area Health Authorities had been abolished and the West Berkshire District Health Authority (WBHA) took over. Mr Geoff Part's Sector was converted into two Units of Management: one the Royal Berkshire Hospital, the other comprising Battle, Blagrave and Prospect Park. Ann Boutall became Battle Hospital Manager, Margaret Jones Director of Nursing Services and Francis Andrews the Unit Medical Representative. The consultants were far from happy with these separate Units; they felt that management should be more streamlined to co-ordinate planning for the move towards a single acute site.

The draft strategic plan 1984/94 by the new District Health Authority did comprehend centralising paediatric services on the Royal Berks site, but this only served to alarm the general surgeons and urologists at Battle whose patients naturally included many children. They urged that piecemeal disintegration of the acute services at Battle must be avoided by a planned transfer of all departments. A special meeting of the Visiting Medical Staff Committee was called in May 1984, where there was again strong support for concentration of all acute services at the Royal Berkshire Hospital. Perhaps for the first time there was debate on the definition of 'acute services'. Some felt there was a danger in not including, for instance, geriatrics and neurology. Peter Dixon's suggestion that cold non-major surgery might be retained at Battle was deemed unacceptable by the surgeons. Even if unanimity had somehow been achieved, nothing could be resolved by the medical staff alone. At its next meeting the West Berkshire Health Authority declared that the consultant preference for all acute services on the Royal Berks site was too expensive to be acceptable to

372

the Regional Health Authority. It did however support the provision of 80 new acute beds there, as well as the transfer of Norcot.

The following year the West Berkshire Health Authority spelled out the situation more clearly. There were 455 acute beds at the Royal Berkshire Hospital, 242 at Battle and 10 at Blagrave. Capital constraints meant it had to be accepted that concentration of all specialist services on one site was unattainable in the next 10 years. The major financial pressures demanded a District strategic review. This review was to lead to the closure of several smaller hospitals such as Hungerford, Wayland and Smith as well as Blagrave and Prospect Park; it would also develop into a coherent plan for the future. In the meantime, an Acute Services Working Party was set up by District Administrator Ian Islip to report on the most appropriate use of the proposed additional acute beds at the Royal Berks. The report was delayed when Mr Islip became ill, sadly soon to succumb.

In the middle of these discussions on the acute hospital service there came further important management changes. Dr Peter Phillips replaced Frank Hampson as Chairman of the West Berkshire District Health Authority in 1986. In the same year, following the Griffiths Report, 'general management' was introduced with abolition of the Unit Management Groups. Mr Michael Taylor was appointed District General Manager and by 1988 Battle and the Royal Berks had been brought back into one fold, the Acute Services Unit, with Alun Jones as General Manager and Ann Sheen as Director of Nursing and Operations. The Unit Executive included Margaret Jones as Manager of Battle Hospital.

When the Acute Services Working Party finally reported, it recommended a complicated reshuffle between the Hospitals, emphasising that funding must be adequate before any redistribution was contemplated. The suggestions included transferring Battle's paediatrics, urology and 25 acute geriatric beds to the Royal Berkshire Hospital, while ophthalmology, ENT and private patients went from the Royal Berks to Battle! For most clinicians, this report was a surprise and a disappointment, serving only to introduce new resentments and false turnings from the path towards unification. Well-reasoned objections flooded in. Of the many counter-suggestions, perhaps the most interesting was to use the Abbey theatre complex as a day care centre and Abbey Block as the core psychiatric unit to replace Fairmile Hospital.

This report was quietly shelved as the goal of a single site edged gradually nearer. The West Berkshire Health Authority annual programme for 1988/90 included this paragraph on a single-site District General Hospital: 'It has been recognised that the achievement of a single-site District General Hospital in Reading would greatly assist the efficiency and effectiveness of the Authority's acute services. Until now there have been no suitable opportunities to resolve this issue, but with the possible sale of the University site adjacent to the Royal Berkshire Hospital rigorous attempts will be made to advance this issue.' No suggestion, we note, of expansion on the Battle site, nor did there come any objections from Oxford to a single large hospital for Reading.

The next management upheaval came with the Government Review of the National Health Service which resulted in the NHS and Community Care Act of June 1990 and the bureaucratic, competitive and divisive internal health care market. From 1st April 1991, hospitals were to be run as businesses, providing services for health authorities and GP fundholders. With no fixed allocation the Acute Services Unit had to gain its income by selling health care in competition with other hospitals. A prospectus had to be produced for the services available; the purchasers would then decide what they could afford, agreements would be reached and contracts signed. All the work had to be costed, recorded and billed for. Further contracts were needed with neighbouring East Berkshire, Oxfordshire and Hampshire. For extra-contractual referrals the Unit had to seek prior authorisation from the relevant provider to ensure payment would be made.

Naturally administrative costs soared. Much more damagingly, the fundamental purpose of the NHS was being set aside. No longer was it a co-operative national network aiming to provide the best treatment for each patient. Instead of sharing best practice, hospitals competing for short-term contracts were encouraged to protect any advantage. The Acute Services Unit appointed a Business Development Team; clinical services were grouped (some bizarrely) into 12 Business Units, each directed by a clinician supported by a business manager and each having to produce its own prospectus. The only purely Battle-based Clinical Director was urologist Derek Fawcett, heading the Surgery Business Unit. Dr Chris Newman led the paediatricians while Consultant Anaesthetist Rachel Hall became Director of Orthopaedics and Anaesthesia, the first rung on her ascent to management heights.

It is to the credit of the Acute Services Unit and the West Berkshire Health Authority that throughout this administrative nightmare not only did the work of both Hospitals continue to advance, but important steps were taken towards rationalisation of Reading's hospital service. The District strategic review had resulted in a series of proposals eventually presented in 1989 as *Prospects II*. There were five key objectives: to overcome the split provision of acute services and provide a fully integrated hospital on one site; improve services for the elderly, integrated with local community hospitals; improve services for the mentally ill and handicapped in modern facilities closer to the centres of population; improve the pattern of services to help recruit and retain staff; modernise facilities in community hospitals, particularly at Newbury. This was further developed into the 1990 consultation document *Prospects III*, prepared by District General Manager Michael Taylor.

In considering Battle, *Prospects III* noted many problems: internal duplication of services in areas such as physiotherapy; patient transfer difficulties because of the split location of buildings; the Abbey Block was in poor physical condition and difficult to maintain; the Thames Block wards were unsuitable for modern medicine. Between the hospitals, as well as duplication of equipment there were different systems of collecting information; division of services was spreading scarce skills; there were difficulties with supervision and training, and in some cases the new statutory requirements on junior medical staff levels and rotas could not be met. A radical change was necessary and the options were reduced to a short list: do nothing; rationalise the services between the hospitals with acute services at the Royal Berkshire Hospital and rehabilitation, rheumatology and continuing care of the elderly at Battle; a single-site hospital at the Royal Berks; a single site at Battle; single site at Borocourt or a new greenfield site.

The document gave a benefit assessment of each option. Using Battle's spacious grounds as the single site scored the highest, next a greenfield site, then the single site at the Royal Berkshire Hospital. But the choice of Battle carried high costs. All the existing buildings would be demolished, and there would be a long period of phasing to allow current services to continue. Estimates were given, but no details, for the cost of the Battle option. Regarding the greenfield option the West Berks Health Authority had spent much time investigating possible sites, including an East Berkshire Health Authority proposal for a joint District General Hospital serving West Berkshire and Bracknell. No suitable site with approval for development could be identified. The preferred option was therefore to have all acute services at the Royal Berkshire Hospital, with Prospect Park as the central location for mental health core services. At Battle the stores, laundry, maintenance and other services in the industrial zone would remain. Any other area not taken up would be sold.

Before submission of this plan to the Regional Health Authority for 'approval in principle', the views of NHS staff, patients and the public were sought. There was just a small outcry in favour of Battle, mainly from residents to the west of Reading. The Visiting Medical Staff Committee after prolonged discussion favoured a greenfield site, if that were possible. If not, redevelopment on the Royal Berks site was still the best option. Further consultations were made on the likely financial problems and their solution. Even if a greenfield site could be found, the possibility was remote of obtaining the £150 million required. Centralisation on the Royal Berks site was estimated to cost £65m and was gaining support from the local politicians, local authorities and from the Regional Health Authority. However, capital from the sale of Battle would not be available until the land was finally released and the Regional Authority had indicated that funding would have to be phased. To maintain full patient services there would have to be some phasing anyway, since the development must include demolition of several poor-quality Royal Berkshire Hospital buildings and re-provision of their facilities.

One option suggested for the first phase was to group all emergency admissions and major surgery at the Royal Berks, retaining elderly care and rehabilitation at Battle together with out-patients, day services and elective surgical in-patients in the Abbey Block. The clinicians were sceptical. All too often, as with South Wing at the Royal Berks, 'subsequent phases' failed to materialise. Further, it would split one-site services such as orthopaedics and gynaecology. The Division of Medicine felt that the Elderly Care Service would be severely downgraded if it were separated from Acute Medicine.

To further complicate an already labyrinthine situation, the Conservative Government was at this time pushing for hospitals to become independent self-governing Trusts. Those accepted as Trusts would remain part of the NHS, but would be run by their own board of directors rather than the local health authority and be accountable directly to the Department of Health. The Acute Services Unit, already coping with the internal market and responses to *Prospects III*, was keen to gain more control over its activities. In October 1991 Mr Alun Jones spoke to the Visiting Medical Staff Committee on possible advantages of Trust status. Again the doctors were sceptical: consultants would become employees of their Trusts and the British Medical Association pointed out that current terms and conditions could not be guaranteed. A ballot in December returned 67 votes out of 86, with only 13 for and 53 against Trust Status.

Despite objections on both fronts, two watershed applications were made during 1992. The Royal Berkshire and Battle Hospitals applied to the Secretary of State to become an NHS Trust; the application and its business plan was founded on rationalisation on to the Royal Berkshire Hospital site. By this time Margaret Jones had retired as Hospital Manager and Director of Nursing Services at Battle and had not been replaced. Alun Jones was still the General Manager, Ann Sheen the Director of Nursing and Operations. The only Battle personnel named in the application were James Lyall, the new Unit Medical Representative on the Executive and Howard Reece-Smith in the list of Business Unit Directors.

The second application was from the West Berkshire District Health Authority and the West Berkshire Acute Services Unit to the Oxford Regional Health Authority for approval in principle of a revised *Prospects III*. This document was titled *Building a Better Future. A plan for new and upgraded facilities to centralise and integrate acute services for the residents of West Berkshire*. It contained over 100 pages detailing development of the Royal Berkshire Hospital so that acute services could be transferred from Battle. Phase 1 would be the transfer of all acute medical and surgical services, vacating Abbey and relocating the Elderly Care Day Unit so that a major section of the Battle site could be sold. This would leave in the older buildings rheumatology, rehabilitation, elderly rehabilitation, the geriatric day unit, interim elderly mentally infirm services and the Child Assessment Centre. The new building at the Royal Berks could start in 1994/95. Phase 2 would be the transfer of the remaining services with rationalisation and refurbishment of below standard accommodation at the Royal Berkshire Hospital.

The submission noted the current provision of beds as 550 at the Royal Berkshire Hospital and 400 at Battle. The Royal Berks site occupied 19 acres plus 2.5 acres of residential site south of Addington Road. Battle had 33.4 acres, but 'a large area was of poor quality made up fill which necessitates special foundations for even single storey buildings'. It estimated that if the project were rejected £10m would be needed to make the Abbey building fully compliant with fire regulations. Many of the older buildings could be renovated to an acceptable standard, but the old Boiler House, Stores and the Accident and Emergency Department were unsuitable for retention.

Both these applications had successful outcomes: *Prospects III* gained a place to progress on the Regional Capital Programme and the Government gave approval for the establishment of a Trust. The Secretary of State appointed Dr Peter Phillips as Chairman and his Shadow Trust commenced in November 1992. In January Ron Cooper, previously Best Practice Programme Director for Lucas Industries, became Chief Executive of the Royal Berkshire and Battle Hospitals as they progressed to full Trust status. Rob Clarke, Director of Finance for the Acute Unit since 1989, was given the same demanding position in the new Trust. With final approval granted by Secretary of State for Health Virginia Bottomley, the Royal Berkshire and Battle Hospitals NHS Trust officially began on 1st April 1993. The Chairman arranged for a Foundation Service on that day, led by the Bishop of Reading, the Rt Revd John Bone, assisted by the multi-denominational team of hospital chaplains. Tactfully the service was held at Battle Hospital.

Peter Phillips was very conscious of the risk that the major efforts might now all be directed towards the Royal Berkshire Hospital development. Many years of service were still needed from Battle and it was vital to maintain morale. To avoid any accusation of bias the Royal Berkshire and Battle Hospitals NHS Trust took for its logo a representation in yellow of Reading's well-known Maiwand Lion statue in the Forbury Gardens. The Royal Berks Coat of Arms was banished from public display. Whether this mollified any Battle staff is doubtful. It certainly infuriated many old hands of the Royal Berkshire Hospital. Tom Boulton was quick to point out that the Lion commemorated both a military disaster for the Royal Berkshire Regiment and the battle where Conan Doyle's bumbling Dr Watson was wounded. Though perhaps an unwise choice, the impartial logo was a signal of the Trust's intention to continue providing the facilities needed at Battle and to do as much as possible to retain the confidence of its staff.

CONSOLIDATION

In 1993 Ron Cooper presented a document on the plan to 'consolidate' the acute services. The first part would involve new parking facilities since the current deficiency of 400 parking spaces at the Royal Berkshire Hospital would increase to 1,000 when all acute services were on the site. It was hoped to convert the garden of the 'headmaster's house' at 17 Craven Road to a multi-storey car park. The second phase would be the required new construction plus refurbishment of existing buildings. Refinement of this outline plan went ahead with the architects Messrs Nightingale Associates. There would be a new Accident and Emergency Department, two multi-storey car parks giving 1,250 spaces, a new Radiology Department, a new suite of theatres, a new elderly care unit, a new day surgery unit, four new wards, a three-storey linkway, refurbishment of the Maternity Block, a new main entrance in Craven Road with offices, shops, health club and food hall, a new nursery for employees' children and refurbishment of the historic buildings. The essence of the project was that common services such as X-ray, theatres and accident and emergency would be placed in the middle of the Hospital with the clinical departments in medicine and surgery sited conveniently around them.

Ministerial approval for comprehensive redevelopment on the Royal Berkshire Hospital site was given in May 1995. The estimated capital cost of £56.3m was to be provided by public money and sale of the Battle site, while the Trust would seek to involve the private sector through the Private Finance Initiative in supplying services such as car parking, office accommodation, rehabilitation and audiology. Planning permission was granted by Reading Borough Council and preliminary work started in 1996. The schedule of new buildings and refurbishment would require Battle to continue treating patients for the next five years.

All this was happening under the weight of further huge changes in the NHS. In October 1993 the West and East Berkshire Health Authorities had merged to become a single Berkshire Health Authority, purchasing services for the population of the county. Regional Health Authorities were also merged from 14 down to 8. What had started as the Oxfordshire Health Authority now covered Oxfordshire and East Anglia plus Bedfordshire. An NHS Executive was created separate from the Department of Health, and the Regional Health Authorities were incorporated into Regional Offices of the NHS Executive. Fortunately these changes had little effect on Reading's new Trust, which was given the promised power to make local decisions and already had firm agreement for development of the Royal Berks site.

The 1997 White Paper of the new Blair Government was much more significant. It would replace the internal market with 'integrated care', not the centralised 'command and control' of the 1970s but a 'third way' with delivery of health care a local responsibility by the Health Authority in partnership with local authorities, the District Health Authorities merging and consolidating with Family Health Service Authorities. Separation would be retained between planning and provision. The White Paper was full of waffly jargon: 'broader set of performance measures', 'quality in its broadest sense', 'incentives to improve performance', 'building on community NHS Trusts and GP-led groups of Commissioners' etc. The NHS Trusts were still given control over key decisions, but now there were some new directives. They would have to embrace 'clinical governance', defined by the Department of Health as 'a framework through which NHS organisations are accountable for continuously improving the quality of their services and safeguarding high standards of care by creating an environment in which excellence in clinical care will flourish'. They would have responsibility for clinical standards, avoiding risks, detecting adverse events, learning lessons and having systems in place to ensure continuous improvements in quality. The new system was unquestionably better; at least the bureaucracy and paper work were switched from financial competition to quality of care.

A new team evolved to carry the Trust through this bright new era. In 1998 Ron Cooper retired, to be replaced as Chief Executive by Mark Gritten MBE, one of the outstanding administrators in the history of Reading's hospitals. Ex-Army officer Mr Gritten was hard-working and efficient, admired and liked by the staff at all levels. In the same year Mr Andrew Pengelly replaced Mr Howard Reece-Smith as Medical Executive Director; when Mr Pengelly retired in 2001 his place was taken by Dr Rachel Hall. Meanwhile the Trust Chairman retired in October 2000 at the completion of his second four-year term. Peter Phillips OBE had reason for satisfaction. He had overseen spectacular progress in both Hospitals; consolidation was well under way and the Trust aim to remove the 'us and them' culture had been largely successful, with nurses and doctors at all levels of administration. In the climate of rapidly changing executives, the new Chairman Colin Maclean was fortunate to have the solid support of Mr Gritten, Ann Sheen and Rachel Hall. Mark Gritten left in 2003 to become Head of Performance at the Department of Health and Social Care in the south. Mrs Ann Sheen OBE, who had taken on the additional responsibility for development of Clinical Governance, now became acting Chief Executive and in January 2004 Chief Executive.

Before these changes of key personnel there had come a severe early set-back to the consolidation plans: no agreement could be reached on the Private Finance Initiative. Treasury funding would have to be pursued for car parking, the new front entrance and offices. Lee Dennis, Head of Consolidation Development, was at this stage also hoping for Millennium Lottery Funds to refurbish the historic frontage of the Royal Berkshire Hospital and for a consortium to develop a private hospital on the site of the South Wing car park. Neither of the latter schemes came to pass, but Tony Blair's 'New Labour' Government, committed to vastly increased funding for the NHS, proved more receptive. An extra £20 billion was announced for the Health Service in general; for Reading's new hospital Secretary of State Frank Dobson agreed to the spending of up to £73m.

By 1998, the 50th anniversary year of the National Health Service, there was visible progress towards what the press were calling 'Reading's new super-hospital'. Over £2m had been spent on refurbishment of the

Maternity Unit and the Nurses' Home had been demolished to make way for the first multi-storey car park. Paradoxically, in view of the staff transfers soon to come, 120 Royal Berkshire Hospital workers were moved to Battle Hospital as their buildings were cleared to create space. Plans were finalised for the Centre Site redevelopment between South Wing and the Eye Block. In 1999 work began on the new clinical buildings to include children's wards, surgical wards, a new Accident and Emergency Department, new main entrance, X-ray, general out-patients, theatre suite and three-storey link corridor.

A totally new plan was now introduced for the final phase of the consolidation project. Instead of a medical/elderly care block on the Greenlands site plus a refurbished Nuffield Block to house medical wards and a cardiac unit, it was proposed to demolish Nuffield Block as well; a single completely new medical block and therapies centre could then be built on the enlarged site. This superior Phase 3 development would provide medical, oncology, neuro-rehabilitation and elderly care wards together with new departments of cardiology, physiotherapy and occupational therapy. The scheme was accepted, bringing the total cost of the redevelopment to an estimated £95m.

The year 2001–2002 saw the opening of the new main entrance, Day Bed Unit, theatres, centre site wards, Out-patients and Radiology Departments. There followed the refurbishment of South Wing and the Eye Block. In May 2003 construction began on the final building, occupying the space where once stood Nuffield Block and Greenlands. Since this was to house most of the remaining departments from Battle Hospital it was given the name Battle Block.

8
GOODBYE TO ALL THAT

Connections, a newsletter for all staff of the Acute Services Unit, replaced *Into Battle* and the Royal Berkshire Hospital's *Messenger* in 1990. *Into Battle* had kept going, thanks mainly to Pam Atkins, the Hospital Manager's secretary. The new combined editorial team included two other long-serving Battle supporters in Stephen Harrold, Assistant Portering Services Manager, and Linda Hanley, who had risen from telephonist to Communications Manager. The first issue of *Connections* described the Grand Re-opening of Battle Social Club after six weeks of refurbishment. This was an encouraging event for those understandably worried that Battle was facing an immediate downhill slide towards closure. In fact, despite the near certainty of consolidation on to the Royal Berks site, there were to be some further important developments for Battle before the curtain finally fell.

More Developments in Abbey
The Abbey Block entered its third decade in upbeat fashion. The Urology Department introduced an ultra-modern service with lithotripter treatment for kidney and bladder stones. (The lithotripter uses a sound shockwave to shatter hard objects, like the early Concorde booms affecting greenhouse glass.) At first, in 1993, a mobile unit was hired once a month, the trailer parked at the rear of Abbey theatres. Mr Andrew Pengelly pays tribute to administrator Alastair Mitchell-Baker for helping to find the finance needed to open a permanent lithotripter suite in 1995. At this time Oxford did not have a lithotripter so as well as kudos the new Trust received more referrals and more benefit from the internal market.

Another important advance was a video camera, funded by Health and Safety money provided to lessen the risk from treating patients with AIDS. Instead of peering through a cystoscope awash with urine, the urologist, his trainees and nurse assistants could all view the procedure on a TV monitor. By 1996 the service had acquired a Training Certificate in Urology and a Senior Registrar rotating with Oxford. Reading was again at the forefront of a trend with agreement by the urologists to sub-specialise. Andrew Pengelly concentrated on urodynamics, incontinence and stones, Derek Fawcett on kidney, bladder and testicular cancer, Peter

Malone on paediatrics, reconstruction work and cancer of the prostate. The Department was again ahead of the field with the trend for flexible fibreoptic cystoscopies to be done as out-patient procedures under local anaesthesia. Most significantly in relation to the rapid changes in nursing, Sister Megan Price became the first nurse in Reading trained to do routine check cystoscopies.

When urology did come to the Royal Berkshire Hospital, in December 2003 rather than 1980 as promised to the young Mr Pengelly, its consultant establishment had grown from one to five. They were by now pleased to move. Without intensive care and paediatrics, Abbey was becoming increasingly isolated from the mainstream and there were difficulties with out of hours investigations and surgery. Their Royal Berks facilities, a new ward and offices together with refurbished theatres, had largely been designed by Andrew Pengelly and Derek Fawcett and the Department was named in honour of their local hero. On 5th February 2004 Professor Hopkins' widow and his son Mr Kelvin Hopkins MP attended the official opening of the Harold Hopkins Department of Urology and Hopkins Ward. The Unit continues to be a leader in urological practice and staff training. Cathy O'Neill, for example, the 'in-house' Radiographer not only operates the lithotripter but herself does ultrasound-guided biopsies for the early detection of prostate cancer. National recognition of the Reading Department has come with the appointment in 2005 of Derek Fawcett as Vice-President of the British Association of Urological Surgeons, prior to his election as President.

Cardiology too made swift progress in staffing, equipment and developing the role of its nurses. John Bell, while continuing in general medicine as well as cardiology, began cardiac ward rounds at the Royal Berkshire Hospital from 1990. By this time specialised techniques were producing a new breed of consultant. Reading's first interventional cardiologist was Jim Shahi from St Mary's Hospital, appointed in 1994. He brought with him Senior Chief Technician Sue Westlake to run the cardiac laboratory team. It was under her direction, says Dr Bell, that the Abbey Department really took off. Battle became best in the country for 'door to needle time' in giving clot-busting drugs to patients admitted following a heart attack. In 1995 a service was begun implanting permanent cardiac pacemakers. The following year thanks to close links with the Middlesex Hospital a mobile coronary angiography laboratory began visits once a week. Cardiac nurses were now getting qualifications in defibrillation and other life-saving skills, and cardiac support nurses were proving their worth in helping anxious patients convalesce from their heart attacks. In 1999 a 12-bedded day case unit and dedicated cardiac catheter suite was opened in Christchurch Ward, the finance this time provided by the NHS. A second interventional cardiologist, Nicos Spyrou, was appointed in 2000. Coronary angioplasty, the use of a balloon-tipped catheter instead of bypass surgery to open the blocked artery, had been done for several years by cardiologists in London and Oxford. In February 2003 Dr Spyrou performed Reading's first coronary angioplasty, the Trust becoming one of the first district general hospitals to provide this service.

Jim Shahi died in 2002 and was replaced by ex-Battle Registrar Will Orr. Two further consultants, Charles McKenna and Anthony Chow, were appointed in the following year. By 2004 the Department was still in the Abbey Block with five Consultants, an Associate Specialist (previous Registrar Karen Luxton), two Specialist Registrars, three Clinical Assistants, two Senior House Officers, one House Officer, four secretaries, and four technicians. They were seeing 480 new patients a month and were doing several angioplasties every day. Many grateful patients could not help commenting on the contrast between this most modern and technological of services and their increasingly tatty surroundings, as Abbey Block entered its final few months.

The new Battle Block has a cardiac village with offices, out-patients, non-invasive investigations and two catheter laboratories occupying most of the first floor. John Bell, however, retired before the move from Abbey. Among other reasons, he did not fancy struggling to find a parking space.

The Respiratory Medicine Unit, relocated and updated following the 1988 fire, received a further fillip when Associate Specialist Joan Thomas was promoted in 1996 to Consultant. After almost 20 years, chest medicine at Battle again had a consultant with responsibilities solely for respiratory care. James Lyall was replaced by Chris Davies in 2000, soon to be followed by two further respiratory consultants. This burgeoning Unit transferred to the Royal Berkshire Hospital in 2003, retaining in-patients in Castle Ward which had been reduced by 13 beds to provide an Acute Stroke Unit. In Battle Block the Respiratory Unit staff have preserved the name Castle for their new ward.

Earlier Departures
While urology, cardiology and chest medicine were going from strength to strength throughout the 1990s, around them Abbey Block was being depleted. As had been planned, and just squeezing into the Health Authority's ten year timetable, paediatrics was first to go when Norcot Ward closed in 1993. (Norcot then become an Emergency Medical Unit which finally closed when the Clinical Decision Unit opened at the Royal Berks in 2004.) The Dingley Child Development Centre was now isolated as the only part of paediatrics left at Battle. Dr Sheila Wallis still had hopes at that time of early resiting into Craven Road, possibly funded by a public appeal. It was not to be. When in 1997 Dr Jenny Chapman was appointed as a new Consultant Community Paediatrician, supporting children with communication disorders and neurodisabilities, she too was based at the Dingley Child Development Centre.

By the last decade of the 20th century intensive care technology had become so complicated and expensive that duplication of equipment and skilled staff could no longer be justified. Once paediatrics had left Abbey, the potentially explosive issue of cancelling intensive care cover for small children was resolved. Consultant Anaesthetist Carl Waldmann, in charge since David Price's retirement, insisted that there could only be one Intensive Care Unit in Reading. Until all emergency surgery was moved to the Royal Berkshire Hospital, any bad-risk surgical patients at Battle could be managed in a high dependency area and transferred to the Royal Berks as necessary. In defiance of pleas from the Abbey clinicians, particularly the surgeons, Lead Sister Evelyn Yardley transferred Battle's Intensive Care Unit into the South Wing Unit in 1994.

The general surgeons very reluctantly moved in the summer of 1995. Their patients might be closer to intensive care, but they were swapping Abbey's still-modern four-theatre suite for the Royal Berkshire Hospital's dilapidated twin theatres, 60 years old and due for demolition. Tony Mee, now separated from his surgical colleagues, was quick to transfer his in-patient medical gastroenterology, initially going into the ex-neonatal section of Kempton Ward. Endoscopies at Abbey continued until 2004, when a new Endoscopy Unit together with a new Pain Clinic were opened in the area vacated by the old Royal Berks Casualty Department.

The Rheumatology Unit took over Redlands surgical ward in 1997 although their offices remained in Thames Block. Tony Bradlow lost a second colleague when Joel David moved to Oxford and was replaced by Dr Jeremy McNally. The longest-serving member of the Department, Associate Specialist Cathryn Murphy, had first joined Ian Meanock in 1978 as a trainee under Dr Rosemary Rue's Part-time Scheme for Married Women in the Oxford Region. She at last gained some female support when Australian Laurel Young became the third consultant appointment.

The expanding rheumatology team moved in late 2005, sharing with general medicine, neurology, diabetes and endocrinology the adjacent Greenlands and Aitken Walker Wards at the Royal Berkshire Hospital. It is more than half a century since a lone Ian Meanock began there with a few borrowed medical beds.

When the rheumatology patients moved to Abbey Block Dr Christine Collin took all the beds in Caversham Ward. Her neuro-rehabilitation service was expanding rapidly and in 2003 she gained a second consultant, Dr Hamid Sultan. That year saw the creation of the Acute Stroke Unit with 12 beds at the western end of Castle Ward. The Stroke Unit is run jointly by Drs Collin and Sultan, geriatrician van Wyk and neurologists Ralph Gregory and Jane Adcock. Patients stay for two weeks of optimal nursing and treatment, observation, nurse-led swallowing assessment and speech therapy. Depending on their progress patients go on from the Stroke Unit to the neuro-rehabilitation or elderly rehabilitation wards, community hospital, nursing home or to their own home with therapists visiting. The stroke team are collaborating in the development of new therapies with the Cybernetics and Psychology Departments at the University of Reading and Drs Collin and Gregory have been made Visiting Professors. It is a level of service and research undreamed of when Dr Vine first began to introduce improved methods of stroke management.

In the summer of 2004 Christine Collin moved her Department to the Royal Berkshire Hospital most reluctantly. In Battle Block 'the bed numbers are down, space and facilities are inadequate and there is no convenient parking'. Rehabilitation would have preferred not to be included as one of the acute services requiring transfer to a single site. Of course it would have been impossible to retain Thames Block, needing expensive maintenance and standing plumb in the centre of the valuable property whose sale was so badly needed. Instead, the 1911 building petered out sadly with offices occupying the old Whitchurch and Cookham Wards and the adjacent operating theatre reduced to a wheelchair park. Tony Bradlow still harbours a soft spot for Thames Block in its heyday. He particularly recalls how ducklings on the courtyard pond, reminders of springtime rejuvenation and the promise of new life, every year provided a boost for both patients and staff – until the ducks were eaten by the hospital cat.

Abbey Block did not fade out quite so sadly. The theatres staggered along losing in-patient general surgery, urology and finally day-case lists and bronchoscopies. Community dental and podiatry lists took over some of the vacant sessions until final closure in December 2003. The Day Bed Unit closed then as well, moving to South Block and amalgamating with the Orthopaedic Day Unit to become the Adult Day Surgery Unit on level 3. Tilehurst closed too when urology departed. Most of the other wards, the out-patients and support services remained active to the end.

Geriatrics in the 1990s and Beyond
At the beginning of the 1990s Battle's geriatric service had 69 acute admission beds, 78 for assessment/rehabilitation, 52 long-stay patients and the 30-place day hospital. Things however were changing. Long-term care was no longer affordable by the NHS and both the community and the politicians had begun to address seriously the problem of a rapidly increasing elderly population. The average hospital stay of the elderly patient had halved over the past 10 years. The West Berkshire Health Authority, Berkshire Social Services, Family Health Services Authority (previously Family Practitioner Committee), the District Councils and voluntary organisations were all working towards helping old people live in their own homes as long as possible. The Local Government and Housing Act 1989 enabled local housing authorities to provide grants and materials for minor works and equipment in patients' homes. Important services such as community nursing, chiropody, occupational therapy, physiotherapy, speech therapy, dietetics, lunch clubs, day centres and meals on wheels were all being improved. But the fundamental change was brought about by the National Health Service and Community Care Act of 1990 with which the Tory Government aimed to separate health from social needs. Residential care of the elderly was to be provided in association with the local authorities; responsibility for funding places in private and voluntary residential and nursing homes transferred to Social

Services. In 1993 the Health Authority engineered a deal with nursing homes in Reading and Wokingham which opened specifically to take long-stay patients. The system of means testing with guaranteed provision of funding was attractive to private enterprise and large companies quickly provided more care homes. During the 1990s to all intents and purposes long-stay patients disappeared from Battle Hospital. No longer was there any doubt that geriatrics was an acute service.

The Constable Rehabilitation Unit moved to Reynolds and Gainsborough's acute/assessment patients to Turner, where the partitions were removed and piped oxygen put in to make it more acceptable as an acute medical ward. Dingley's Paediatric Assessment Unit crept into the vacated adjacent wards while part of Gainsborough was also used by medical records and occupational health. When the Primary Care Trust not surprisingly found more facilities were needed for intermediate care between the acute hospital ward and long term residence, Gainsborough was set up in this role. (This unit and the Dellwood GP unit are scheduled to go to vacant ward accommodation in the rebuilt facilities at Prospect Park.)

The Geriatric Day Hospital was transferred in 1996 to the Centre Block day rooms and new conservatory. After 20 years, proximity to Abbey was no longer needed since the hospital phlebotomists came round to collect blood samples, the four-ward block now had a quick X-ray service and there were more junior doctors in the main geriatric wards. It was sensible to have the Day Centre there too and to combine it with out-patient clinics. Occupational therapy and physiotherapy were sited at each end, making this a most efficient and convenient multi-function unit. Although the number of places was still constrained principally by transport problems, the Day Centre continued to provide for up to 30 patients who could be cared for at night in their own home. The previous Day Hospital building next to Abbey, now called Elm House, was converted to offices mainly for the refugees from demolition at the Royal Berks.

Among other advances in the 1990s came the important multi-disciplinary nutritional assessment scheme introduced on all the elderly care wards in 1997. Age-related admission was changed to the more appropriate needs-related admissions policy in 2001. To help house 'delayed transfer' patients a temporary ward was provided in 2002. This portacabin erected on hardstanding left behind from an ill-fated cook-chill building was named by its patients 'Nightingale Ward'. A nice thought, even if it was the complete opposite of the traditional long, high-ceilinged Nightingale wards once typical of the large British hospital.

There were many changes too in the consultant staffing for geriatrics. Charles Weinstein replaced Ros Allen-Narker when she returned to New Zealand in 1993 and was himself replaced in 1999 by Andre van Wyk. Glenn Foubister retired in 2000. Sadly he died later in the same year and his eventual replacement was Dr Zahid Hussain. The most spectacular boost for the specialty came when Professor Margot Gosney was appointed in 2003 as Professor of Elderly Care Medicine jointly between the University of Reading and the Royal Berkshire and Battle Hospitals NHS Trust. This first clinical academic appointment at the University was soon followed by that of Dr David Oliver as a Senior Lecturer in Elderly Care Medicine. Specialist Elderly Care now began on the Royal Berkshire Hospital site with 13 beds on Aitken Walker Ward, 'delayed transfer' beds on Greenlands, followed in January 2004 by an orthopaedic rehabilitation service run by Dr Hussain. When the Clinical Decision Unit was opened in March 2004 the consultants began a new rota: three times a day patients in the Clinical Decision Unit are visited for repeated assessments by a gerontologist (the term now preferred to geriatrician).

Until transfer to the Royal Berks was complete, Battle continued its programme of up-to-date care for the elderly in Centre Block and the Abbey medical wards. On the eve of departure Miriam Palk, Lead Sister or 'Modern Matron' (the same job as old matron but not for a whole hospital) was justly proud of the standards achieved at Battle. The Gerontology Department was no longer a Cinderella service. No soulless, depressing long-stay wards; no need for an assessment flat, thanks to intermediate facilities and home visits by the occupational therapists; no specific beds for psychogeriatric patients, instead a mental health liaison nurse and close ties with the psychiatric hospital at Prospect Park; instant active therapy in the Acute Stroke Unit; high-quality nurse staffing, specialisation among the consultants, university-based teaching and research ... gerontology has indeed taken its place as a vital acute service. The patients have chosen the ward names for the move to Battle Block. Woodley, Emmer Green, Burghfield, Calcot and Mortimer Wards may hark back to local place names as chosen by Les Parcell half a century ago, but the specialty has come a long way since a lone consultant and his Austin A40 'office'.

Industrial Zone
The laundry played such an important part in the life of the Oxford Road Union and the municipal hospital that it is worth briefly reviewing its history under the NHS and eventual demise. As early as February 1950 the Finance and General Purposes Committee approved a plan to extend the laundry to serve the needs of both Battle and the Royal Berkshire

Sewing Room

Hospital. There was some small development until in the mid 1960s a new 'interim' Group Laundry was agreed (interim because there were already plans for a new laundry in conjunction with the proposed Export Hospital). From April 1964 the 'executive duties' of the Laundry Manager at the Royal Berks, Mr T Main, were extended to include Battle. In 1966 Messrs Charles Smith and Son were appointed architects for the interim laundry and a tender for equipment from Isaac Braithwaite Ltd was approved. Two laundry machine operators, Mr F Didcock of Battle and Mr D Oxley at the Royal Berkshire Hospital, were given leave with pay to visit Burnley General Hospital laundry to gain experience in the use of Braithwaite washer/hydros. Mr G Marven, Head Electrician at Battle, similarly visited the Braithwaite factory at Kendal. The total cost for the laundry and electrical distribution improvements was £51,687 including new presses, tumblers, washing and weighing machines. The laundry from the Royal Berks transferred in June 1967, but the Group Laundry suffered repeated breakdown problems with the new machinery. By 1972 the Group Engineer reported that the machines, although rebuilt in 1968, had further faults and 'now have only scrap value'.

Even the brand new laundry had early difficulties soon after the Abbey complex was opened, the Hospital Visitors expressing concern about a problem with ventilation. This was regarded as a design defect and the Hospital Management Committee was pleased to pass responsibility on

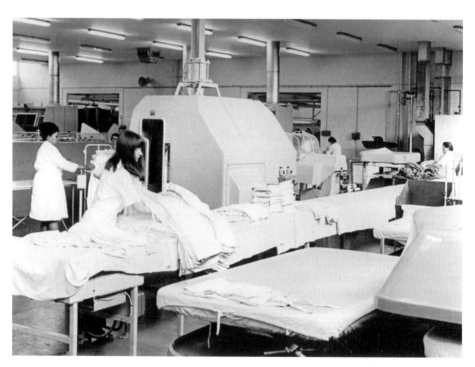

New Group Laundry

to the Oxford Regional Hospital Board. At last in 1973 the Laundry Consultative Committee could produce a more upbeat report. Additional financial allocation for more linen and positive action on linen distribution had greatly reduced difficulties. An incentive bonus scheme was working well; output was up to 95,000 pieces per week and staff hours down. Unfortunately performance of the tumbler dryers was still unsatisfactory.

For a quarter of a century the NHS laundry workers in the largest building of the industrial zone served both Hospitals and some outside the Group. This finally came to an end in 1999 when the service was contracted out and the equipment sold off. Only the sewing room continued while the huge building was used just for records, storage and mattress decontamination until the Hospital finally closed.

The Pharmacy Production Unit adjacent to the Portman Road entrance was opened in 1987. It had been commissioned by the Oxford Regional Health Authority to fill the gap in the supply of commercial products, those where the demand was too small or the shelf-life very short. A single-floor building was completed for the proposed regional production unit when someone decided this was too wasteful of valuable space. By the time it had been re-commissioned as two floors and the second storey added, most of the problematic pharmaceuticals were being produced more cheaply in plastic containers and the commercial gap had closed. The new building, fully equipped with industrial size autoclaves was simply handed over to West Berkshire's Pharmacy Department. For a few years it was run by just a handful of staff as the quality assurance laboratory and for making some items such as eye drops. Chief Pharmacist Bill O'Donnell tried without success to sell it as a commercial concern with the trading name of Portman Pharmaceuticals. The unit was decommissioned in 1995, the quality assurance function moving first to Constable, then Gainsborough Ward. It leaves in late 2005 for a portacabin in the South Wing car park. After lying idle for a couple of years 'Portman House' received more than 70 finance staff relocated from the Old Pathology Building at the Royal Berks and current proposals envisage its continuation as Trust offices.

The Central Sterilising and Disinfection Unit, having taken over the function of Abbey's Theatre Services Sterilising Unit some time earlier, was leased to Hays Commercial Services in December 1998 to provide a centralised cleaning and sterilisation service for the Trust's surgical instruments, thus also replacing the service from the Theatre Sterile Supply Unit at the Royal Berkshire Hospital. Hays sold the contract on to Synergy Healthcare PLC in 2003.

In 1992/3 a cook/chill (as opposed to cook/freeze) central production unit was built at Battle by the Oxford Regional Health Authority on a £3.8 million budget. The plan was to service many hospitals along the southern border of the Authority's 'patch' including Wycombe Health Authority as well as Berkshire. This initiative was supported by West Berkshire Health Authority but the timing was unfortunate because the hospitals intended

BATTLE IN THE 1990s

Top left: Abbey Block still busy; *Top right*: From roof of Thames Block. Doctors' flats mid-photo, 1944 huts in foreground; *Bottom left*: Purley Block; *Bottom right*: Gainsborough/Constable, the original Workhouse infirmary

as users were becoming Trusts. When given the option they chose in the majority of cases to remain with traditional catering teams. Thus although the building was completed and commissioned it had no customer base and without any revenue-generating contracts attempts to lease the plant to commercial operators failed. Was Battle's industrial site at risk of becoming a white elephant farm? The Regional Health Authority sold off the catering equipment and the building was dismantled and transported to Poland. At least its hardstanding served for a couple of years as a base for the Nightingale portacabins.

Southern Supplies Division, an offshoot of Regional Supplies, created a large warehouse development in the mid 1980s on the north-east corner of the site, used as a bulk store for the supply of consumables to local hospitals. The area became the property of the Royal Berkshire Ambulance Trust at its inception in 1993, although the warehouse continued to be operated by Southern Supplies (latterly NHS Supplies) till the late 1990s when it fell into disuse. The incinerators were made obsolete by new environmental laws and were closed down, the Trust's clinical waste going to Bournemouth for incineration. At least the waste energy serves the NHS, as it is used to heat Bournemouth Hospital.

Battle in the 1990s

Top left: Capt. Les Warth MBE,TD, Founder of Hospital Radio Reading broadcasting in the converted wartime hut; *Top right*: Cook-chill unit, 1994; *Bottom left*: Committee Room interior; *Bottom right*: Redundant Chest Clinic buildings, 1996

Finale

That barometer of morale, the revitalised Social Club, began to fade during the 1990s. But Club Treasurer Barbara Gatward thinks many factors other than morale were involved – 'captive' members were lost when nurse training stopped on the wards, lunch-time drinking was forbidden for staff on duty and novelty pubs with cheap drinks swamped Reading town centre. With Battle's fate certain, the Club finally closed its doors in August 2000, a few years before the very end.

The last in the succession of magazines for the staff of both Hospitals must be *ROBA* (from ROyal Berks and BAttle), first edited by the late Trevor Bentley. *ROBA* remained resolutely light-hearted during Battle's last few years although very sympathetic towards staff distressed by the slow erosion of their Hospital and its way of life. The NHS Trust very early on formed an Action Group led by Cathy Osselton to help Battle staff cope with the difficult period of transition. This Group organised a Battle Hospital Thanksgiving Service in Abbey Block on 27th April 2005. The Service was held in the foyer while Abbey was still a busy clinical centre. Many hundreds of present and past staff attended to hear prayers from representatives of the Muslim, Jewish, Buddhist and Christian faiths and an outstanding address by retired Hospital Chaplain Elizabeth Jackson commemorating the work and the people of Battle Hospital.

What of the estate? Most of the Battle Hospital estate was actually sold in the spring of 2004 with a leasing agreement to cover the remaining period of occupation by the Trust. The industrial zone will stay in the immediate future primarily because of the vital work of the Sterilising Unit. Practicality, not simply nostalgia, suggests that this area of Battle should be permanently retained to help cope with overspill from an increasingly congested Royal Berkshire Hospital.

On the old hospital site, demolition of unused buildings began early. Old Casualty, the original Workhouse building, had never been fully re-used after the service was transferred to the Royal Berks. It had become a health and safety risk and was demolished in 1994. The Vagrants Ward, turned Out-patients, turned Chest Clinic is long gone, as is the old Nurses' Home. Purley Ward, the 'imbecile block' of 1911 is doomed, after long and varied subsequent service encompassing geriatrics, chiropody, nurse changing, education for auxiliaries and care assistants, back care and podiatry. All the in-patient buildings and derelict Elizabeth House will surely soon fall to the wreckers.

From the viewpoint of hospital heritage it is fortunate that some buildings at the Oxford Road entrance will be preserved. The western side of the Gatehouse and the range of buildings behind including the lovely Boardroom building have been transferred back to Reading Borough Council. They are now on long lease free of charge to the Oxford Road Community Centre. Chairman Rajinder Sohpal is proud of what has already been achieved by the collaboration of the Muslim, Hindu, Nepalese and Afro-Caribbean communities. Matron's flat has provided teaching and seminar rooms and offices and the Committee Room is a fine lecture theatre. The ultimate plan is for a new two-storey building connecting these two, perhaps to include a heritage display on the history of the Battle site. A Mosque is planned on the site of the old Casual Ward. Between there and the Community Centre, the gatehouse and adjoining cottages of Battle Terrace are still in NHS Trust ownership, while to the rear an area is to be developed by Reading Primary Care Trust. It remains to be seen how the estate between the Portman Road and Oxford Road enclaves will unfold and what homage, if any, will be paid to Battle's history.

9

THE ROYAL BERKSHIRE HOSPITAL SINCE 1989

Since its 150th Anniversary, apart from the listed buildings fronting London Road, the Royal Berkshire Hospital has changed almost beyond recognition. Gone are the Nurses' Home opened in 1925, the general theatres of 1928 and adjacent pathology laboratories, the out-patients block, Cyril Taylor Unit, the Nuffield Block for Women and Children, the once stately Greenlands Private Nursing Home. On Craven Road the cramped telephone exchange, the delightfully turreted Occupational Health building and most sadly the Social Club have all been sacrificed to make way for the impressive new main entrance. More of the residential properties across the road have been gathered into the Health Service; while some provide staff accommodation, most of the elegant houses have completely changed their function. Here Community Paediatrics and Family Planning can now be found; the 'Headmaster's House' is a warren of Trust offices, with the Maintenance Department squeezed into portacabins in its grounds. At No.19 the purpose-built staff nursery was opened in 1999; next door is the new headquarters for Dr Anne Ross's flourishing Department of Occupational Health.

Battle Block now massively fills the area between North Wing and the Eye Block. The cost of this final building was some £48m, bringing the total for the consolidation programme to well over £128m and the total beds at the Royal Berkshire Hospital to 813. The multi-storeyed new edifices, together with the refurbished and extended older buildings, occupy the island site to an extraordinary degree. During construction even more space had to be found for the contractors' massive cranes and other plant and for their vehicles and services. The planners, construction workers and particularly the Hospital staff can all be proud of the organisation and the willingness to co-operate which allowed work in the Hospital to carry on despite all the disruptions and noise of being part of a major building site. A prime example was the use of temporary portacabins to continue serving meals during the 1997 £1.2m refurbishment of the kitchens. In August 1999 the Accident and Emergency Department actually moved to Orthopaedics for 12 days to allow strengthening work for the new Day Bed Unit to be constructed above. In 2002 a temporary 'hospital street' was created which connected

Battle Block under construction

North Wing to the Eye Block, by-passing the demolition work and the construction of Battle Block; this wide wooden corridor was unlovely, but provided comfortable passage for the hundreds journeying north and south every day.

Some of the advances in the development programme have been noted in the changeover of departments from Battle, but there have been many others. In 1990 the Radiology Department installed two new scanners, one MRI and one CT Pace scanner, partly funded from the astonishing Ken Thomas Appeal, which finally wound up in 2005. When the Department moved into its central new home in November 2002 it could boast two CT scanners, two new Magnetic Resonance scanners and separate suites for vascular, ultrasound and fluoroscopy work. The new Picture Archive and Communication System replaced X-ray film with digitised images stored and distributed by computer. There is no longer a need for films in envelopes; images can be viewed immediately on work stations and computer screens across the Trust, giving huge advantages in both speed and convenience.

Nearby the new Accident and Emergency Department, also opened in 2002, has similar high-tech imaging equipment, four resuscitation bays with the most advanced facilities, and a special area reserved for children. Staff establishment has grown to four consultants, ten middle grade doctors, six juniors and five accident and emergency nurse practitioners who are expert in such skills as triage, establishing intravenous drips and giving intravenous drugs. The speciality has come a long way since Mike Squire began to organise both accident and emergency and orthopaedic services in 1949.

Paediatrics has been transformed since the move from Norcot to Victoria Ward in 1993. A Paediatric Assessment Unit was provided within Accident and Emergency; upgrading D floor of the Maternity Block gave a new paediatric ward; the Neonatal Unit, as well as refurbishment, was given national television coverage when Carlton TV and Sky followed the work of the Unit in a 26-week series during 2000 entitled 'Special Babies'. In 2002 the purpose-built Paediatric Unit opened within Centre Site – Lion and Dolphin Wards, with a high-dependency unit and eight-bedded adolescent unit, nearby the Paediatric Assessment Unit and Kempton Day Bed Unit retaining the name of Reading's first specialist paediatrician. The ideal of one dedicated children's area for all admissions had been achieved. By 2005 the Department had six Hospital Consultant Paediatricians and four Community (Developmental) Consultants. In addition, following the precedent of academic appointments in gerontology, Professor Gary Butler took up his post in April, soon to be supported by a Senior Lecturer in Paediatrics. The last link with Battle will be severed when the 'Nightingale' portacabins exchange their elderly patients for young ones by transferring to 3-5 Craven Road and the Dingley Child Development Centre finally joins the rest of the paediatric service.

On preventative child care, special tribute is due to the campaign for cycle helmets begun in 1992 by Sister Angela Lee of the children's orthopaedic ward, leading to the Childhood Injury Prevention Service. After local success in halving the number of bicycle-related head injuries in children, the campaign was backed by the Departments of Health and Transport for a national relaunch in 1998. The now almost universal use of children's helmets in Britain can be traced directly to the pioneering and indefatigable work of Angie Lee and her colleagues.

Improvements and reorganisation in the orthopaedic service included a fifth ward created in 1997. Chesterman Ward was named in honour of the late Mr Patrick Chesterman who did so much for the speciality, not least ensuring its establishment in South Wing. As part of the upgrading of theatres two new laminar flow ventilation systems were installed. Their purpose is to reduce the risk of infection, especially important during internal fixations and joint replacement surgery. The expansion in orthopaedics has been dramatic. In 2005 there are 12 consultants between them providing additional expertise by sub-specialising in hips, knees, feet and ankles, shoulders and elbows, hands, spines and children's orthopaedics.

When the head and neck surgical specialties – eye, ENT, oral, orthodontic and facio-maxillary – were combined into a single unit, 'Eye Ward' became a misnomer. In 2003 it was renamed Dorrell Ward to commemorate Mr E A Dorrell who preceded Geoffrey Cashell as Honorary Ophthalmic Surgeon from 1923 to 1933. The North Wing ENT operating theatre which had opened in 1896 still soldiered on, using Alice Ward as its Day Bed Unit. Eye surgery moved to the new central theatres in 2004, leaving the old Eye Theatre redundant, its fate still to be decided.

Upstairs in the Eye Block Greenlands is no longer the Private Ward. Because of congestion it is perhaps as well that the hoped-for private hospital did not eventuate. The only private patients now are child day patients and those major cases needing facilities at the Royal Berkshire Hospital such as intensive care. Greenlands and Aitken Walker Wards served many purposes during the development reshuffling, until the take-over by general medicine, rheumatology and the other medical specialties in mid 2005.

Below Dorrell Ward, the Pharmacy has continued to expand. In 1995 an Aseptic Unit was created, mainly for preparation of chemotherapeutic agents. As Battle closes, the work load is being taken up by a second Dispensary sited on the new Concourse, close to the out-patient clinics. However, the most remarkable change in recent years has been switching of the main pharmacy activity from production and supply of medications to an advisory service on their safe, economic and appropriate usage. A further advance has come with Royal Berks pharmacists joining nurses in a course at the University of Reading which will allow them to prescribe for chronic conditions. In September 2005 the University accepts its first student intake for a degree course in pharmacy, giving the Hospital Department even closer academic links.

The Maternity Unit, while remaining in its 1968 purpose-built Block, has undergone many changes. Some have been in response to altered public attitudes such as the demand that midwives be given a more important role. The Unit was one of the first to offer midwife-managed beds and in 1994 two of the midwives raised funds to provide a new birthing pool. Senior midwives have been given added responsibilities such as ventouse deliveries. The increasing significance of Foeto-Maternal Medicine was recognised by the appointment in 1996 of two new consultants, Pat Street and Jane Siddall. The following year saw the start of a massive programme of upgrading throughout the Maternity Block, improving all the facilities and bringing maternity and gynaecology together – theatres, wards, clinics and day unit – a logical consolidation of specialities within the hospital consolidation programme. In 2002 an Integrated Birth Centre was introduced, providing 'home from home' rooms for low-risk deliveries, with comfortable furnishings and all medical equipment hidden away, yet the security of being just one floor above the delivery suite. The Integrated Birth Centre offers a practical solution for mothers concerned about having to choose between natural birth at home or the safety of full hospital facilities.

Alongside all the projects directly related to consolidation, there have been many other advances, often supported by charitable funding. The highlight of the Anniversary Year was undoubtedly the visit on April 4th 1989 by Her Majesty the Queen and the Duke of Edinburgh. This proved to be the last public appearance by Sir Gordon Palmer, the Lord Lieutenant for Berkshire who braved illness and severe pain to ensure personally that the day went well. The main purpose of the Royal visit was to open the redeveloped Radiotherapy Department, funded by the 150th Anniversary Appeal and Cancer Relief Macmillan Fund. Such is the rate of progress that new technology was soon needed, including a further linear accelerator paid for by the New Opportunities Fund, a by-product of the National Lottery. What was now The Berkshire Cancer Centre required further expansion, which was again supported by a successful Macmillan appeal. In 2003 the cancer patients gained new consulting rooms, pleasanter waiting areas, a quiet room for complementary therapy, an information room with access to the internet and space for support groups to meet. Above, some of the offices have moved upstairs to occupy the old 'Greenlands Flats', once the quarters for private nursing staff. They look across the forecourt car park to the old 'Maids' Home' where ambulances now bring patients for haemodialysis. A chronic dialysis facility was created here in 2000 using the Private Finance Initiative, and replacing the unit at Dellwood.

In August 1989 a fire started while workers were in the roof over Adelaide Ward. More than 100 patients were safely evacuated without any panic but Adelaide and Victoria wards were wrecked by falling rubble and water from the firemen's hoses. Although restoration took a long time, a positive benefit was the creation of the Charlotte Starmer-Smith Isolation Unit, opened by Princess Anne in 1994. Funding for this Unit was mainly due to the efforts of Nigel and Ros Starmer-Smith and the generosity of the rugby world. The appeal came under the umbrella of the West Berkshire Hospitals Charity, which succeeded the 150th Anniversary Appeal and was later renamed the Reading and District Hospitals Charity. Of the many appeals it has co-ordinated the largest was for the Diabetes Centre in Melrose House, opened in 1996 by Olympic oarsmen Steve Redgrave and Matthew Pinsent. Much fund-raising has been independently organised, most notably the £200,000 Audiology Unit Appeal, led first by John Bamford and then Carol Town. The handsome new Unit was opened in 1990, strongly built to allow for future upward expansion.

Every hospital department has seen major development over the past 16 years and all have increased their consultant staffing in line with the Calman Report on medical training and reduction in junior doctor hours. Most of the key changes in the medical specialities have been mentioned. General surgery, after some difficult years in the old theatres and in distant, scattered wards (someone coined the term 'safari ward round') finally settled into the new Centre Block with all facilities in close proximity. The Adult Day Surgery Unit opened with 12 trolleys in 2001, expanding in stages to accommodate 28 patients when Abbey Day Bed

Unit transferred across in December 2003. Anaesthetics moved from North Wing to its new headquarters in the South Block extension in July 2003, better equipped, closer to theatres and the Intensive Care Unit and with much more space, as befits a Department now numbering 24 consultants.

Pathology, one of the first departments to move into the old South Wing, has had some internal structural improvements but the most remarkable change has been in the use of automation and information technology. The major advance in Cellular Pathology has been immunohistology which detects specific antigens such as tumour markers. In Clinical Biochemistry the Battle 'stat lab' providing a day-time service on urgent requests was phased out in the 1990s and replaced by Point of Care testing, with the Department training medical staff in the use of the equipment. Automated immunoassay of eg hormones replaced radioimmunoassay and the whole of the Department of Medical Physics was incorporated into Clinical Biochemistry. Haematology has switched from the old microscopic cross-matching technique to a gel card system which would have delighted Dr Mills – the time to make blood available for transfusion has been halved. In microbiology the only presence at Battle was closed when the tuberculosis work was transferred in the early 1990s to a new Royal Berkshire Hospital laboratory for high risk cases. The Public Health Laboratory closed in 2003 with all the microbiology services being devolved to the NHS Trust.

The automated laboratory work is one example of how the Hospital has changed not only physically but functionally. In 1993 Ron Cooper, the ex-businessman Chief Executive, introduced the principle of re-engineering to streamline and simplify all hospital services in a programme called Hospital Process Redesign. Senior managers, led by Betty Evans, formed design teams to take a fresh look at the work throughout the Trust. New care pathways and procedures were developed for routines such as the patient journey from first hospital contact to return to GP (for example accident and emergency, X-ray, plaster-room, orthopaedic ward, discharge home). Benefits such as better use of computers, reduced paperwork and fewer delays are still being accrued.

Perhaps the most interesting and significant changes have been in the broadened role of the nurse, where in many fields the Royal Berkshire Hospital has been a leader. When nurse training became a university diploma or degree course, the Nurse Education Centre was affiliated firstly with the University of Reading, then Thames Valley University. In 1988 Benyon Ward was the first in the Trust to introduce primary nursing, allocating patients to a specific primary nurse who took responsibility for their care from admission to discharge. The staff developed patient-focused nursing with information booklets and such measures as self-medication for selected patients. In the early 1990s Benyon achieved official status as a Nursing Development Unit. The Trust has continued to lead in nurse training and development, being one of the first to assign

Practice Educators specifically to teach the student nurses. In every speciality qualified nurses have been encouraged to extend their professional practice. Nurse-led pre-operative clerking was started in the ENT/Maxillo-Facial Department and during the 1990s it was taken up by nearly all departments. Also at this time nurses were being trained in such skills as venepuncture, venous cannulation, electrocardiogram recording and pain control. Appropriately qualified nurses perform endoscopies, act as first assistant in theatre and lead specialised clinics in ENT and ophthalmology. Emergency Nurse Practitioners began in 1995, dealing unsupervised with minor injuries in Accident and Emergency; nurse prescribing is about to happen. Of the media's 'super-nurses', Reading has two. Sue Duke was appointed Nurse Consultant in Palliative Care in 2000. A year later Mandy Odell became Nurse Consultant in Critical Care. A major development in safety for the severely ill has been the nurse-led Critical Care Outreach Team which started visiting the general wards in May 2001. Their system for early detection of those patients requiring augmented care, the Reading Modified Early Warning System, went Trust-wide in January 2003.

From the public's viewpoint, the most obvious alteration to the Hospital has been the relocation of the main entrance and the total transformation in architectural style. Only a small number of visitors now use Henry Briant's neo-classical entrance of 1839. The switchboard moved here from its portacabin on Craven Road. When the Battle and Royal Berks switchboards merged in 1998 Linda Hanley came from Battle as Manager, to be succeeded two years later by her daughter Sharon. In 2004 current Manager Bob Dell and the team moved again, to much-needed space and new equipment in the vacated Huntley and Palmer Ward.

Much of the clinical work has gone from the North Wing wards, totally changing the nature of the original Hospital buildings. For Benyon Ward a switch from surgical to medical patients occurred when gynaecology went up to join maternity, and surgery took over the Nuffield Block. The present plan is for Benyon and Victoria to remain medical wards. Sidmouth and Adelaide have moved to Battle Block, with West and King Edward Ward as the Haematology Day Unit still using the Huntley and Palmer name. Albert continues as an out-patient Chronic Ambulatory Peritoneal Dialysis Unit. The West Wing occupiers – the expanded Cancer Centre and the Reading Pathological Society Library – happily remain, as do the Haemodialysis Unit, offices and doctors' accommodation in the East Wing. In the basement there are still the North Wing housekeeping services and the vitally important Medical Records Department, since 2000 hidden deep in this historic building. Immediately adjacent is the now digitised Photographic Department where, until he retired in 2004, Head of Department Lionel Williams was the longest serving member of the Hospital staff.

The new main entrance from Craven Road was officially opened in September 2001, the ceremony attended by the Deputy Lord Lieutenant for Berkshire, the former Trust Chairman Dr Peter Phillips, the current Chairman Mr Colin Maclean, many senior hospital staff and local dignitaries. The ultra-modern open style of architecture met general approval, as did the immediate accessibility from bus stop and from the multi-storey car park. Centre Site and South Wing development brought increasing enthusiasm for the reception facilities, catering and retail outlets and broad throughways to wards and clinics. The five-metre double helix light sculpture suspended from the entrance foyer ceiling was more controversial, although most detractors have come to appreciate its varying colour patterns and artistic imagery of the coil of life. Commissioning this sculpture, designed by local artists Anne Arlidge and Jancis Smithells, was one of the first projects of the Trust's Arts and Gardens programme. This has been aimed at improving the environment for the benefit of patients, staff and visitors on the increasingly busy and congested site. The League of Friends provided the first sponsored garden, 'The Peace Garden' beneath the multi-faith Sanctuary in Centre Site. In October 2002 local religious leaders took part in a service of dedication to mark the opening of the Sanctuary and garden. Under the Arts and Gardens scheme painting exhibitions, heritage displays, donated sculptures, courtyard shrubs, plants and garden furniture have all served to help make the now vast Hospital a less threatening and more interesting place.

The Voluntary Service, having done so much for both Hospitals, has become even more valuable in promoting a friendly welcome to the all-new wards and clinics. The Welcoming Service and especially its sponsored electric buggies are essential in helping patients and visitors around the new facilities. How sad that their most eminent Welcomer died in 2004 before consolidation was complete; The Hon. Lady Palmer DL was probably the Royal Berkshire Hospital's most staunch supporter.

The Patient Advice and Liaison Service was launched by the Trust in both hospitals in 2000. Now with its office near the main entrance, the service has become more accessible to patients, carers and relatives. Manager Sue Jackson, her volunteers and unique Patient Panel transmit a wide range of information to patients and staff, provide help for the bereaved and improve communications for those with complaints or problems. By contrast, to keep the environment safe for patients, visitors and staff some new services must perforce be less than friendly. It is a grim reflection on modern society that Health Service monies are increasingly called upon to fund restriction of access by swipe-card locks, surveillance by closed circuit TV and 24-hour security patrols.

Battle Block finally opened in mid 2005 providing 344 beds and modern accommodation for Acute Adult Medicine, Neuro-rehabilitation, Acute Stroke Unit, Cardiology In-patients and Out-patients, Cardiac Day Case Unit, Coronary Care Unit, Acute Renal/ Haemodialysis, Respiratory Medicine, Occupational Therapy and Physiotherapy. Here too Haematology/ Oncology have a permanent home after disruptive

Battle Block entrance from West Drive

journeyings involving Greenlands, Adelaide and Huntley and Palmer Ward. Transfer of nearly all the services from Battle Hospital took place in just a couple of weeks in May/June 2005, another triumph of organisation and co-operative teamwork.

Congestion
With the arrival from Battle of hundreds of patients and clinical staff, parking, which was almost the first consideration in Ron Cooper's 1993 planning document, became one of the most contentious issues. Although the Trust worked conscientiously with Reading Borough Council, supporting green commuter plans is no simple matter for a large acute hospital. Such projects as park and ride, improved facilities for cyclists and

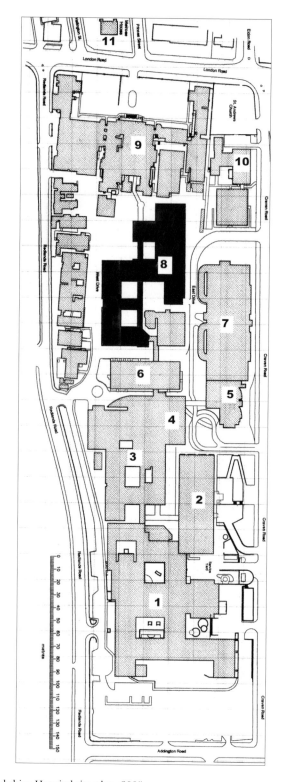

1. South Block
2. Maternity Block
3. Centre Block
4. Accident & Emergency
5. Main Entrance
6. Eye Block
7. Multi-storey car park
8. Battle Block
9. North Block
10. Trust Education Centre
11. Melrose House

Royal Berkshire Hospital site plan, 2005

better bus services all make a valuable contribution yet are unlikely to prove sufficient with only one hospital multi-storey car park. For staff, inability to park may be an aggravation but for frail patients and their escorts it can be a matter of the greatest anxiety.

Without doubt 'consolidation' has vastly improved Reading's hospital service although there is general acceptance that too much has been crammed into too small a space. The pressure for 'all acute services on one site' came before changes in attitudes and in technology meant that geriatrics, rheumatology and non-major elective surgery also demanded inclusion. Although research has shown that specialisation and centralisation give better outcome, smaller hospitals and their local populations are not persuaded that these principles should apply to every patient. Comfortable, friendly surroundings and proximity to family and close supporters can be more important than access to MRI scanners and intensive care. From a medical viewpoint the ideal is probably to have all types of patient cared for within one vast complex, sharing the expensive facilities and staff expertise while offering the full range of in-patient and day-care accommodation. Instead of being cramped and congested, this centre would offer open green spaces with gardens and sport facilities. A first-class system of transport, both external and internal, would be essential. Rather than being constantly at full stretch the whole would function well below capacity, giving more time for staff training and the ability to deal with such exigencies as terrorist attack or a virulent new type of infectious disease. Under current NHS financing this can only be a pipe dream.

The 'super-hospital' for Reading was always going to be a compromise; would consolidation at Battle have been a better option? Although more area was available, the site was rejected primarily on financial grounds. At the Royal Berkshire Hospital the Cancer Centre, Trust Education Centre, Eye Block, Maternity Block and South Wing have all been used in the consolidation programme while Battle had few facilities worth preserving. Its potential development was hampered physically by narrow congested roads and less obviously by an underlying local wish to erase memories of the Workhouse. Concentration of services on the Royal Berks site was the more feasible rather than the most desirable solution and like all compromises has been less than perfect.

The fervent hope is that hospital work will continue to be reduced as more services are taken up in the community. It is therefore most fitting that the Reading Primary Care Trust has retained part of the site of the original Oxford Road Union for a primary care resource centre. This new unit, to be purpose-built in about two years' time, will thus offer something of the services transferred from Battle and the tradition of health care on the same site since 1867 will not be entirely lost. Increased community health provision is nevertheless unlikely to resolve the congestion at the Royal Berkshire Hospital. With nowhere to expand, when will planning start on a second hospital for Reading?

Epilogue

The Berkshire Medical Heritage Centre's Museum in the Royal Berkshire Hospital's Old Laundry has more than 3,000 mementoes from the medical past. Sadly few are specifically from Battle Hospital. None of the artefacts from everyday workhouse life have survived. There are some original architect's plans, interesting photographs, particularly from the first World War, nurses' certificates from Reading Borough Council and a little equipment from the early years of chest medicine and surgery. The largest item is the iron lung used firstly at Prospect Park Hospital, then for just a few years in Abbey Intensive Care Unit. Doubtless in some homes there are Battle-related family papers and photographs. Within Battle Block a few objects and photographs have been preserved at the request of patients or staff and more importantly the building itself retains the name reaching back to 1066. None of these, however, guarantees lasting remembrance – memories fade, once-treasured documents are scrapped, official records disappear, buildings are demolished. This book is written in the hope that the many contributions of the Oxford Road Union and Battle Hospital will not so easily be forgotten.

APPENDIX

by

MARGARET RAILTON

MAY PEARSE 1877–1967

May Pearse died in Battle Hospital in 1967 aged 90. She had been a patient there for over 50 years. First admitted when the Hospital was the Reading Union Workhouse, she was still there when Battle Infirmary became Battle Hospital in the 1930s and in 1948 when it became part of the National Health Service.

Her medical history was not exceptional a century ago. In 1901, aged 23, May was admitted to the Royal Berkshire Hospital twice suffering from a tubercular knee. Two operations did not cure the problem and in 1903 her leg was amputated by Dr Guilding at the Workhouse. She returned home but found it increasingly difficult to cope on crutches and eventually, when she became bedridden, she returned to the Workhouse.

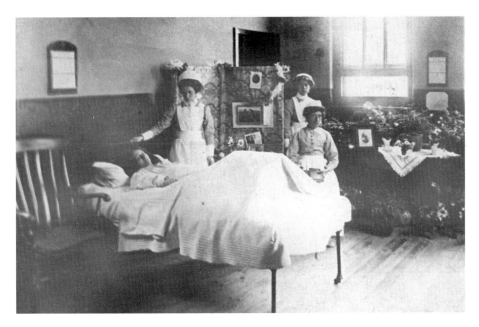

May Pearse in Basingstoke Workhouse Infirmary 1915

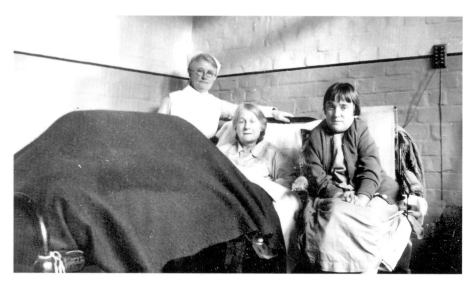

Battle Infirmary 1920s

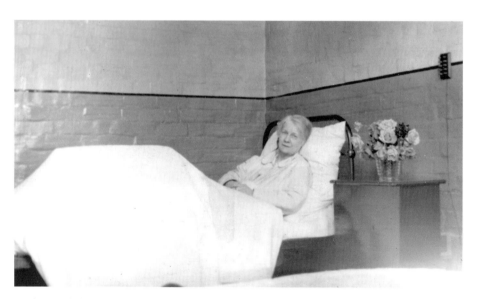

Battle Hospital 1930s

May was among the inmates who were moved to Basingstoke Union in 1915 when the Reading Workhouse was taken over to become a military hospital during the First World War. She returned to the Workhouse when it reopened in 1921 and remained there for the next 46 years until her death in 1967.

Attempts to make her walk again were unsuccessful and Battle Hospital became May's home. Among her regular visitors were her close

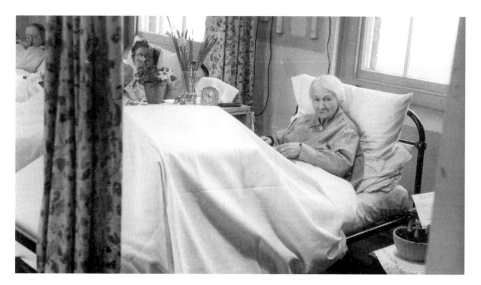

Battle NHS Hospital, Shiplake Ward, 1950s

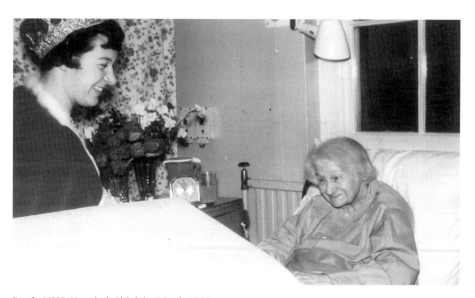

Battle NHS Hospital, Shiplake Ward, 1960s

friend Mrs Fisher and her daughter Valerie (Mrs Ayres). They recalled that May was a very remarkable person who was always cheerful and never complained. An article published after her death in the *Evening Post* noted that it was a tribute to the 'careful and devoted medical and nursing care' which she had received that, apart from mumps in 1932, she had never suffered any illness. When May died in 1967 the nurses in Shiplake Ward were in tears. The life of their special patient had ended.

INDEX

Entries in italics refer to illustrations

Index

410

264–5, 268, 269, 275, 277, 280–2, 284–7, 294, 299, 314, 328, 341, 343
Act 208
of Labour 278–9
Minkley, Dr H R 247, 271
Minster Ward *360*, 361
Mitchell-Baker, Alastair 381
Moore, Nurse Julie 361
Morgan, Miss Gladys 326–7, 356
Moring, Mr F E 237–8
Morris, Canon B 274
Morris, Miss I W 262
Morris, Mr Joseph 8
Morris, Sister T 317
Mortimer Ward 365
Mortuary 61, 143, 248, 273
Motorbike outing *188*
Moulsford Asylum 27, 45, 60, 69, 70, 95, 123–4, 148
Mumford, Dr 271
Municipal Hospital 245, 291–2, 387
Reading 245
Murphy, Cathryn 384
Murray, Revd J Wilford 274
Myszor, Dr Margaret 359

National Assistance Act 295
National Health Service 211, 277–9, 285–6, 289–91, 293, 295–6, 300–1, 308–9, 312, 318, 328, 365, 372, 374, 378, 385, 403
Bill 284
Trusts 378–9, 387
Naylor, Frank 343
Nelson, Nurse Christine 361
Neonatal unit 324, 362, 395
Neurological Clinic 298, 312
Neurologist 298
Neurology 341, 344–5, 370, 372, 384
Neurosurgical Services 352
Newbury Hospital 358
Workhouse 215
Newman, Dr Chris 362, 374
Newton House 178
Nicholls, Mr 274
Niles, Mr L C 290–1, 295–6, 303

Nixon, Dr 90
Norcot Ward 348, 353, 362, 373, 383, 395
Norris, Mr T 209, 223, 231, 234
North, Ken 354
NSPCC 86
Nuffield Block 326, 380
Nuisances, Inspector of 56
Nurses 20, 23, 27, 28, 34, 37, 38, 66, 89, 101–4, 127, 130–1, 137–9, 141, 142, 161, 180, 183, 190–1, 209, 211–4, 230, 233, 243, 248, 256, *257*, 261–2, 265, 269–70, 273, 278, 280, 282, 284, 287, 291, 294, 304, 309–10, 318, 328, 334–5, 338, 361, 396
Assistant 283–4
Education Centre 347, 398
Enrolled 327
Head 45–6, 65–6, 85, 89, 91, 93, 103, 129
Male 214, 250, 256
Practitioners 399
Private 152
Probationers 19, 91,129–131, 138, 151, 209, 213–4, 218, 230, 233, 256, 263, 269, 279
Queen Alexandra 150, 158, 161, 190, 192
Queen Victoria Institute 126, 209
State Registered 327, 333
Superintendent 19, 103–4 129–131, 136–137, 139, 147, 209, 212, 258
Training School 218, 239, 248, 282, 285–6, 309
Workhouse nurse *2*, 207
Nursery 132, 253, 262–3, 273, 276–8, 284, 286, 298, 324–5
Attendent 132, 276
Premature Babies 306, *307*
Nurses' Home 102, 136, *137*, 139, 161, 210–1, 222, 224, 233, 237, 248, 252, 256, 262–3, 264, 267, 284, 291, 294, 310–1, 313, 326, 352, 380, 393

Nursing Association, Workhouse 67
Nursing 346
Services 372, 376
Department 217
Nutt, Mr 50, 51

Obstetric Unit 308, 328
Obstetrics 282, 286, 305–6
Department 309
Occupational Therapy 288, 314, 318, 321, 370, 380, 385, 400
Therapist 289, 297, 316, 362
Oddie, Dr J A 339, 341
O'Donnell, Bill 389
Ogden, Dr 321
Old Age Pensions Act 135
Oldfield, Dr R H 331
Oliver, Dr David 387
Oliver, Mr 210, 238
O'Neill, Cathy 382
Ophthalmic Dept. 142
Ophthalmology 301–2, 373, 399
Orthodontic 395
Orthopaedic: Clinic 248
Centre, Nuffield 330
Day Unit 385
Department 362
Patients 315
Service 312, 335, 387, 395
Surgeons 302, *364*
Theatre 309
Orthopaedics 248, 251. 259, 301–2, 304, 315, 318, 324, 331, 341, 344–5, 358, 362–3, 365
Regional Area of 305
Outdoor Labour Test 54, 55
Out-patients clinics 386
Department 236, 244, 255, 264, 267, 271–2, 282, 299, 305, 330, 344, 347, 362, 370, 380
Dispensary 236
Service 303
Oxford: Base Hospital 151–2, 161
Regional Health Authority 376, 389
Regional Hospital Board (*see under* Regional)

To Dear Sue
with love
mary.
Xmas 2014.

BATTLE HOSPITAL MID-1970s

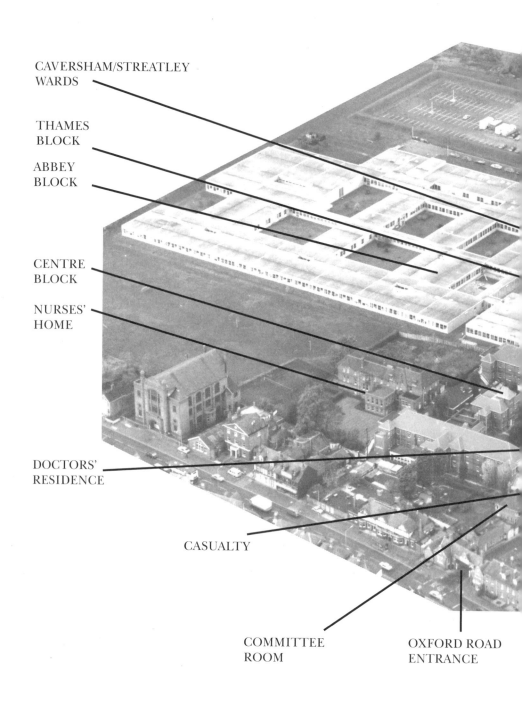

CAVERSHAM/STREATLEY WARDS

THAMES BLOCK

ABBEY BLOCK

CENTRE BLOCK

NURSES' HOME

DOCTORS' RESIDENCE

CASUALTY

COMMITTEE ROOM

OXFORD ROAD ENTRANCE